LIMESTONES AND CAVES
OF THE
MENDIP HILLS

THE LIMESTONES AND CAVES OF BRITAIN

Series Editor : T. D. Ford

published

Limestones and Caves of North-West England
A. C. Waltham and M. M. Sweeting

in preparation

Limestones and Caves of the Peak District
Limestones and Caves of South Wales

LIMESTONES AND CAVES
OF THE
MENDIP HILLS

compiled and edited by
D. I. Smith
assisted by
D. P. Drew

published by

DAVID & CHARLES

NEWTON ABBOT   LONDON   NORTH POMFRET (VT)   VANCOUVER

for

The British Cave Research Association

ISBN 0 7153 6572 X

Set in 11 on 13 pt Baskerville
and printed in Great Britain by
Bristol Typesetting Company Limited for
David & Charles (Holdings) Limited
South Devon House   Newton Abbot   Devon

Published in the United States of America by
David & Charles Inc
North Pomfret   Vermont 05053   USA

Published in Canada by
Douglas David & Charles Limited
3645 McKechnie Drive   West Vancouver BC

Contents

List of Illustrations

PLATES

7

The authors would like to express their grateful thanks to N. Barrington, P. Davies, R. Godwin, A. E. Mc R. Pearce, H. Taylor and the University of Bristol Speleological Society for permission to use the photographs listed above.

Copies of the oblique air photographs acknowledged to West Air Photography can be purchased from West Air Photography, 28a Bedford Rd, Weston-super-Mare by quoting the appropriate reference number. West Air Photography also have a wide selection of other oblique air photographs of the West Country.

TEXT FIGURES

A*

LIST OF TABLES

The authors would like to thank the Somersetshire Archaeological and Natural History Society for permission to reproduce
figures 95 and 96, and the University of Bristol Speleological
Society for permission to use many figures based upon those that
have appeared in that Society's Proceedings.

Foreword

Much of the limestone scenery of Britain is of high scenic, recreational, and educational value. Two of our main National Parks, in the Peak District and Yorkshire Dales, and many of our nature reserves are in limestone country, and, by its very nature, most of our caves are in these areas. Yet no comprehensive account of the limestone scenery and caves of each of these areas is to be found. The general review *British Caving— an Introduction to Speleology* was written a generation ago by members of the Cave Research Group of Great Britain, and it stimulated so much interest that a whole series of volumes is necessary to summarise the present state of knowledge. Once again, members of the Cave Research Group (now merged within the British Cave Research Association) have given freely of their time in writing the chapters within.

Though of the same geological age, the limestones of our different areas, of the Yorkshire Dales, Peak District, Mendip Hills and South Wales, each have their own subtleties, and each has a distinctive pattern to the landscape, partly resulting from the character of the limestone itself. The history of that limestone through subsequent geological periods has stamped further variations and contrasts between the regions, not least during the Ice Ages of the Pleistocene. These factors have further controlled the nature and distribution of the cave systems and underground drainage. In turn these differences are reflected in the degree of prehistoric habitation by early man and contemporary animals, and by the present-day occupation of the cave environment by insects and other life specially adapted to permanently dark and damp conditions.

The present state of knowledge of all these aspects of our limestone areas is reviewed within. One purpose of this book is to bring together the essentials of our knowledge, but, in so doing, the authors hope they have highlighted the gaps in our knowledge; the gaps which must be filled by further investigation, whether it be more accurate measurement of underground water flow, the rate of limestone solution, the life of prehistoric man, the metabolism of modern insects underground, or, more simply, the discovery of new caves.

It is hoped that this series of books will provide a survey of facts for the landowner, quarry industry and water authorities alike, where a conflict of interests is sometimes manifest. The books should provide guides for teachers and students who use these areas so much to gain an understanding of the weathering and other processes affecting our environment. It is hoped that the cave descriptions will encourage the sporting caver to seek a greater understanding of the features visible in his favourite caves, and the cave scientist will have a clearer background into which to fit his own piece of research.

As Series Editor for these books, I wish to express my sincere gratitude to all those who have contributed, in particular to the co-ordinating authors of each volume. The sense of their feelings towards their respective areas comes through vividly in the pages that follow. I hope that you, the reader, will enjoy reading this book as much as we have enjoyed preparing it for you.

Trevor D. Ford
Series Editor

I

The Caves of Mendip— An Introduction

D. P. Drew

Yet Ochy's dreadful hole still held herself disgrac'd
With th' wonders of this isle that she should not be plac't.

But that which vex't her most, was, that the Peakish cave
Before her darksome self such dignity should have:

And Chedder for mere grief his teens he could not wreak,
Gush'd forth so forceful streams that he was like to break
The greater banks of Ax, as from his mother's cave
He wander'd to the sea . . .

Drayton, *Polyolbion*, 1612

Drayton's lament no longer holds true, and indeed the caves of
Wookey Hole and Cheddar are now embarrassingly well known,
whereas Peak Cavern has declined into relative obscurity as a
tourist attraction.

Equally famous, both to the caver and to the professional
speleologist are the non-commercial caves of the Mendips. For
an area of its modest size it is probable that more intensive cave
exploration and karst research has been carried out within the
Mendip Hills than in any comparable area in the world.

Stretching from Brean Down in the west to Frome in the east,
and less than 10km in width, the Mendip Hills form a compact

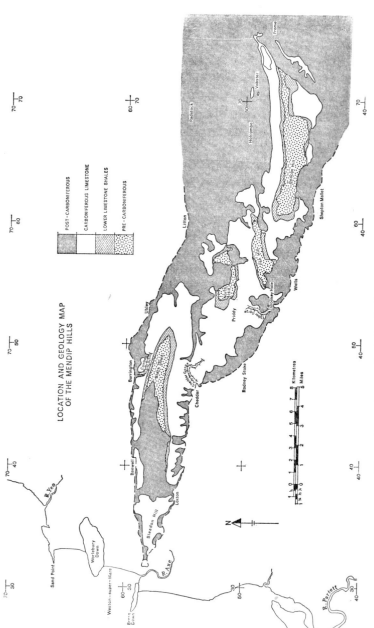

LOCATION AND GEOLOGY MAP
OF THE MENDIP HILLS

POST-CARBONIFEROUS
CARBONIFEROUS LIMESTONE
LOWER LIMESTONE SHALES
PRE-CARBONIFEROUS

Fig 1 Location and geological map of the Mendip Hills

unit geomorphologically, hydrologically and topographically. Fig 1 gives an overall location and geological map. They are a distinct 'region' in themselves, markedly different in both their physical and human landscapes from those of the lower country to the north and south; and it is perhaps, in part, because of this distinctiveness that they have become the object of such assiduous study.

The history of karst research on Mendip is closely linked to the history of cave exploration, more so than in other limestone areas of Britain. It is of some interest that, in contrast to other British caving areas, very few of the major Mendip caves had naturally accessible openings—Wookey Hole and Stoke Lane Slocker being notable exceptions. Hence, most of the caves and extensions to known caves have been discovered by digging, an unheard of phenomenon in much of the caving world.

The early history of exploration of the Mendip caves has two distinct aspects. First, the activities of lead miners—especially on central Mendip—who accidently encountered natural cavities whilst tunnelling. The discovery of Lamb Leer in the eighteenth century is the prime example, though the miners also explored many of the smaller caves in their search for ore.

Secondly, speleological interest was stimulated rather more directly and scientifically by the activities of the peripatetic gentlemen—archaeologists of the nineteenth century of whom Boyd Dawkins was perhaps the archetype. It was men such as Dawkins who first gave to cave exploration some degree of respectability, and who gave some intimation of the value of caves to the prehistorian and the geologist.

In large measure, Dawkins and his contemporaries were the inspiration of H. E. Balch (1869–1958). If any one person may be said to be pivotal to the whole development of Mendip caving and speleology it is Herbert Balch. An excellent biography of the man has been published by Stanton (1969*a*) and therefore only a brief account of his work will be given here.

It was Balch and his contemporaries (especially Baker and

Troup) who were responsible for opening up two of the Mendip's largest cave systems—Eastwater Cavern and Swildon's Hole—exploration of the latter at least, is still an active concern today. However, Balch's influence was far greater than simply in encouraging caving. His lifelong interest in the prehistory and geomorphology of the Mendip area, summarised in his series of books on Wookey Hole, Cheddar and the swallet caves, considerably advanced our knowledge of these topics and influenced several generations of cavers into taking an interest in the scientific aspects of caving. Although some of Balch's hypotheses have been modified by later workers, much of what he said is still relevant.

A further impetus to the study of the Mendip caves has been given by the existence of several major caving clubs based in the area: for example, the University of Bristol Speleological Society, the Wessex Cave Club and the Mendip Nature Research Committee. All of these societies are well established in comparison to most caving groups, and they have shown a continuing interest in the speleological aspects of caves as well as in the purely sporting approach. In addition, they have provided a valuable element of continuity in both exploration and investigation.

Reflecting the approach of geomorphology in general, the study of the Mendip karst in the pre-1950 period tended to be essentially qualitative and speculative in nature, with comparatively little objective work being undertaken. Notable exceptions to this were the water tracing experiments carried out by the Bristol Waterworks Company in the early part of this century, and the rather more ambiguous traces by members of the Wessex Cave Club in the 1930s.

As the study of caves became increasingly academically respectable during the late 1950s, so Mendip experienced the beginnings of a flood of geomorphologist-cavers which now threatens to overwhelm it. Amongst these pioneers of a more rigorous approach to the study of Mendip karst were W. I.

Stanton and D. C. Ford. Indeed Ford's work on the genesis of the central Mendip caves is the basis for much of the discussion of the Mendip systems within this book.

Since about 1960 the geography department of the University of Bristol has taken a special interest in the karst of the Mendips, and this has led to more specialised and quantified studies of the hydrology of the area being undertaken. In addition, the local river authorities have taken an active interest in the area.

Mendip today is in the healthy position of being studied both by professional hydrogeologists and by members of the—now many—caving clubs. For example, the Bristol Exploration Club, with a particular interest in St Cuthberts Swallet, is producing a comprehensive study of the system from both the exploratory and scientific aspects.

It is probably true to say that more is now known about the hydrology and the caves of the Mendip Hills than of any other limestone area of Britain. Almost all the sinking streams have been traced to their resurgences, most of the major cave systems have been investigated geomorphologically—even to their most distant and dismal ends—and much is known of the surface geomorphology of the area. For this reason the Mendips provide a good 'laboratory' for more sophisticated studies of a karst area. In addition to the flattering (if undeserved) distinction of having the eponymous term 'Mendip' absorbed into the geomorphologist's vocabulary, the Mendip Hills may become a 'type area' for karst studies.

2

The Rocks of Mendip—
Their Structure and Succession

D. I. Smith

Any understanding of the character and personality of the Mendip Hills requires a basic understanding of the rocks of which they are formed. In a study devoted to speleology this is especially true, for the very presence of caves is intimately related to the rocks of which the region is composed. It is necessary, therefore, to consider the geological background of the region before enquiring further into the questions of the origin and development of the caves themselves.

The first task undertaken by a geologist in studying an area is to establish a sequence for the local rocks. Such a sequence is known as a stratigraphical succession. The results of such studies are usually expressed in the form of a columnar section which includes all the rocks of the area in a sequence, with the oldest rocks at the bottom and the youngest at the top. Such a column presents a model representation of the kinds and thicknesses of rock which would be encountered if a borehole could be sunk through the whole succession. However, the construction of such an ideal vertical section depends on the recognition and acceptance of the major principles of stratigraphy. These principles can be set out in various ways, but for our purposes they can be divided into three.

THE PRINCIPLES OF STRATIGRAPHY

First, the principle of uniformity : succinctly, this states that natural conditions and processes are the same today as they were in the geological past. It is essential to realise that the processes responsible for the origin of the rocks on Mendip may no longer be typical of that particular region today.

Secondly, there is the principle of the superimposition of strata. This states that in a normal geological sequence one bed, or stratum, of rock is laid down upon another, and that the upper bed was laid down after the lower. This is not only applicable to those rocks deposited by marine sedimentation but also includes those laid down by rivers or by wind, as well as those originating from the deposition of lava. It must also be remembered that earth movements subsequent to deposition can cause inversion of the original sedimentary sequence.

Lastly, there is the principle of palaeontological correlation. Many sedimentary rocks, especially those originally deposited in a marine environment, contain the remains or traces of former organisms. Any such evidence of earlier life is a fossil, and the study of fossils is known as palaeontology. Palaeontological correlation relies upon the facts that once a species has become extinct it never reappears in younger strata, and that no two species are ever identical. Thus a collection of fossils from a particular bed or group of beds is often diagnostic of the geological age of those beds, and if a similar assemblage of fossils is obtained from another locality the two sets of beds are of the same stratigraphical age. Many difficulties occur when an attempt is made to study the palaeontological composition of a given set of beds and to correlate them to other beds in the area. The occurrence of fossils demands special circumstances for their preservation. Many sedimentary beds contain no fossils, and others yield only poorly preserved specimens which even a specialist cannot identify exactly as regards species. Further, only certain species are useful in providing a detailed indication of the exact stratigraphical age of the rock concerned. Such distinctive species, which flourish for only a short span of geological time, are known as index fossils. Despite all the difficulties, the use of fossil evidence as an indicator of geological age, and as a major tool in stratigraphy, is essential.

THE HISTORY OF GEOLOGICAL MAPPING IN THE AREA

The task of producing a stratigraphical column and a geological map for most of Britain was initially undertaken in the earlier part of the last century. Indeed, the Mendip area merits a special place in the history of geological mapping. The principle of palaeontological correlation was first clearly outlined by William Smith in the last decade of the eighteenth century, and this was followed by the production of the first true geological map by Smith in 1799. This map was of the country within a radius of some five miles of Bath. Smith was first and foremost a practical man, and his full comprehension of the principles of stratigraphy was obtained during his employment as surveyor to the Somerset Coal Canal in the 1790s. He appears to have lived in a number of houses in the Bath district; that at Rugbourne Form (651583) at High Littleton, where Smith lived for the period 1792–5, is particularly closely associated with Mendip. In 1815, Smith published the first complete geological map of England and Wales at a scale of approximately five inches to the mile. One of the original copies of this map is displayed in the geology museum in the Queen's Building of the University of Bristol. No better tribute can be paid to the prodigious efforts of Smith, and his painstaking attention to detail, than to compare this original map with the modern ten miles to the inch geological map of Britain, published by the Geological Survey. The comparison is most marked. Smith applied his newly enunciated ideas of palaeontological correlation in the construction of this map, and denoted the Mendip Hills as 'Derbyshire Limestone', thus recognising not only the similarity of the rock type between what would now be termed the Carboniferous Limestone of

Derbyshire and Mendip but also demonstrating their contemporaneous formation. He also marked on this map all the other major occurrences of Carboniferous Limestone in England and Wales, including the Isle of Man!

Thus Smith's original maps, and all later map series of the Geological Survey, delimit the geology first and foremost according to stratigraphical age, with the nature of the rock as a secondary classification. This is undoubtedly the most useful single overall form of map to portray the geology of an area, but the emphasis upon stratigraphical age is not necessarily the major criterion required of a geological map for purposes such as speleology or civil engineering, etc. The emphasis for these is undoubtedly upon the type of rock or, more properly expressed, upon the lithology of the rock; in other words, its physical and chemical characteristics. We shall see that the uninformed use of a stratigraphically based geological map to obtain information with respect to lithology can lead to misunderstandings. However, if the concern with the existing geological map is to obtain information as to the geological structure, then a map based on stratigraphical divisions can be of considerable assistance.

The early impetus given to British geology by William Smith, and the formation of the Geological Survey of Great Britain in 1835, resulted in the production of a series of one inch to the mile geological maps. The mapping commenced in the south-west of England, and the mapping and publication of the 'Old Series' geological maps for the Mendip region was completed by 1850. We are fortunate in the Mendip region as the publication of the 'New Series' one inch to the mile maps has recently been completed (with the exception of sheet 279). In addition, a 1:25,000 map was published in 1969 for the Cheddar area, and six inch to the mile maps exist for selected areas of eastern Mendip. In addition to the geological maps, accompanying texts known as geological memoirs were issued. There is a memoir of a regional nature for the Old Series (Woodward, 1876) and a subsequent sheet memoir for the New Series, sheet 280 (Green and Welch,

1965). A regional guide for the Bristol and Gloucester district describes the Mendip area in a wider setting (Kellaway and Welch, 1948).

A guide to the reference numbers, and further information regarding these various Geological Survey maps, is given in Appendix 1 on page 87.

From the wealth of geological information available for the Mendip region in maps, memoirs and published papers, it is possible to extract the salient aspects of broad speleological significance. First, we will consider the stratigraphical succession, and then the geological structures into which these rocks were deformed subsequent to their formation. The further question of how these rocks have been sculptured to form the present-day landscape will be reserved for consideration in a later chapter.

ROCK CLASSIFICATION

There are two main methods of classifying rocks. They can be divided into distinct lithological divisions such as shales, sandstone etc, or alternatively, into zones, which are time divisions with a characteristic fossil content. The recognition of a zone depends on the presence of zonal fossils that are known to have existed only for a limited period of geological time. Such fossils evolve and become extinct in a short time interval, which lithologically is sometimes represented by only a few feet or less of strata. The problem of such a duality of classification is that frequently the time units do not correspond to the lithological units. At first sight this lack of accord may appear strange, but the explanation is not difficult to comprehend.

At any one time in geological history, deposits are being laid down under a variety of environmental conditions. If our considerations are restricted to marine deposits this point can be readily illustrated. In the immediate region of the shore, the type of sedimentary rock material deposited is frequently of sand, and not infrequently of coarser-grained particles such as pebbles or boulders. If this material becomes consolidated and part of the geological column, it will be recognised as sandstones or conglomerates. The fossil content will be that of organisms adapted to living in this disturbed in-shore region, many of the species having coarse shells able to withstand the buffeting of the waves in this shallow water. On moving away from the shore-line, into deeper water, the sediment size will tend to decrease, and also the fauna will be of a different type. The shells of the marine molluscs and brachiopods in this deeper water are often thin, as they are not subject to the turbulent conditions of the in-shore zone. The bottom-dwelling organisms of the off-shore zone are in the relatively calm water below the surface layers of the ocean affected by wave action. Sediments of this type are sometimes referred to as shelf-zone type. The term shelf refers to the continental shelf, which is an area surrounding the world's major land masses. Typically the continental shelf has depths of less than 200m. The deeper parts of the oceans are remote from the land masses and receive a very limited amount of sediment. They are far away from the rivers and the coast which supply much of the sediment, and it is only possible for the finest particles to be transported, in suspension, to such distant parts of the ocean. Such deposits are usually referred to collectively as ooze but can be further sub-divided into calcareous ooze, siliceous ooze etc, depending on the composition of the sediment involved. It is relatively uncommon for true deep-ocean deposits to be found in the sedimentary record of the present land masses.

Thus, in-shore, shelf, and deep-water deposits clearly can be formed at the same period of geological time. Stratigraphically such deposits are of the same age, but as regards the type and thickness of deposit they are extremely varied. Many of the organisms, later to be preserved as fossils, are also restricted in areal extent to specific depth environments. This is particularly true of the bottom-dwelling species. Palaeontological correlation of marine deposits from the different zones is difficult and is only made possible due to the preservation, as fossils, of certain species of marine life that live in the surface waters of the ocean. These are collectively referred to as planktonic species. When a planktonic organism dies, its remains can be preserved either in the sediment of the deep ocean or in the shallower waters of the shelf or in-shore zones, and thus correlation between the different marine zones becomes possible. It will be realised that although the fossil forms may show deposits to be of the same age, the deposits themselves can be, and are, very different.

The assemblage of rock type and fossil content are therefore frequently related, and referred to as a facies. For example, the in-shore facies would be such a distinctive assemblage. In addition to marine sediments there are also corresponding non-marine deposits. These are known as continental facies and include material deposited by rivers (fluviatile), or by the wind (aeolian), or sediments laid down in fresh or brackish water. The correlation of a continental facies with that of the corresponding marine facies is particularly difficult.

On a world scale there is an accepted standard stratigraphical geological column. This represents an agreed palaeontological correlation, dividing the rocks deposited in the last 600 million years or so into major units. This, in fact, only represents about a sixth of geological time, but the construction of a stratigraphical column depends on the presence of clearly recognisable fossil evidence, and this is not found in the earlier sedimentary rocks. The broadest division of the stratigraphical column is into eras. For Mendip the Palaeozoic and Mesozoic eras are represented (see Fig 2). The next division of the standard column is into systems or periods; the Silurian, Devonian, Carboniferous, Triassic and Jurassic periods are found in the area we are considering. Further sub-division into deposits representing smaller time units is possible and is important in the detailed consideration of local areas. In Britain, for example, the Carboniferous is divided into three major units, namely the Carboniferous Limestone, the Millstone Grit, and the youngest unit, the Coal Measures. Division into smaller and smaller units is possible,

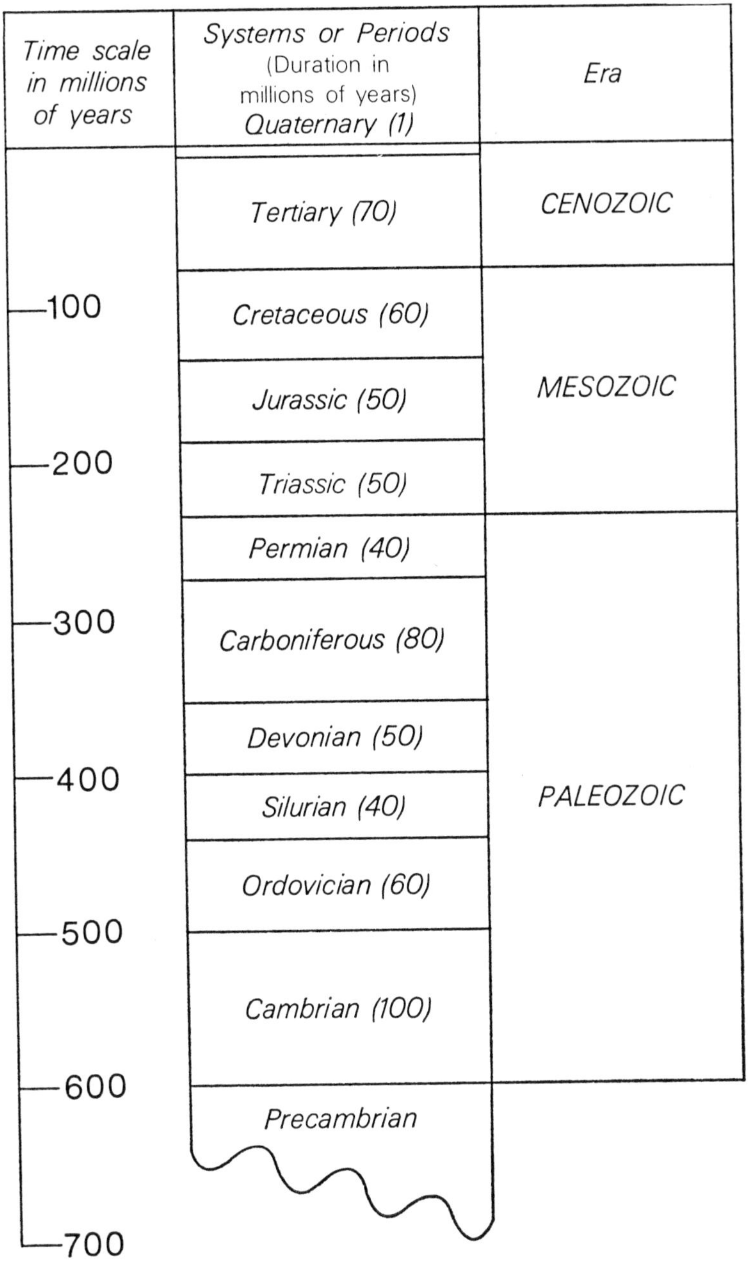

Time scale in millions of years	Systems or Periods (Duration in millions of years) Quaternary (1)	Era
	Tertiary (70)	CENOZOIC
—100	Cretaceous (60)	MESOZOIC
	Jurassic (50)	
—200	Triassic (50)	
	Permian (40)	PALEOZOIC
—300	Carboniferous (80)	
	Devonian (50)	
—400	Silurian (40)	
	Ordovician (60)	
—500	Cambrian (100)	
—600	Precambrian	
—700		

Fig 2 Columnar section for the standard geological column

particularly if the beds contain abundant fossil evidence. With optimum conditions the ultimate palaeontologically based sub-division can be into units with strata a few metres (or even less) in thickness.

THE SILURIAN

The oldest rocks exposed on Mendip are of Silurian age. These are of limited areal extent and are only found in an elongate outcrop in eastern Mendip. The total thickness of the Silurian rocks is in excess of 350m, and the bulk of the succession is composed of rocks of volcanic origin. The volcanic material is of two main types: the lava itself, and material ejected in associa-tion with the lava and composed of ash and small, consolidated fragments of the lava. Such ejected material is known as volcanic tuff.

The manner of deposition, particularly of the tuff, suggests that the volcanic deposits were laid down under water, probably in a marine environment. However, neither the tuff nor lava is of direct stratigraphical value as there is no satisfactory way to date the rock. The stratigraphical dating of volcanic deposits is only possible by considering the fossil content of any sedimentary rocks contained within the sequence of volcanic deposits. Such strata occur in this area as inter-bedded fossiliferous tuff. Near the bottom of the sequence of deposits, and at the top of the volcanic deposits, there are fossiliferous mudstones.

The fossil species obtained from these beds are sufficient to show that the volcanic deposits are sandwiched between rocks that are of undoubted Silurian age. Reynolds (1929a, p 84) states that representatives of thirty-six recognisable species were found in the lower sequence of fossiliferous tuff, and forty species from the mudstones at the top of the succession. The species from the tuffs, however, do not enable an assignation to a particular part of the Silurian to be made with certainty, although Reynolds (1912a, p 80), and Green and Welch (1965, p 7), consider them likely to be of Llandovery age (Lower Silurian). The fossils from the higher mudstones show them to be of undoubted Wenlock age (Middle Silurian).

Despite the detailed information contained in the above papers, the Silurian rocks are, with one exception, poorly exposed. The volcanic rocks, the exception, have been quarried on a large scale for many years, mainly for the production of roadstone. The active quarries at Moon's Hill (663461) and Sunnyhill (660461), and the disused quarries near Downhead (687461), contain excellent exposures of these rocks. However, even these good quarry sections are disappointing in that the rocks are extremely fine-grained and not infrequently deeply weathered and stained. The lava was formerly considered to be andesitic (see, for example, Green and Welch, 1965, p 7), but recent detailed geochemical analyses of a larger number of samples demonstrate that the dominant rock type is a rhyodacite (Van de Kamp, 1969). This revised petrological description is only of consequence to the specialist, and indicates that the lavas are of a more acid type than was previously supposed. In mineralogical terms this acidity is expressed by the presence of more free quartz. As the rhyodacites were extruded at the surface, they follow the normal pattern of such rocks in being extremely fine-grained—a response to the relatively rapid rate of cooling of the molten lava. Thus, in the field, the individual grains can be seen by the naked eye only with difficulty; it is possible to identify the constituent minerals which form the grains only by the use of a microscope. The mean grain size of the lava is less than 0.01mm. Van de Kamp distinguished some fifteen units within the exposed volcanic rocks; in addition to the lavas, there is included debris thrown out during the course of the eruptions. The size of many of these so-called volcanic bombs is such that the original volcanic vent could not have been more than some 3km distant.

The true sedimentary rocks, the fossiliferous tuff and the upper series of mudstones, are extremely poorly exposed in the field. In consulting a geological map it should always be remembered that, by convention, geologists leave no area of the map un-coloured, so that a visit to the non-volcanic Silurian areas marked on the geological map is disappointing, as the area has a soil cover and few actual exposures of the rock itself can be seen. The fossiliferous mudstones have only been seen in place in specially dug trenches, prepared in 1911 and described by Reynolds (1912*a*). In the earlier studies by Reynolds the situation is clearly stated: 'The mutual relations of the different rocks were, however, very difficult to ascertain, as much of the mapping was based on material thrown out by moles and rabbits' (Reynolds, 1907, p 218).

A generalised columnar section based upon the various studies mentioned above is given in Fig 3.

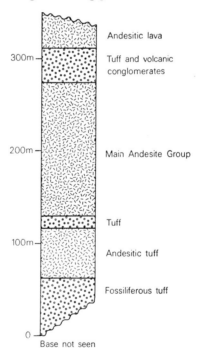

Fig 3 Columnar section for the Silurian rocks in the Moon's Hill area

THE DEVONIAN

The Devonian of parts of Britain is normally referred to as the Old Red Sandstone or more familiarly as the 'Old Red'. This is to distinguish rocks of this age from those lithologically similar but stratigraphically younger, which are known as the New Red Sandstone. The term Old Red Sandstone is restricted to areas where the strata is not only Devonian in age but is of a continental facies. However, it need not necessarily be red in colour, or even of sandstone lithology! In the Mendips, the Devonian deposits are all of Old Red Sandstone type and all the outcrops are associated with high ground. The Old Red underlies the catchments of many of the streams which flow into the swallets, which are developed in the Carboniferous Limestone.

Rock exposures on Mendip are mainly limited to beds exposed in streams; the exposures in the East and West Twin streams in Burrington Combe are particularly good. The lithology ranges from mudstone and fine-grained sandstones to coarse-grained conglomerates. The beds are dominantly composed of quartz grains although felspar is an important minor constituent. Their colour on a local scale is varied but, if the term is loosely used, could be said to exhibit a red hue. Some of the uppermost beds in the sequence have a limited calcareous content.

Examination of samples of the sandstone under a microscope or hand lens frequently shows the individual grains to be rounded, and the red colouration to be due to a dusting on the surface of otherwise colourless grains. This surface coating is mainly of haematite, which is an iron oxide. Close examination will sometimes show a secondary, post-depositional growth of mineral material around the individual particles. This cement is usually siliceous, and is important locally in decreasing the pore space of the sandstone. For example, Whittard (1949, p 479) referring to the Old Red Sandstone of Mendip states that they usually possess an exceedingly low porosity ratio because secondary silica occupies the voids'. The

B

effects of this silicification of the original pore space of the sandstones has important consequences when the groundwater hydrology of the region is considered.

Many of the sandstone beds of the Old Red Sandstone have a tendency to fracture along the original lines of sedimentation (called bedding planes) to give rise to coarse flagstones. These bedding planes, which act as the planes of weakness for the fracturing of the rock when it is exposed to weathering in the atmosphere, are frequently micaceous. The mineral mica has the property of splitting into very thin flakes, and when deposited in a sandstone the individual mica particles impart a perceptible gleam, particularly in freshly fractured surfaces. Such a rock would be termed a micaceous sandstone.

In addition to the sandstone beds of the Old Red, a number of bands of conglomerate occur. These coarse-grained beds are more frequent in the lower part of the succession. The conglomerates are particularly resistant to erosion, and form minor waterfalls where they occur in stream beds, and bluffs along hillsides. They are composed dominantly of white quartz pebbles in a matrix of quartz sand bound together with siliceous cement. Individual pebbles can be up to some ten centimetres in length. They could, indeed, be best described by the homely geological term 'puddingstone'.

The thickness of Old Red Sandstone varies throughout Mendip. Green and Welch (1965, p 10) consider that the fullest succession of about 500m is exposed on Blackdown, and that 400m of Old Red Sandstone can be found overlying the Silurian rocks of eastern Mendip.

There is no real doubt that these rocks are of Devonian age, but as with most continental facies the rocks are almost totally devoid of datable organic remains. Occasionally, the impressions of plants can be found but these are so poorly preserved that they are of no stratigraphical importance. Hepworth and Stride (1950, p 136) mention 'a thin impersistent, bright coal, no more than an inch thick' from the section exposed in the adit driven into the hillside in the valley of the West Twin Stream (476582). This thin coal seam contained plant and fish remains but it appears that it was impossible to identify the species accurately. The paucity of fossil evidence from the Old Red Sandstone of Mendip in fact precludes their direct stratigraphical dating, and they are presumed to be of Devonian age from their relationship to the proven Silurian rocks in the Moon's Hill quarry area, and by the proven overlying Carboniferous rocks at numerous localities. The general nature of the deposit also corresponds closely to other occurrences of Old Red Sandstone which contain diagnostic fossil remains in the Bristol region. By analogy with neighbouring regions, the Devonian rocks of Mendip are considered to be all of Upper Old Red Sandstone age and are correlated to the Portishead Beds (Kellaway and Welch, 1955a). The uppermost beds of the sequence merge into strata of Carboniferous age and will be considered below.

A generalised vertical sequence of the Old Red Sandstone of Mendip is given in Fig 4.

THE CARBONIFEROUS

The Carboniferous system in the United Kingdom is divided into two major stratigraphical units: the Upper and Lower Carboniferous. In the United States the Upper Carboniferous is known as the Pennsylvanian, and the Lower Carboniferous as the Mississippian; this is the only major international departure from the standard geological column. The more familiar classification in the United Kingdom is, however, into three lithologically based divisions. These are, in ascending order, the Carboniferous Limestone, the Millstone Grit, and the Coal Measures. Every caver will realise that all the major caving regions in the British Isles are developed in the Carboniferous Limestone.

In outlining the succession for the Mendip area it should be remembered that significant differences in the type and thickness of limestones occur between the various British caving regions.

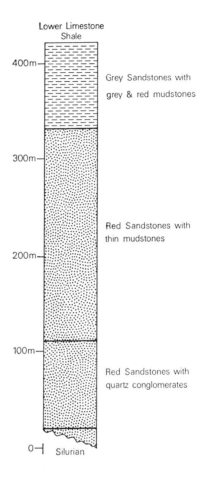

Fig 4 Columnar section for the Old Red Sandstone of the Beacon Hill area

CLASSIFICATION OF THE CARBONIFEROUS LIMESTONE

The classification of the formations within the Carboniferous Limestone of the South West has a very considerable history of its own and has generated a most impressive bibliography. The limestones were deposited in a shallow water, marine environment and are generally rich in fossil material. The exposures tend to be good, and the continuous exposures of several hundreds of metres of strata in the gorges at Burrington and Cheddar (see Plate p 65) are particularly impressive. The combination of fossiliferous material and good exposure led to detailed palaeontological and stratigraphical studies, pioneered by Professor A. Vaughan of the University of Bristol at the beginning of the century. Initially, Vaughan worked in the Avon Gorge near Bristol, and some texts refer to the Carboniferous Limestone of Britain as the Avonian.

Vaughan's major contribution was to divide the Carboniferous Limestone of the Avon section into five major zones and numerous sub-zones (Vaughan, 1905, 1906). These zones were preeminently palaeontological divisions, with the lithological variations as secondary consideration. The work is a classic example of palaeontological zonation, and as such has been taught to generations of geology students, not only in Bristol and in Britain, but on an international scale. The same zonal system, with minor modifications, was applied by Sibly (1905) to the Carboniferous Limestone of Burrington Combe and was later extended (Sibly, 1906) to the Carboniferous Limestone of Mendip as a whole. Vaughan and Reynolds (1911) revised Sibly's work in Burrington Combe and, in fact, slightly modified the Avon section zonation. The zonal sequence was then applied to other areas of Carboniferous Limestone throughout Britain. Detailed maps of varying parts of Mendip, employing Vaughan's zonal notation, were published. Bamber (1924) dealt with the country between the Severn Estuary and the Cheddar Valley, and Welch, in three separate papers (1929, 1932*a* and 1933), extended this work to cover the remaining Carboniferous Limestone outcrop of central and eastern Mendip.

The recognition and application of zonal sub-division is a specialist study, and interested cavers may take heart from the fact that this method of geological mapping for the Carboniferous

Limestone has now partly fallen from grace. The detailed mapping upon which the current geological maps of the region are based is entirely in terms of lithological units. For the purposes of the study of the origin and development of caves, it is the lithology that is of fundamental importance with the palaeontological stratigraphy a poor second. The reason for this change in portrayal on the geological maps is that the detailed zonal classification of Vaughan cannot be sustained as more than a broad guide. This problem is discussed by Kellaway and Welch (1955*b*) for the Bristol region as a whole, and Mitchell and Green (appendix 1 in Green and Welch, 1965, pp 177–97) present a detailed study for Burrington Combe.

The major difficulty with the palaeontological form of zonation is that it is applicable only to a very local area, and the type of fossil found relies heavily on the local conditions of sedimentation at the time the bed was formed. This view is stressed by George (1958, p 231) and succinctly stated as 'the technique of dating beds by a rigid pigeon-holing of fossils can only be expected to break down when "assemblage" zones are traced laterally'. In fairness to the pioneer work of Vaughan it should be added that George (p 233) goes on to say 'but with all their shortcomings they [the zones] are found to be far more widespread and persistent than the highly local lithological groups recognised by "formational" mapping'.

There is no need for us to dwell further on this problem, fundamental though it is to stratigraphy, but as so much of the relevant literature for the Mendips is presented in zonal terms a brief introduction to the basis of the classification is considered useful. For parts of Mendip, notably the western section, the only detailed maps are in terms of Vaughan's zones, and the mapping of the zones enabled the detailed structure of the area to be unravelled.

Vaughan's zonal system
The Carboniferous Limestone was divided into five zones;

four of these bear the names of corals and the fifth that of a brachiopod. The arrangement of the zones, in stratigraphical order, is given in Table 1. It has become common practice to

TABLE 1 *The zonal classification of the Carboniferous Limestone* (based on Vaughan and Reynolds, 1935)

Zone	Name of index fossil and type of fossil	Sub-zones, faunal overlap and phases
D zone	*Dibunophyllum* (coral)	D_3 Base of Millstone Grit and horizon ε D_2 Upper *Dibunophyllum* zone D_1 Lower *Dibunophyllum* zone
S zone	*Seminula* (brachiopod)	S_2 Upper (main) *Seminula* zone S_1 Lower *Seminula* zone
C zone	*Caninia* (coral)	Upper *Caninia* zone C_2 Upper *Syringothyris* zone Lower *Caninia* zone C_1 Lower *Syringothyris* zone γ horizon of overlap of *Caninia* and *Zaphrentis*
Z zone	*Zaphrentis* (coral)	Z_2 Upper *Zaphrentis* zone Z_1 Lower *Zaphrentis* zone β horizon of overlap of *Zaphrentis and Cleistopora*
K zone	*Cleistopora* (coral)	K_2 Upper *Cleistopora* zone K_1 Lower *Cleistopora* zone K_m Base of K_1, forming passage beds to the Old Red Sandstone.

refer to the zones by the initial letter of the zonal fossil: D zone for the coral *Dibunophyllum*, S zone for the brachiopod *Seminula*, etc. The only exception is that the lowest zone of all is known as the K zone although the name comes from the coral *Cleistopora*; this avoids confusion with the *Caninia* zone which is known as the C zone.

A similar principle was used to break the zones down into sub-zones. Vaughan (1905, p 185) explains the method as follows: 'Sub-zonal indices were next adopted, to designate the parts of a zone, whenever a marked change of fauna naturally called for a sub-division of a zone.' The notation adopted to differentiate the sub-zones was to use a suffix such as K_1, D_3 etc. The zones are sub-divided into a total of ten sub-zones.

It was realised that the fossil content of the zones often overlap and to allow for this problem Vaughan used a system of Greek letters: 'faunal overlaps of zones form very definite horizons, and I have designated them Horizons etc' (Vaughan, 1905, p 185).

Lastly, phases within the succession were recognised. These were defined as follows: 'Any interuption of a zonal sequence, by deposits formed under conditions distinct from the standard conditions which have been selected for the purpose of zoning, is termed a "phase" ' (Vaughan and Reynolds, 1935, p 36). The phase is indicated by a suffix such as K_m which represents the *Modiola* phase within the K zone and is marked by shallower sedimentation conditions than the other beds in the K zone.

It is essential to remember that although each zone (or sub-zone) bears the name of one fossil, the recognition of these divisions is determined by the whole fossil assemblage that they contain. This is important since at some exposures even a pro-longed search will not produce even a single specimen of the zonal index fossil.

The literature cited above will act as a guide to the palaeon-tology and stratigraphy of the Mendips, but a consideration of the lithology and thicknesses of the various units is necessary.

The total thickness of the Carboniferous Limestone strata is approximately 1,000m. This can be divided into two distinct units—the Lower Limestone Shale at the base of the succession, and the overlying limestone beds formerly known as the Mountain Limestone. It is worth noting that the Lower Limestone Shale, defined in lithological terms, corresponds in this region to the K zone defined on a palaeontological basis.

Lower Limestone Shales

The Lower Limestone Shales are very similar in lithology and thickness throughout the area. The thickness varies from about 150m on Black Down to 120m in the Beacon Hill area. As the dominant type of rock is a shale, the natural exposures are low-lying compared to those of the more massive limestones typical of the rest of the sequence. The general pattern of the outcrop is usually mapped by its relationship to the topography and soils. Much of the surface expression is marked by an area of relative lowland with waterlogged soils. The base of the formation has only been described in detail from sections exposed in the East and West Twin Streams, and from a better exposed section in the adit associated with the West Twin Stream (475582). The sedimentation is continuous with that of the Upper Old Red Sandstone below, but the junction in this locality is easy to distinguish on lithological grounds. The lowest limestone band is taken as the base of the Lower Limestone Shales, and the sandstone immediately below as the top of the Old Red. This is convenient as no limestone bands then occur in the Old Red and no sandstone beds in the Lower Limestone Shales. The fauna of the lowest limestone bed is marine, in contrast to the continental facies of the sandstone (Hepworth and Stride, 1950, p 137).

The lithology is composed of black or dark-grey shales with inter-bedded bands of limestone, the thickness of the differing bands varying from a few centimetres to several metres. The
B*

shales themselves are frequently calcareous although no major caves are developed in rocks belonging to this group.

LIMESTONE LITHOLOGY—COMPOSITION AND ORIGIN

The upper 1,000m or so of the Carboniferous Limestone succession in the region was formerly known as the Mountain Limestone. In palaeontological terms this includes zones D to Z. The Mountain Limestone was described by Woodward (1876, p 20) as 'generally a bluish-grey limestone, tough and crystalline, and which emits a peculiar sulphurous odour when fractured'. Such a generalised picture is of little use to any detailed understanding of the genesis of caves, and as caves are so intimately related to the limestone strata it will be necessary for us briefly to consider the various types of limestone.

Classification is the necessary curse of any science and in a field science such as geology we are immediately plunged into a morass of terminology. The classification problem commences with 'what is a limestone?', and is soon wrestling with the merits of such terms as calcilutite, intramicrudite–intramicrite, oösparrudite–oösparite and the like. For the reader who would like to extend his knowledge of this subject the published symposium entitled *Classification of carbonate rocks* (Ham, 1962) is a comprehensive account. It is not the purpose of this account to review fully the many classificatory terms that have been suggested, but rather to give the background to those terms in common usage in texts referring to the area, to dispel some of the more common misconceptions, and finally to stress that variations in limestone rock types are likely to have a profound effect on the questions of limestone solution and cave formation.

The mineralogy of limestones is in fact simpler than for almost any other common rock type. The dominant mineral constituents are only two in number—calcite and dolomite. Expressed in chemical terms these are respectively calcium carbonate ($CaCO_3$), and the double carbonate of calcium magnesium ($CaMg(CO_3)_2$). In addition, other related carbonates are also known, the most important one being aragonite. Aragonite is chemically identical to calcite, but it exhibits a differing crystal form and has different physical properties and is, therefore, a separate mineral. This simple picture becomes clouded, as there is a complete gradation as regards chemical composition between the two end members of the calcite to dolomite series; in mineralogical parlance this is known as an isomorphic series. Dolomite, however, cannot exceed the equivalent molecular proportions of 54.35 per cent $CaCO_3$ and 45.65 per cent $MgCO_3$.

It is upon this chemical composition that the modern definition of limestone is based—in contrast to the original lay-definition of any rock that could be burnt to produce lime (CaO). As the essential mineral components are all carbonates, many recent texts refer to such rock collectively as carbonates. For a rock to be correctly termed a carbonate it must be composed of more than 50 per cent, by weight, of carbonate minerals. In part, the term carbonate was coined to avoid the use of the word limestone for rocks with a high content of the mineral dolomite, which are better termed dolomites. Applying these criteria, limestones are carbonate rocks composed of more than 50 per cent, by weight, of the mineral calcite and dolomites then become rocks that contain more than 50 per cent, by weight, of the mineral dolomite. The qualifying adjective 'dolomitic' refers to rocks which contain 10–50 per cent of the mineral dolomite. Exact agreement over the figures is lacking among geologists, but the definitions suggested are certainly useful field terms, and their specific application depends on chemical analysis of the rocks and these are, at best, infrequent. In reality the 50 per cent criterion is not usually a problem as most limestones and dolomites have a carbonate content that is in excess of 90 per cent. There is some evidence that the magnesium carbonate content of carbonate rocks shows two peaks—one at less than 5 per cent, and the other between 40 per cent and the theoretical maximum of 45.65 per cent (Robertson, Simpson and Anderson, 1949, p 32). This is certainly the case for the limestones and dolomites of Mendip. The most significant compositional factor of carbonate rocks, as regards solutional erosion, is the Ca/Mg ratio.

Another fundamental criterion of the classification of carbonate rocks is that of grain size. For field use, it is usual to distinguish three grain sizes. Fine-grained samples are those where the dominant constituent particle size cannot be seen with the naked eye (see Plate p 66, *ul*). Variations occur in the exact limits of this definition but an upper size limit of about o.o5mm would seem commonly acceptable. Medium-grained is then used to define rocks with an average particle size of between o.o5 and 2mm. Coarse-grained limestone deposits are then those in excess of 2mm mean grain size.

A third widely used criterion is that of colour. Simple as this may sound it is capable of leading to considerable confusion. Ideally, a standard colour range should be used. Such a standard does exist and is known as the Munsell Colour Chart, but it is rare to find this chart employed in describing rock colour. Some misunderstandings are avoided if it is remembered that the quoted colours for a rock refer to a newly-fractured, unweathered surface—unless, of course, the colour is specifically referred to as that of the weathered surface. The variation between weathered and unweathered limestone on Mendip can be extremely marked.

Having established the chemical composition, size and colour, further classification is dependent upon the specific purposes for which the classification is required. The choice normally lies between a genetic or a descriptive approach. The latter has the advantage of easier field application, greater applicability to speleology, and avoids the 'cart before the horse' argument often involved in attempting to apply a genetic classification. However, some acquaintance with the broader aspects of genetic classification is necessary as they are used so frequently in geological accounts.

A long-standing three-fold division used for limestone classification was into those of organic, inorganic or mechanical origin.

Organic limestones were those dominantly composed of the skeletal remains of various marine organisms and were frequently prefixed by the dominant form of fossil present. Thus on parts of Mendip the lithological succession is referred to as crinoidal limestone (see Plate p 99, *u*) and other terms are foraminiferal limestone which is composed chiefly of the microscopic shell remains of foraminifera (see Plate p 66, *ur*). Also included in his organic group would be algal limestone which is composed of calcite deposited by algae and bacteria. Fortunately none of the local limestones are of a 'reef type'. This term has become so abused and misused as to be meaningless; certainly it is a gross oversimplification to consider organic shelly limestones, whether containing fossil corals or not, to be the equivalent of the present-day coral reef. Corals can live happily far away from any reef, and reefs need not be composed of corals.

Inorganic limestones, alternatively referred to as chemically deposited limestones, typically include many of the fine-grained mudstones. These are thought to have been chemically precipitated in areas of shallow warm water and the minute particles to have accumulated like falling snow on the sea floor. A fascinating rock type normally placed in this class is oolitic limestone (see Plate p 99, *u*), and other terms are foraminiferal approximate to spheres in shape, are composed of concentric layers of carbonate material, an individual grain being known as an oolith (see Plate p 66, *ll*). In rare cases the grains can approach the dimensions of a pea, for which the homely term pea grit is used. However, if the dimensions of an oolith exceed 2mm it is known as a pisolith and the rock type as a pisolithic limestone.

Finally, mechanical limestones are those composed of broken and worn organic or inorganic limestone fragments laid down in a comparable fashion to sandstones. These are now often referred to as clastic limestones.

This three-fold classification, which at first sight may appear descriptive is, in fact, genetic in that the origin of the limestone is intimately involved. However, the terms are in such frequent usage that they have become commonplace in geological accounts. There is no need to investigate the classification closely to see its shortcomings. There is no way of stating how far a shell must have been transported to move out of the organic pigeon-hole into the mechanical class. Current views on the origin of oolitic limestones suggest that they are not solely the result of chemical precipitation but that algal or bacterial activity is also intimately involved. This has led some writers to suggest modifications, so that the word 'organic' is replaced by 'biochemical' and 'inorganic' by 'physio-chemical'. A further complication fast gaining wide assent is that sediment–burrowing or sediment–ingesting organisms may obliterate the original texture of the rock. Such organisms can cause additional confusion on their death by adding their own skeletal remains to the deposits which they have ingested.

The situation described above relates to the original deposition of the strata, but carbonate rocks are more susceptible to post-depositional change than any other commonly occurring rock type. Such changes are of real importance, and are especially important as regards the origin of dolomites and dolomitic limestones. Dolomites are not known to form on sea floors at the present day, and since it is unlikely that there has been any fundamental change in this environment compared to the geological past, this argues for chemical change at a time after deposition has taken place. Such changes in the composition or texture of the sediment that occur at low temperature in a rock are known as diagenesis or diagenetic changes. These are distinct from changes that may occur in a rock due to subsequent heat and/or pressure which are generally referred to as metamorphisms. Thus dolomitisation of limestones is purely a diagenetic change. The reasons for this marked susceptibility to diagenetic change will now be considered.

The carbonate minerals as a group have a higher solubility than other common rock-forming minerals. Although both calcite and dolomite have high solubilities, they differ slightly from each other; and this is also true of the relationship of calcite to its isomorph aragonite. Thus in a rock with a variable carbonate composition some redistribution of the constituent elements is possible, these changes taking place whilst the rock is in a completely solid state. However, for dolomitisation to progress on anything but a local scale, the addition of magnesium is necessary, and it must be possible for the magnesium to migrate through the rock. Many carbonates have, on deposition, a particularly large void space, which is more usually stated as the carbonates having a high porosity. In addition, the ability of water to flow through many forms of carbonate sediment is considerable. This ability to allow water to flow or percolate through a rock is known as permeability. A combination of high porosity and high permeability renders the carbonates particularly liable to compositional changes due to solutions migrating through the rock.

The problems of post-depositional change, and particularly of dolomitisation, are still largely unanswered. There is little doubt that the dolomitisation of the Carboniferous Limestone on Mendip is of diagenetic type (see Plate p 66, *lr*). In some cases the rock is partly dolomitised, in others the dolomitisation is complete, whilst in other areas there is no dolomitisation at all. The situation as regards dolomitisation of the Lower Carboniferous of Britain as a whole is summed up by the following quotation which, if a little unhelpful, is admirably frank: 'The dolomites, however, are probably all or almost all of subsequent origin in being the product, at an unknown time and by an unknown process, of the diagenetic alteration of other kinds of limestone' (George, 1958, p 247).

A discussion of the dolomitisation for the Mendip area is given by Green and Welch (1965, pp 21–3).

THE LIMESTONE SEQUENCE OF THE LOWER CARBONIFEROUS

Having considered the variations in the types and origins of limestones, let us now consider the main limestone sequence of the Lower Carboniferous. It is thought to be more helpful for the purpose of this study to follow the dominantly lithological division of the strata rather than the zonal classification. In so doing, the account rests heavily upon the Geological Memoir but, where possible, additional information has been incorporated. A columnar stratigraphical section correlating the lithological and zonal schemes is given in Kellaway and Welch (1955*b*, p 10).

The formations recognised are as follows :

> Hotwells Group
> Clifton Down Group
> Black Rock Group
> Lower Limestone Shale.

Black Rock Group

The Black Rock Group is represented by the Black Rock Limestone, which varies in thickness between 250 and 300m. The strata, in contrast to the underlying Lower Limestone Shales, are well exposed in numerous natural and artificial exposures. From the caving viewpoint the formation is of major importance, as many stream swallets and the entrances of major cave systems are developed in these beds, eg Goatchurch, GB, Swildon's, Eastwater, etc. The exposures in Burrington Combe are particularly splendid and have been described in great detail by Green and Welch (1960, pp 180–7); the vertical section in Fig 5 is based upon their published results. For the specialist, a study of the microscopic remains of the foraminifera of the Burrington Combe section is given in Cummings (1958).

The Black Rock Group is composed dominantly of bioclastic limestones, which are generally dark-grey or near black in colour; variations in the lithology are small throughout the region. The rock contains vast amounts of crinoidal debris but the groundmass of the limestone has a tendency to be fine-grained. Throughout the succession this group is richly fossiliferous. At some

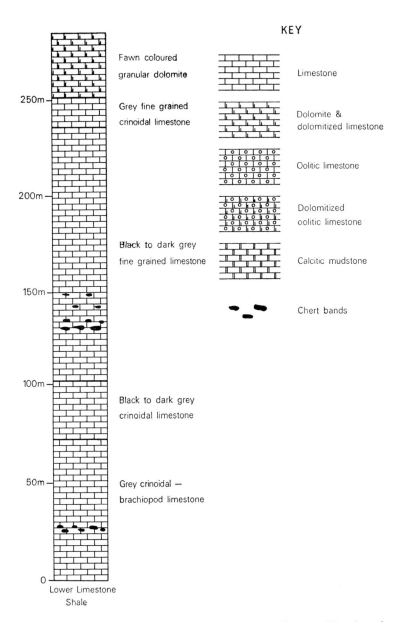

KEY

Fawn coloured
granular dolomite

Grey fine grained
crinoidal limestone

Black to dark grey
fine grained limestone

Black to dark grey
crinoidal limestone

Grey crinoidal —
brachiopod limestone

Lower Limestone
Shale

Limestone

Dolomite &
dolomitized limestone

Oolitic limestone

Dolomitized
oolitic limestone

Calcitic mudstone

Chert bands

Fig 5 Columnar section for the Black Rock Group. The key is
also applicable to Figs 6, 7 and 8

horizons the details of many of the fossils are well preserved (as the original calcitic skeletal remains were silicified) and are therefore particularly resistant to weathering. Silicified fossils of this type can frequently be found protruding from dry stone walls in the area, and also occasionally in cave walls (see Plate p 99, *u*). Exposures and rock debris in the westernmost quarry at Waterlip (658445) are a well known collecting ground for silicified fossils of Black Rock age. The lowest levels of the formation are marked by the preservation in many areas of abundant horn corals, more properly referred to as zaphrentoid corals.

The lower boundary of this group is difficult to separate lithologically from the Lower Limestone Shale below, and the lower half of the Black Rock Group, whilst dominantly composed of massive limestones, also shows some development of thin bedded shales. In addition to the silicification of many of the included fossils, silica also occurs in the form of nodules and sheets of chert. Chert is composed of silica (SiO_2) and is comparable in composition and origin to flint. The division between the two is somewhat arbitrary but chert does not give such sharp edges when fractured. Much of the chert is clearly of secondary origin and not directly deposited in the form in which it is now found; another example of diagenetic change enhanced by the property of limestones to transmit migrating solutions.

A continuous chert band is developed near the middle of the Black Rock Limestone, whilst a band apparently only present in the Black Down area occurs some 30m above the base of these beds. This former bed is often in excess of 15m in thickness.

The uppermost beds of the Black Rock Limestone are locally dolomitised, particularly in the north of the Mendips. In some instances the crinoid remains, which are frequent in these beds, were resistant and are not dolomitised. The distribution of the dolomites is described by Green and Welch (1955, p 18) who state that '. . . their limits, both laterally and vertically, are often difficult to draw in the field due to their gradual passage into non-dolomitised limestone'.

Clifton Down Group

This group has a thickness of between 300 and 400m and exhibits more lateral variation within the region than either the Black Rock Group below or the Hotwells Group above. There is a virtually unbroken series of exposures of the whole group in Burrington Combe. This section is described in detail by Green and Welch (1965, pp 187–94) and the columnar section in Fig 6 are based upon their findings.

Two major lithological divisions are recognised in the Clifton Down Group in the Burrington area : the Burrington Oolite at the base of the succession, and the Clifton Down Limestone above. The Burrington Oolite is indeed oolitic for the whole of its thickness, and as such does not exhibit the marked bioclastic composition typical of most of the Carboniferous Limestone succession in this area. Macrofossils are comparatively sparse in the Burrington Oolite. In parts, the succession is completely composed of ooliths, whilst other beds consist of some ooliths associated either with calcitic mudstones, or limestones consisting of crinoidal debris. The oolites are thought to have developed under very shallow water conditions and there is no indication in this area of the break in sedimentation known from rocks of this age at many British localities. The individual ooliths appear to have formed by the accretion of layers of calcite around a central core which can sometimes be shown to be a minute fragment of crinoidal or foraminiferal material.

The Clifton Down Limestone throughout Mendip shows considerable variations and this is true for the deposits of the Burrington area. The lowest beds are oolitic, whilst the succession includes various forms of calcitic mudstone, and the middle section exhibits silicification both in the form of chert bands and nodules and the preservation, in the form of silica, of included fossils. The mudstones, whilst by definition fine-grained, have in some cases a particularly distinctive appearance. Some of the mudstones weather to a pale-grey or white colour

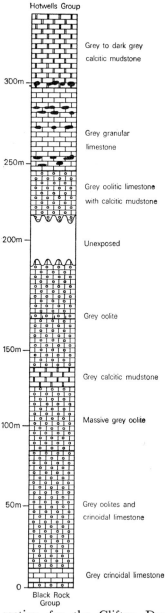

Fig 6 Columnar section for the Clifton Down Group of the
Burrington area. For key see Fig 5

and have a characteristic fracture of a flinty or conchoidal nature. The correct terminology for these rocks is to describe them as porcellaneous but the long-established local term for these calcite mudstones is 'chinastone'.

The stratigraphy of the Clifton Down Group for other areas on Mendip shows considerable variations from that described above. The variations shown on the current geological maps are the Cheddar Oolite and the Cheddar Limestone, and to the east the Vallis Vale Limestone.

Green and Welch (1965, pp 28–32) describe in detail the succession of the Clifton Down Group stratigraphically above the Burrington Oolite. These strata are exposed in the sides of Cheddar Gorge itself. Due to the marked lateral variation, the type of limestone differs from that of the Burrington exposures: It should be stressed, however, that both sequences are composed of particularly pure limestones and that the beds have a tendency to be massively bedded. Green and Welch recognise two local formations, the Cheddar Limestone and the Cheddar Oolite, at the base of the Clifton Down Group in this part of southern Mendip. These are overlain by the Clifton Down Limestone. The salient points of the lithology can be seen from the vertical sections in Fig 7 which are constructed from the information given by Green and Welch (1965).

A final example of the variability of the Clifton Down Group is the local occurrence of volcanic rocks. There are small outcrops within the confines of our area at Uphill and at Woodspring, and also at Spring Cove near Weston-super-Mare. The deposits consist of basalt and associated tuffs (as the basalts contain the mineral olivine they are more specifically olivine-basalts). The Spring Cove exposures show signs of pillow structures, which are taken to indicate that the original volcanic eruption was of a submarine nature. This statement is further strengthened by the inclusion of broken limestone fragments within the sequence of basalts. The deposits were described in some detail by Reynolds (1916), and further comments regarding

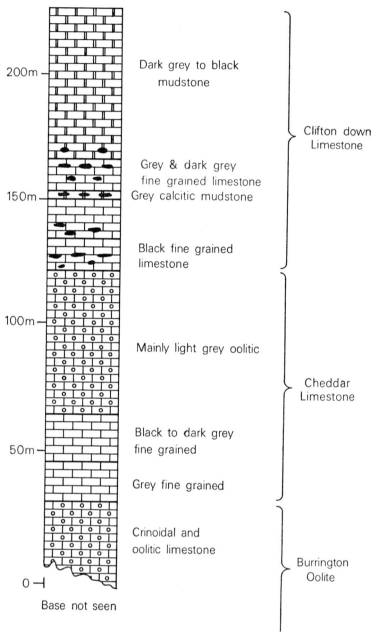

Fig 7 Columnar section for the Clifton Down Group of the Cheddar area. For key see Fig 5

the age of the deposits are given in Curtis *et al* (1955, p 16). There is disagreement over the exact age, but the deposits occur low in the Clifton Down succession.

The final mapped unit recognised by the Geological Survey within the Clifton Down Group is the Vallis Limestone. This corresponds in stratigraphical position to the lower part of the Burrington Oolite. The Vallis Limestone is mapped only in eastern Mendip, and the most westerly exposure is in a quarry near to the Hunter's Lodge Inn (547499). At its maximum development the formation has a thickness of some 100m and is well exposed in the quarries at Vallis Vale. The limestone is light-grey in colour, typically oolitic–crinoidal in composition, and sometimes coarse-grained.

These are the major lithological units recognised within the Clifton Down Group, and it has been stressed that they show considerable lateral variation. The recognition and mapping of such units is difficult, and the best overall comment is that the Clifton Down Group is indeed extremely variable.

Hotwells Group

The uppermost division of the Carboniferous Limestone Series distinguished on Mendip is the Hotwells Group. This is represented on Mendip by the Hotwells Limestone which corresponds almost exactly with the original D zone classification. The complete succession is found infrequently on Mendip, but at Ebbor Rocks the thickness is about 150m.

Only the lower part of the formation, approximately 30m in thickness, is seen in the Burrington area, where the exposures form the northernmost flank of Mendip; the upper parts of the Hotwells Limestone are buried under younger deposits. The thickness of the exposed beds is greater in the outcrops on the eastern parts of Cheddar Gorge with a succession in excess of 100m. In both localities the lithology is distinguished from the Clifton Down Limestone by a change from dark-coloured mudstones to a grey, dominantly crinoidal limestone. The beds concerned usually have a massive appearance. The basal part of the succession is exposed in crags above Gough's Cave and reaches road level near to the foot of Jacob's ladder. Long Hole and Great Oones Hole are developed at the very base of this formation. A geological map and description of the Cheddar Gorge area are given in Green and Welch (1965, pp 28–32), and the vertical column for parts of the Hotwells Limestone for Burrington and Cheddar are given in Fig 8. These too are based on Green and Welch.

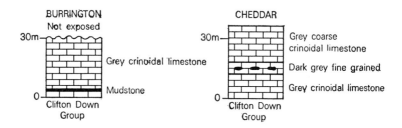

Fig 8 Columnar section for the Hotwells Group of the Burrington and Cheddar areas. For key see Fig 5

The other exposures of the Hotwells Limestone are in more easterly parts of Mendip. The Hotwells Limestone is exposed in the Cook's Wood Quarries (670479), and the risings at St Dunstan's Well are associated with the youngest rocks of the formation. The whole sequence is also present in the Ebbor area. Unlike the Clifton Down Group the Hotwells Limestone retains a consistent character throughout the area; everywhere the limestones are grey in colour, massive and bioclastic, and in the Ebbor and Cook's Wood area the crinoidal nature becomes crinoidal–oolitic. Shale and chert bands form a minor but important element in the stratigraphy.

The upper parts of the Hotwells Limestone and its relationship to the Quartzitic Sandstones of Millstone Grit age above are not well exposed. It would appear that the contact between the carbonate-rich rocks of the Hotwells Limestone and the Quartzitic

Sandstones is sharp, although locally a thin series of sandy limestones is encountered.

UPPER CARBONIFEROUS

The Carboniferous Limestone, which forms the Lower Carboniferous, is succeeded in most parts of Britain by the Millstone Grit and the Coal Measures, which together correspond to the Upper Carboniferous.

The Millstone Grit

In most British regions the Millstone Grit has a total thickness of several hundred metres, dominantly composed of sandstones. Northern cavers will be aware of the striking effect that the Millstone Grit has on the landscape of the Pennines. In the Mendips, however, the situation is very difficult. Overlying the Carboniferous Limestone Series there is a series of beds known as the Quartzitic Sandstone Group. This has a thickness of less than 6m. At first sight it would seem likely that these beds correspond to a condensed sequence of the Millstone Grit, which they closely resemble lithologically. These beds are only sparsely fossiliferous, especially as regards the presence of goniatites which are the zonal fossils used for the Millstone Grit. The only undoubted specimen of a zonal goniatite indicative of the Millstone Grit was obtained from the faulted and overthrust rocks at Upper Vobster (705498). Fossils from the lower part of the Quartzitic Sandstone Group would suggest that stratigraphically these beds are dominantly of Lower Carboniferous age. The uppermost beds contain fossils indicating a Coal Measure age. There appear to be no breaks in the sedimentation sequence, and this thin development of rocks of apparent Millstone Grit age remains an unsolved problem— the more mysterious as undoubted Millstone Grit deposits are well developed in the corresponding South Wales caving region! The problem was recognised by De La Beche as early as 1850 and it has become common practice to refer to these beds as 'Millstone Grit', always employing inverted commas.

The thickness of the Quartzitic Sandstone Group on Mendip is everywhere less than 6om and in the northern outcrops nearer 5om. The deposits are all in the eastern half of Mendip, and the dominant element in the succession is a quartzitic sandstone with only minor occurences of other rock types. There is some secondary silica enlargement of the quartz grains. Rocks of this type are exposed near Ashwick in Harridge Wood (649481). The quartzites can often be seen in natural exposures and in quarries which worked the stone for building purposes. Several accounts (eg Sibly, 1906, p 362 and Woodward, 1876, p 30) draw attention to trial working for coal in the Ebbor area where it would appear that at least one thin coal seam was found, although of no commercial value.

Coal Measures

Rocks of undoubted Upper Carboniferous age (corresponding to the Coal Measures) are well displayed in the Bristol region and to the north of Mendip, but they have little direct effect on Mendip itself. The Somerset coalfield has a total thickness of nearly 3,000m of Coal Measure strata, which completes the Upper Palaeozoic succession. This area is renowned for the preservation of its fossil plant remains, particularly in the Radstock area. However, most of the coalfield is concealed below younger rocks.

The succession can be grouped into three major divisions : the lowest is the Lower Coal Series, followed by the Pennant Series and the Upper Coal Series. The lithology of the Upper and Lower Coal Series is largely composed of mudstones and shales, whilst the Pennant Series consists of coarse sandstones. It should be remembered that although these series collectively form the Coal Measures, the thickness of the actual coal seams accounts for only 1 per cent or so of the total thickness of the strata. The coal seams in the Somerset coalfield are amongst the thinnest worked seams in Britain.

On Mendip itself the only occurrences of Coal Measure strata are the uppermost beds exposed in the Ebbor area. These consist of shales with inter-bedded sandstone bands, and would appear to follow the Quartzitic Sandstone Group without a break in sedimentation. The Coal Measure strata are exposed immediately to the north of Mendip between Nettlebridge and Mells, and again would appear to indicate a continuous sedimentation from the Carboniferous Limestone and the 'Millstone Grit'. The strata in this area continue well up into the Pennant Series and formerly supported a small but prosperous group of coal mines.

Sedimentation was virtually continuous in the Bristol region from the Upper Old Red Sandstone to the highest beds of the Upper Carboniferous. In terms of absolute time this represents a period of about 100 million years. The sedimentation then ceased and the area was subject to a marked phase of tectonic activity and sub-aerial erosion. The stratigraphical record is then a blank until the renewed deposition of material of Mesozoic age, commencing with rocks of Triassic age. There are no deposits from the intervening Permian period.

THE TRIAS

In most parts of Britain the Trias, and the Permian, are composed of strata laid down under continental conditions. There are similarities with the Old Red Sandstone sedimentation, and in parts of Britain the deposits of Permian and Trias age are collectivly known as the New Red Sandstone. The continental nature of the sediments is associated with a paucity of fossiliferous material, and therefore exact stratigraphical dating is difficult. However, it is generally agreed that the Triassic deposits in the Bristol and Mendip region are of Keuper age, which corresponds to the latter part of the Trias system. Throughout the Permian, and for much of the Trias, Mendip was a land mass and, normally, no direct geological evidence is available for such periods. This is true for Mendip with one notable exception, which is the occurrence of Triassic fissure deposits which allow us a direct glimpse of the land fauna, and have fascinating overtones as regards cave formation in this geologically remote period. These aspects will be considered later in more detail.

A study of the lithology and thickness of the Keuper deposits for Mendip is difficult if we attempt to summarise the available information in the form of columnar sections. The difficulty is due to the variations in the type and thickness of deposit laid down— even in localities separated by only a few metres. In geological terminology these deposits are said to belong to diachronous facies. A facies is a term used to describe all features of a deposit laid down under a recognisable set of environmental conditions. The three facies involved in the Upper Trias of Mendip are the Rhaetic the Keuper Marl and the Dolomitic Conglomerate. Both of the latter two names are singularly unfortunate in that they give misleading ideas as to the nature of the deposits to which they refer. Both, however, are so firmly established in the literature that to consider renaming the deposits is impossible—if only for the reason that the names now have a meaning as regards stratigraphical age.

The Keuper

The Keuper Marl is in fact not a marl, for the term, if correctly used, describes a strongly calcareous clay soil. A better description of the lithology of the Keuper Marl would be a mudstone—in our area dominantly red in colour. The 'Tea Green Marls' (another antiquated, unscientific, descriptive term) are only found in areas peripheral to Mendip. In a fresh exposure the Keuper Marl is almost structureless, weakly calcareous and, if studied under a microscope, often found to contain minute crystals of dolomite. The grain size and lack of clear stratification are indicative of an origin as a wind blown deposit, with similarities to the loess deposits of China. In many localities outside our immediate region saline deposits are found, and even if the supposition regarding wind transport is correct there is little doubt that the deposit finally settled out in water. The only fossils are ultramicroscopic spores and unicellular plankton.

The distribution of the land and sea masses—the palaeogeography—at this period will be considered later, but to understand the nature of the Dolomitic Conglomerate a broad outline of the distribution is necessary at this stage. In Upper Triassic times, what we now know as Mendip can be considered as an upstanding mass of resistant Palaeozoic rocks, largely limestone, slowly being engulfed in progressively deepening deposits of Keuper Marl. The Upper Carboniferous cover was apparently eroded entirely during Permian times. The hillsides that developed on these resistant rocks were mantled by scree deposits, and it is the remains of these screes that are today preserved as the Dolomitic Conglomerate. These deposits are thus the diachronous equivalent of the Keuper Marl. Critics have suggested that the Dolomitic Conglomerate is neither dolomitic nor conglomerate. In the strict sense a conglomerate is a water-lain deposit of rounded pebbles; these scree deposits are angular and not normally the product of water action, so that a preferable term would be a breccia. The individual components composing the breccia are fragments of the rock weathering to form the scree. Thus the lithology of the particles can differ locally but is frequently derived from limestones of the Carboniferous Limestone succession, although it is, occasionally, composed of Old Red Sandstone material. The size of the constituent particles varies from about pea size to boulders over a metre in diameter. The matrix in which these particles are now embedded is varied, sometimes consisting of sandstone but more commonly a cement composed of carbonates frequently of a dolomitic type. The Dolomitic Conglomerate has often been affected subsequent to its deposition, not only by dolomitisation of the cement and occasionally the whole deposit, but also by local silicification and by the formation of ore deposits, of which the various iron oxides are dominant (often imparting a red or yellow colour to the deposit). These iron oxides have been worked in past periods for red or yellow ochre.

The thickness of the Triassic deposits on Mendip is extremely variable. The Dolomitic Conglomerate probably reaches a maximum thickness of some 100m, but its origin as a scree deposit or an alluvial fan resulted in marked local variations. The Dolomitic Conglomerate is coarsest near the cliffs from which the material was weathered, and grades to finer material away from the cliffs. No detailed sedimentological studies of the Dolomitic Conglomerate have been undertaken on Mendip, but studies on similar deposits in the Vale of Glamorgan by Bluck (1965) indicate that there the Dolomitic Conglomerate was laid down in fan-like deposits associated with fluvial activity. It is thought that a similar origin can be postulated for part, at least, of the Mendip deposits. In some areas the Dolomitic Conglomerate passes imperceptibly into the silt grade particles of the Keuper Marl. The Keuper Marl itself has a thickness of 50–150m to the north of Mendip and a thickness of 500m to the south of the area. The cover on Mendip itself is everywhere probably less than 100m, but as the lithology mantles an irregular surface it is impossible to make useful generalised statements as to the thickness over the area as a whole.

The uppermost beds of the Keuper Marl in the Bristol region differ from the red mudstone and siltstone which form the dominant lithology. These youngest Trias deposits are known as the Tea Green Marl. The lithology is again composed of mudstone, but the major variation is the colour which tends to be grey or green. This colour change is due to a differing form of oxidation of the iron compounds and is thought to indicate formation under less extreme arid climatic conditions. The Tea Green Marl is not exposed on Mendip itself. Exposures are to be found on the Isle of Wedmore, where the total thickness of the Tea Green Marls is approximately 30m. Some 5m of strata of the Tea Green Marl is exposed in a section in Madwoman's Lane (427471). This section passes up into the overlying beds of Rhaetic age.

The Rhaetic

The Tea Green Marls of Upper Triassic age grade, without any break in sedimentation, into the Rhaetic succession. The

Rhaetic deposits differ from those of the Upper Trias in that they represent a progressive change from conditions of continental deposition to those of a marine environment. The Rhaetic itself grades, again without any break in sedimentation, into the lowest Jurassic beds. The Rhaetic, therefore, represents a time of changing environment, and such beds are often referred to as passage beds. The difficulty in stratigraphy is how to divide the strata corresponding to this gradual change into acceptable units. One earlier notation was to consider the Rhaetic as representing a full system of comparable status to the Trias or Jurassic. This solution is not now generally accepted and the beds of the Rhaetic Series are usually linked with either the Trias below or the Jurassic above. The Geological Survey now groups the Rhaetic with the Trias in accordance with continental practice.

Generally, in Britain, the Rhaetic succession is only about 15m thick. (The base is taken as the occurrence of the first marine fossils.) The deposits on Mendip are usually less than 10m thick and are poorly exposed. The main outcrop occurs in the area between the Castle of Comfort, and Chewton Mendip. In part, the Rhaetic is underlain by Keuper Marl but in other localities it lies directly on a folded and eroded surface of Carboniferous Limestone. The beds of the Rhaetic can be considered as resulting from a marine transgression lapping around, and slowly covering, a small number of islands corresponding to the present area of Mendip. The deposits therefore vary from sandstones and conglomerates representing the original Rhaetic beach and in-shore facies, to shales and pale-grey calcareous mudstones which were deposited away from the immediate shoreline. The details of the lithology on Mendip are often masked by later modification which affected the Rhaetic and other beds. This modification takes the form of silicification, and the beds so affected are mapped and referred to as the Harptree Beds. The best exposure of the Harptree Beds is on the sides of Wurt Pit (559539). These beds comprise the lowest units of the Jurassic, although the lower portions of Wurt Pit are probably in rocks of Rhaetic age (Donovan, 1958). The

Rhaetic deposits are famed for the Bone Bed which occurs near the base of the succession. This bed is remarkably continuous over large areas despite its thickness of only a few centimetres. The Bone Bed is composed of myriad remains of fish in which the scales, bones, and teeth are particularly notable and, in addition, occasional reptilean remains are found. A temporary exposure of the Rhaetic Bone Bed was described by Savage (1962) from the Emborough area (626509). The Rhaetic deposits and the included Bone Bed are well exposed in a famous section at Aust Cliff adjacent to the Severn Bridge.

Fissure infillings of Rhaetic and Lower Jurassic age have been described from eastern Mendip (Moore, 1867; Kuhne, 1946; Halstead and Nicoll, 1971). Unlike the Triassic fissures, these deposits were laid down under water, probably in a shallow near-shore environment. The deposits were trapped in an underwater cleft, usually formed from an enlarged bedding plane or joint in the limestone. The deposited material includes a large number of fish teeth. These teeth are extremely small and are found by sieving the material filling the fissure. The sieving and sorting of several tons of material at Holwell Quarry (726450) yielded some 70,000 fish teeth and also 29 small mammalian teeth. These fossil remains are the earliest known occurrence of mammals in the British geological column. In appearance these mammals were probably similar to marsupials about the size of the modern mouse. Although the fossils are of Rhaetic age they were finally deposited in a sea of Middle Jurassic age. In geological parlance such fossils are termed derived. Nevertheless, the fossils give a clear indication that islands existed in Rhaetic and Middle Jurrassic times.

THE JURASSIC

Jurassic strata in Britain are often several hundred metres thick and typically include considerable thicknesses of oolitic limestones and clays. The Cotswold edge at Cheltenham is composed entirely of Jurassic material and is nearly 250m high. On Mendip the Jurassic is not directly associated with the caves, but in the eastern

Page 65

The lower section of Cheddar Gorge (view is down the Gorge) showing
the degree of rock exposure and the massive nature of the limestone

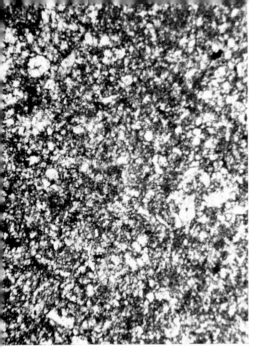

Micro-photographs of various limestones found on Mendip (*above left*) Fine grained limestones of Carboniferous age. Magnification 40 times (*above right*) An organic limestone, composed in part of foraminifera. Magnification 40 times (*below left*) Burrington Oolite, showing the spherical nature of the individual ooliths. Magnification 40 times (*below right*) Dolomitised limestone. Magnification 40 times

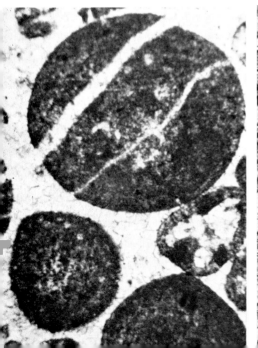

section the Carboniferous Limestone is masked by rocks of this age. Indeed the whole of Mendip must originally have had a covering of Jurassic material, although limited areas would have continued as land masses in the Lower and Middle Jurassic. The Jurassic stratigraphy of Mendip differs from the succession to the north and south in that it is very much reduced in thickness and includes a number of periods of non-deposition. For the moment let it suffice that the axial east–west line through Mendip was one of structural activity throughout the Jurassic.

For the purposes of stratigraphical description the Jurassic is divided into three. The Lower Jurassic is often referred to as the Liassic whilst the Middle Jurassic includes the Inferior and Great Oolite. The Upper Jurassic does not outcrop within the region with which we are concerned and therefore detailed consideration is not necessary.

The Liassic sedimentation continues the marine sequence established in the Rhaetic without any major break or change in lithology. Only the Lower Lias is represented on Mendip, the total thickness being only about 15m. The lithology is dominantly composed of light-coloured limestones which are frequently coarse-grained and bio-clastic, with very thin clay bands as a minor constituent. The deposits are sometimes composed of conglomerates, and it would appear that small islands continued into the Liassic. The lithology is in marked contrast with the Lower Lias to the north and south of Mendip where the deposits consist of well over a hundred metres of clay.

The Middle and Upper Lias are not represented on Mendip although they are well developed within the region. The lack of these deposits on Mendip is due in part to non–deposition, the area being above the sea level of the times, and in part to erosion of material before the sea inundated the area afresh to continue the stratigraphical succession.

A widespread advance of the sea into the region occurred in the Middle Jurassic. More specifically this was of Upper Inferior Oolite age. The Inferior Oolite strata often lie directly upon a

c

surface of marine-eroded Carboniferous Limestone, confirming the transgressive nature of the sea at this time. The exposures in the Vallis Vale quarries, which show the contact of the buff-coloured oolitic limestones, juxtaposed against the dark-grey Carboniferous Limestone have assumed the status of a classic in the geological literature. The Carboniferous strata shows a planed marine surface, which has become buried under accumulated oolitic material. Such marine planation surfaces cut in limestones can be found at numerous localities around the present British shoreline and it is easy to imagine a comparable situation in the Jurassic. This reconstruction is vividly supported by the occurrence at Vallis Vale of holes and tubes bored into the Carboniferous rocks by Jurassic marine organisms, and preserved with an infilling of lighter-coloured Jurassic materials. The exposure is normally easy to see as the quarrying operations have stripped back the top few feet of Jurassic overburden to exhume the original marine surface. The site has particular merit for the teaching of introductory stratigraphy and is a splendid example of an unconformity. Cloford Quarry Cave (717444) is developed at the plane of unconformity between the Inferior Oolite and the Carboniferous Limestone. The details are described in Drew and Smith (1972).

On the periphery of Mendip, the Doulting Stone quarries extract rocks of Upper Inferior Oolite age for use as a building stone. Sections can be seen in several quarries but those in the St Andrew's Quarry (648434) are particularly noteworthy. The thickness of the Upper Inferior Oolite strata at this locality is a little over 15m, of which 6m of massively bedded freestone is suitable for building purposes. The succession is composed of bioclastic limestones, some of which are shelly, and some oolitic. The Inferior Oolite strata of Mendip are similar in lithology to the corresponding deposits at Cheltenham, but the thickness is reduced to nearly a tenth.

The Inferior Oolite series forms the older of the two divisions of the Middle Jurassic and is the youngest of the geological strata in the Mendip area. The upper portion of the Middle Jurassic is represented by the Great Oolite succession. The terms Inferior and Great Oolite were originally proposed by William Smith in the late eighteenth century; the term 'inferior' was used in the sense of meaning 'lower than' rather than any suggestion that the Inferior Oolite was less well developed or in any other way a lesser rock than the Great Oolite. The Great Oolite succession is well displayed in the Bath region.

Although the stratigraphical record on Mendip ceases in the Middle Jurassic, it should be stressed that the region was undoubtedly covered by later rocks. The fact that none of these younger rocks are now present is due to erosional processes and should not be taken to suggest non-deposition. Considerations of the palaeogeography of the British Isles for the periods subsequent to the Middle Jurassic clearly indicate that the Mendips must originally have been covered with a very considerable thickness of Upper Jurassic, Cretaceous, and possibly Tertiary material.

For example, the Upper Jurassic rocks preserved in Dorset comprise a total thickness of some 700m and it is thought that a similar sequence would have been laid down on Mendip. The structural effects that limited the thickness of the Lower and Middle Jurassic are thought to have ceased in the area during the Upper Jurassic. It is even more certain that the Cretaceous would have given rise to extensive deposits. The edge of the Chalk escarpment at Warminster is only some 15 km from eastern Mendip and palaeogeographical reconstructions apart, it is not difficult to imagine that the Mendip mass has only recently emerged from beneath its former cover, which could have included at least 150m of Cretaceous chalk. The former extent of the Tertiary cover gives rise to much less agreement in geological literature.

The processes by which the Mesozoic rocks were stripped from the area are best considered together with the processes that shape the physical landscape as it is seen today.

THE GEOLOGICAL STRUCTURE OF THE MENDIPS

Several geological factors are of significance in the formation of a cave. Of these we have already outlined the lithology of the rock and the thickness of the various stratigraphical units. This leaves us to consider the geological structure of the area. The structure is of direct importance in that it is an essential control on the form of the cave system. This control affects the major features of the system both as regards its vertical and horizontal plan, and also some of the minor aspects, such as passage cross-section.

The geological structure of an area can be conveniently considered under three headings. At a minor scale there are the bedding planes and joints which are common to most sedimentary rock types. If, however, an area has been exposed to tectonic activity, the originally horizontal or sub-horizontal bedding planes will show some form of tilt which, with increasing tectonic severity, will pass into fold structures. Finally, associated with the same tectonic activity it is likely that the strata will give some evidence of movement along fracture lines, which are known as faults.

Prior to describing the structural geology of Mendip a short introductory guide to the appropriate terminology will be given.

Bedding planes and joints

A bedding plane is a natural parting in the rock associated with the original sedimentation. Bedding planes are normally horizontal unless the rock has been subject to post-depositional movement. The thickness of individual beds can vary from fractions of a millimetre in a shale, to over a metre, as in many Carboniferous limestones. In the latter case the strata would be described as 'massively bedded'.

Joints are not a feature of the original sedimentation although it is likely that they are formed soon after the rock has become indurated. In unweathered rock, joints are normally composed of hairline fractures, but no movement occurs relative to the fracture. The spacing of the joints varies with the lithology and the tectonic history. The joints usually exhibit a distinct pattern as regards their orientation; each set of joints maintains a constant orientation and is related geometrically to other set of joints in the rock. This relationship can assume a variety of forms, but commonly the two major sets of joints in a rock are approximately at right angles to each other.

Both bedding planes and joints act as planes of weakness within a rock and as such, often form the paths for water flow. In limestones particularly, the water movement leads to chemical erosion along the joints, and the initially minute cracks become enlarged and are thus readily visible. The rectilinear pattern of many cave plans is a direct result of erosion along two or more sets of joints, and the detailed form of passage cross-sections is frequently due to the differing resistance to erosion of the limestones forming adjacent beds. It is also common for calcite veins to be emplaced along the joints, and in unweathered rock surfaces this is often the easiest way to recognise the presence and orientation of joints.

Folding

In common with most Palaeozoic rocks in the British Isles the Mendips have been subject to phases of severe tectonic activity. The response of strata to the compressive forms set up during tectonic activity is either to fold or to fault. The exact form of the folding or faulting depends on the rock type and on the intensity and direction of the forces involved.

To unravel the structural history of a region it is necessary for the tilt, or in geological terms the dip, to be measured. The dip is measured in terms of the angle that a bedding plane makes with the horizontal. This angle varies according to the direction of measurement, and the dip angle referred to in a geological context is the *maximum* angle between the bedding plane and the horizontal. The direction at right angles to the line of dip is known as the strike of the rock; by definition, therefore, the strike drawn on a bedding plane is a horizontal line (see Fig 9).

When the dip and strike directions are mapped it is possible to recognise patterns which act as a guide to the overall structural

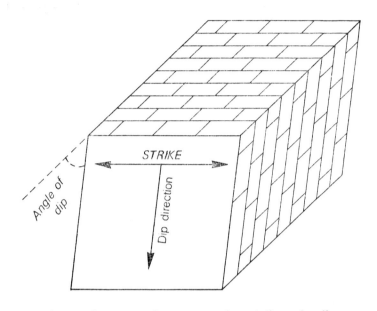

Fig 9 A diagrammatic representation of dip and strike

forms. The pattern of folds which emerge from such structural maps can take a variety of forms but essentially the basic units are comparable to the wave-like forms that occur on a wrinkled tablecloth. The crests of the waves are referred to as anticlines and the troughs as synclines; the plane drawn through the crest or trough is known as the axial plane of the fold or more simply as its axis. The amplitude, or height, of the corresponding

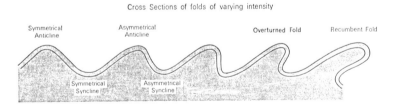

Fig 10 A diagrammatic representation of differing fold types

geological features can vary from a matter of a few centimetres to several kilometres. The length of the folds can also vary between wide limits. The overall cross-sectional form of a fold can also exhibit a variety of forms. These are illustrated in Fig 10 where the simplest cross-sectional form is that of a symmetrical syncline or anticline. An increase in the compression first causes the folds to become asymmetrical, and then one limb of the fold becomes overturned. A final case is that of a recumbent fold which is sometimes referred to as a nappe structure. Overturned and recumbent folds result in the beds on one limb of the structure becoming inverted. In an individual exposure it can be extremely difficult to establish whether the beds are in fact inverted, and the structure of a region can only be really appreciated from the mapped pattern extending over a considerable area. It should also be remembered that it is in fact rare for synclines or anticlines to extend as parallel folds for long distances; the more usual case is for a series of folds to assume a staggered pattern often referred to as an *en echelon* arrangement. In such a pattern the structure of individual anticlines more closely resembles the form of an upturned rowing-boat rather than an infinitely long wave crest. Such an upturned boat form is referred to as a pericline, which can be considered as a type of anticline.

Examples of all these fold structures are encountered in the Palaeozic rocks of Mendip, and an understanding of folding is essential to a study of form and distribution of the cave systems.

Faults

The resistance of strata to tectonic forces depends on the lithology, and other factors such as the spacing of the bedding planes. There is, however, a limit to the capacity of the strata to respond to tectonic forces by folding, and once this limit is exceeded the rock fractures and the stresses are taken up by differential movement along the two sides of the fracture. Such a fracture is known as a fault. The movement between the two sides of the fault can vary from less than a metre to several tens

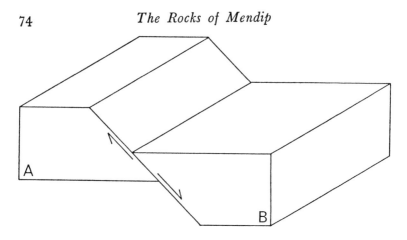

Fig 11 Block diagram of a normal fault

of kilometres. Faults are, in general, near-planar surfaces and can be divided into a number of distinctive types.

The simplest type is the 'normal' fault (Fig 11). In this case block B has dropped relative to block A. In the second case block B has been forced up over block A, and this is known as a 'reverse' fault (Fig 12). In the examples illustrated in Figs 12 and

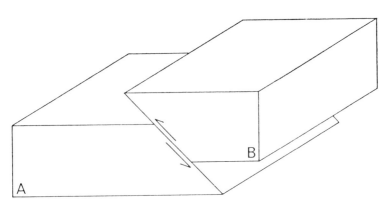

Fig 12 Block diagram of a reverse fault

13 the relative movement has been shown as vertically up or down the fault plane. In reality the movement is rarely confined solely to the dip or strike direction of the fault plane, and more often the movement is oblique to the plane, as illustrated in Fig 13. In limited cases the movement is restricted to the strike direction (Fig 13 example C). Such faults are known by a variety of terms of which strike-slip, wrench or tear fault are in common usage. The amount of vertical movement on a fault is known as the 'throw' of the fault.

The dip of the fault plane in both normal and reversed faults is usually high, exceeding say 60°. A special case of the reverse

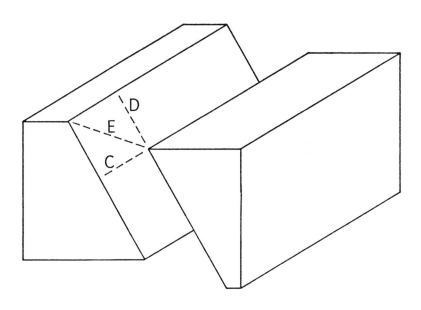

C = Strike Slip   D = Dip Slip   E = Oblique Slip

Fig 13 Block diagram showing strike slip, dip slip and oblique slip faults

c*

fault, distinguished by its low angle of dip, say less than 10°, is the 'thrust' fault.

The block diagrams used to illustrate the differing types of fault are unrealistic in that they show a marked surface feature where the plane of the fault intersects the ground surface. Such features only occur in regions which are tectonically active at the present day, and when associated with the actual fault movement are known as fault scarps. Introductory text books usually illustrate fault scarps from New Zealand or the west coast of America. However, in the British Isles there are no known fault scarps, and any topographic expression associated with faults is due to differing erosion rates on the two sides of the fault.

All the fault types described above occur in the Mendip region. The overall disturbance of the geological pattern by faulting naturally affects the form of caves and caves systems. Additionally, the fault planes are associated with broken rock material (fault breccia) which often affords a relatively easy path for the passage of groundwater.

STRUCTURES ON MENDIP

It is usual in generalised accounts of the structural history of the British Isles to recognise three major periods of tectonic activity during the portion of the stratigraphical column of post– pre-Cambrian age. Such periods are known as orogenies, and each of these major orogenies is differentiated by name. The earliest is known as the Caledonian orogeny, which attained its peak of activity at the end of the Lower Palaeozoic period. A comparable period of tectonic activity occurred at the close of Upper Palaeozoic and is known as the Armorican or Hercynian orogeny. The last is referred to as the Mid-Tertiary or, alternatively, the Alpine orogeny. It must be stressed that the folds and faults assigned to an individual orogeny are formed over a very long period of geological time, and the so-called mountain building aspects of an orogeny should not be considered as some form of sudden or catastrophic event.

The Silurian rocks of eastern Mendip are the only example of Lower Palaeozoic strata in the region, and these are so poorly exposed that little comment can be made as to the possible effects of the Caledonian orogeny, although Green and Welch (1965, p 127) describe an angular unconformity between the Upper Old Red Sandstone and the Silurian in the Beacon Hill area. The most striking feature is the fact that much of the Silurian sequence is composed of volcanic material. There are only four other known occurrences of Silurian lavas in north-western Europe, all of which are situated along a belt from the west of Ireland to Bohemia. Volcanic activity is commonly associated with areas that are tectonically active, and it may well be that the Silurian volcanics in eastern Mendip are the earliest indicator of a major zone of structural weakness that was reactivated on numerous occasions later in geological time. The break in sedimentation between the Upper Old Red Sandstone and the underlying Silurian rocks in Mendip is undoubtedly associated with the better exposed and described Caledonian structural forms of neighbouring regions.

The stratigraphical sequence from Upper Old Red Sandstone times to the close of the Carboniferous times, is virtually complete on Mendip. Apart from the most minor events this was a period of tectonic calm—to be completely shattered by the effects of the Armorican orogeny. The evidence from the wider Bristol region would suggest that the major period of folding and faulting, referred to as the Armorican, occurred after the deposition of the Upper Carboniferous rocks, presumably in Permian times. The strata were subjected to severe compression from the south and therefore the folds and major faults have their axes trending in a general east–west direction. The Mendips are situated on a tectonic line of international importance that can be traced completely across Europe. The line marks the so-called Armorican Front, which separates intensively folded and faulted rocks to the south from relatively lightly folded rocks to the north. The Armorican structures developed on Mendip, therefore, are relatively highly folded, and result from a 'pushing' of the strata from the south.

The major fold structures developed in the Palaeozoic rocks on Mendip are a series of periclines arranged in an en echelon formation. From a study of the exposed strata four periclines can be distinguished; from west to east they are the Black Down, North Hill, Pen Hill and Beacon Hill periclines, the periclines being divided one from another by synclinal troughs. There is little doubt that similar parallel structures, developed in Palaeozoic rocks, extend eastwards along the Armorican Front, but they are completely masked under later sediments. It is probable that the corresponding periclinal structures may underlie the several hundred metres thick Triassic strata that obliterate the Palaeozoic basement rocks to the south of Mendip.

Geological cross-sections, drawn in a north–south direction across the Palaeozoic structures of Mendip, clearly demonstrate the asymmetrical nature of the folds, indicating that the compression was from the south. For example, the dips on the northern limb of the Black Down pericline show a general value ranging from 50° to 80° whilst the southern limb ranges from 25° to 35°. A well exposed example of the inverted strata associated with the Blackdown pericline can be seen in a small disused quarry (445593) beside the main A38 road to the south of Churchill. Detailed study of this section is necessary to establish that the strata is indeed inverted and the best indicator is a wider consideration of the geological outcrop pattern of the area. Geological cross-sections illustrating the asymmetry of the periclines are presented in Fig 14.

The amplitude of these folds is some 1500m. It is erroneous to envisage the original folds as forming east–west mountain ranges with a height of several hundred metres, as the folding is far from an instantaneous occurrence even if considered on a geological time scale. As the structures were developing, erosion took place. The Palaeozoic rocks of Mendip as we see them today—emerging from beneath a cover of Mesozoic deposits—

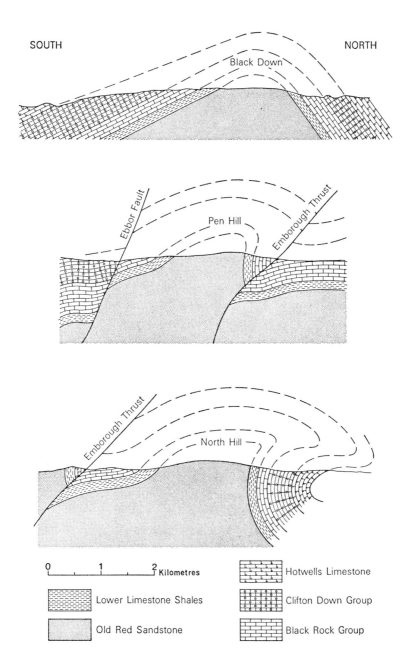

SOUTH   NORTH

Black Down

Ebbor Fault   Pen Hill   Emborough Thrust

Emborough Thrust   North Hill

0   1   2 Kilometres

	Hotwells Limestone
	Lower Limestone Shales
	Clifton Down Group
	Old Red Sandstone
	Black Rock Group

Fig 14 Geological cross-section drawn in an approximate north–south direction across the Black Down, Pen Hill and North Hill periclines

show only a limited range of relief. The fold and fault structures were planed down during the succeeding Permian and earlier Triassic phases. This is a theme to which a return will be made.

The major faulting of the area is closely related to the folding, and several large faults occur—again emphasising the severity of the Armorican orogeny in the region. The most important of these faults are, like the folds, aligned in an approximate east–west direction and consist of thrusts. In detail, the situation is complex as the thrust planes sometimes bifurcate and often take the form of thrust zones composed of a number of individual thrust faults which, locally, pass laterally into tear faults. This situation is well shown by the complex of thrusts in the southern section of Mendip between Cheddar and Wells. There is the Ebbor Thrust exposed at Ebbor Rocks (547477) with the associated Emborough Thrust, and the Cheddar Thrust. The details are discussed in Welch (1929) and by Green and Welch (1965, pp 134–43).

A similar, complex situation occurs to the north of Mendip with the Farmborough Fault Belt. In this case the zone of faulting is several kilometres wide and, whilst not well exposed at the surface, it is known in some detail due to the coal mines sunk in the area to work the seams of the Upper Coal Series involved in the faulting. In the case of the Farmborough Fault Belt the faulting consists mainly of reverse faults rather than thrust faults, the differences in nomenclature indicating that the angles of fault planes are less in the Farmborough area than in the Cheddar–Wells complex. The differing styles of faulting may represent a differing response of the lithology to the compressive stresses. The Carboniferous Limestone acts in a more resistant, or in geological terms, competent, fashion than the less competent Coal Series. In general, the Carboniferous Limestone is in large, open folds in contrast to the incompetent Coal Measures to the north which show all manner of contortions as regards the folding, as well as repeated low-angle overthrusts.

The intensity of the folding and the immense amount of

subsequent erosion are perhaps best illustrated by considering the structural features known as a klippe (a German word meaning cliff and whose plural is klippen). The rocks involved in a klippe at first sight contradict the law of superimposition of strata, in that a mass of older strata rests directly on younger. The situation can only be explained in terms of intense folding and thrust folding where the nose of a recumbent fold comes to rest on younger strata as shown diagrammatically in Fig 15. Subsequent erosion removes much of the recumbent fold and leaves the isolated mass of older rock to form a klippe.

There are several examples of such detached outcrops of Carboniferous Limestone situated to the north of Mendip. The best described of these is at Upper Vobster (705498). The first full description of the tectonics involved at this locality was given by

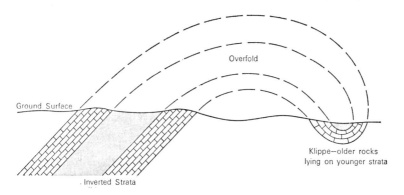

Fig 15 A diagrammatic representation of a klippe structure

Sibly (1906), and additional descriptions dealing with new exposures revealed by the extension of the quarrying can be found in Welch (1929 and 1933). The Upper Vobster klippe is aligned in an east–west direction, having a length of about 1km and a maximum width of about 400m. Despite the extent of the quarry faces it is difficult to distinguish the details of the tectonics. The rocks show extensive shattering and many forms of minor faulting and folding. There can be no doubt that the feature is indeed a klippe, and the evidence of the severe tectonic disturbance accords with what would be expected with an overthrust and faulted mass. The Carboniferous Limestone is undoubtedly underlain by Coal Measure strata, and further evidence is afforded from the geological records of former coal mines in the immediate vicinity. The Upper Vobster locality is probably one of the best examples of klippe structure in the British Isles.

Three other smaller klippen occur in this area, although they are poorly exposed in comparison to the example described above. The first of these occurrences is at Vobster itself, where a small detached mass of Clifton Down Limestone forms a crag-like feature immediately to the east of Vobster Inn (507491). A mile or so to the west-north-west is the klippe at Luckington Farm (692502), which consists of poorly exposed Clifton Down Limestone, and of which a description and map is given by Welch (1933, p 42). The third of these small klippen in eastern Mendip is to the north of Soho (695483). This was not in fact differentiated as a completely detached mass by Welch (1933, p 21) but it is clearly shown as such on the latest Geological Survey maps (see especially Geological Survey Sheet ST64NE). This change of interpretation is indicative of the relatively poor nature of the exposure and the difficulty of interpreting the complex tectonic activity.

The klippen at Upper Vobster and Soho consist, in part, of rocks of the Quartzitic Sandstone Group. These are of particular interest in that it is from a mass of faulted shale (at Vobster) associated with this Group that the only fossil specimen of undoubted Millstone Grit has been obtained.

Green and Welch (1965, p 128) also consider that the isolated Carboniferous Limestone outcrops to the north of central Mendip at Churchill (443602) and East Harptree (569548) are probably the remnants of comparable klippe structures. Again the Carboniferous Limestone overlies the younger Coal Measure strata.

In addition to the east–west trending thrusts, other major faults are developed on Mendip. Many of these other faults radiate out from the periclinal structures, particularly from the Pen Hill pericline which Welch (1929, p 76) considered to be especially unstable when compared to the other Mendip periclines. There is still no firm agreement as to the exact type of many of these faults, some being tear faults and others normal faults. As well as affecting the overall pattern of the geological outcrops, some of these major faults directly affect the cave systems. For example, the Priddy fault is interpreted as a normal fault with a throw of about 150m, and its surface outcrop has been related to its subterranean effects on Swildon's Cave.

The surface expression of the fault structures does not often give rise to any marked topographic feature and the faults are generally not well exposed. The faults marked on many geological maps are difficult to see in the field, and their effects can only be fully appreciated by a consideration of the pattern of the surface outcrops of various stratigraphical units. Where exposures of the faults do occur, the strata frequently show extensive shattering and the development of many minor folds. The shatter zones are often associated with the later emplacement of calcite and, occasionally, mineral veins. In addition to the mappable structures many minor faults can be seen, especially in cave passages. There is no doubt that careful geological observation in the caves and cave systems could assist greatly with the deciphering of the structural geology of Mendip, as the geologically-minded caver has the advantage of seeing the otherwise theoretical geological cross-sections from the inside!

The third and last major orogeny reached its peak intensity in the Mid-Tertiary era and, as the effects were particularly marked in the Alps, an alternative is to refer to the effects as belonging to the Alpine orogeny. The ideal situation for the recognition of Mid-Tertiary tectonic activity would be for rocks of an earlier age to be succeeded by strata of Upper Tertiary age, and for an angular unconformity to separate the two sequences. This is the situation well shown for the Armorican orogeny on Mendip, where the much folded and faulted Palaeozoic rocks are succeeded by gently-folded Mesozoic strata. There are, however, difficulties in distinguishing the effects of the Mid-Tertiary orogeny in the British Isles, as there is no extensive outcrop of rock post-dating the major period of the folding and faulting.

The tectonic activity in south-eastern England affected rocks of Lower Tertiary date, and the major faults and folds developed are assigned to the Mid-Tertiary orogeny. As one moves away from southern England there are no rocks of Tertiary age, and the normal geological methods of dating are therefore of little help. On Mendip, and elsewhere, Mesozoic rocks of Triassic, Jurassic and Cretaceous age are undoubtedly folded and faulted, although the intensity of these structural forms in very much less than the older Armorican structures seen in the Palaeozoic strata. The problem is to assign a date to the formation of these structures. On Mendip, tectonic movements along the Mendip axis affected the sedimentation during Jurassic time. The variations in the type and thickness of various units of the Jurassic stratigraphical column in this area, when compared to the corresponding beds to the north and south, are due to the tectonic activity along the Mendip axis; that is movement along the trends of the Armorican structures. This phenomenon of renewed tectonic activity along a previously active structural zone is known as posthumous movement.

One example of such posthumous movement is the Biddle fault, which had a throw of approximately 100m due to the Armorican orogeny, but was reactivated at a later date and affected Triassic and Liassic deposits. The subsequent displacement amounts to a further throw of perhaps 30m (Green and Welch 1965, p 146) and, since the youngest rocks cut by the fault are Liassic, it can be stated with confidence that the fault is post-Liassic. However, such a statement is somewhat inexact as the fault could have originated in the Jurassic, Cretaceous or

Tertiary. Other faults which affect Liassic strata include the Chewton Fault and the Mudgley Fault Belt to the south of Mendip near Wedmore. The Mudgley Fault has a maximum throw of about 100m. Other major faults on Mendip of Armorican age pass under a cover of later rocks with no observable effect; in these cases the faults have remained inactive since Armorican times. The major thrust faults in southern Mendip pass under Triassic material without any associated displacement.

Posthumous movement applies to fold structures as well as to faults, although the technique for recognising fold movements is different. The method employed for demonstrating the details of fold movements in the Mesozoic strata is to construct a map with structural contours drawn at the base of a suitable stratum. For Mendip, the most convenient stratum is the base of the Rhaetic. The assumption is made that the Rhaetic beds were laid down in shallow water and that the base of the deposit was essentially horizontal. Thus a map with contours drawn at the base of the Rhaetic as it occurs today would show, as 'hills and valleys', the form of any folding that affected these beds in post-Rhaetic times. Such a map is presented by Green and Welch (1965, Fig 14, p 144) for central Mendip, and a more detailed map for the area of the North Hill pericline by Green (1958, p 76). An earlier map for the Bristol Channel region was constructed by Jones (1931, Plate 2).

These structural maps vary in detail but clearly show that the difference in height between the base of the Rhaetic, in central Mendip, and comparable beds to the south of Mendip (the details here are from borehole data), is well in excess of 300m. The overall form of the fold would appear to be that of a flat-topped, steep-sided structure, with its long axis paralleling the crest of Mendip. Such a structure is best interpreted as due to posthumous movement along the earlier established east–west tectonic Mendip axis. The work of Green (1958) for the central Mendip area would suggest that this broad anticlinal structure is composed of smaller fold structures. Again there is difficulty in suggesting the date, or dates, at which this folding occurred.

The date, or dates, of these structures affecting the Rhaetic and Liassic deposits cannot be established on Mendip by direct geological methods as younger strata does not occur in the area. Dating by comparison with neighbouring regions where younger strata are found leads to the conclusion that the movements responsible could be of one or more possible ages. The Jurassic rocks exposed topographically below the Chalk edge a few miles to the south-east of Mendip were folded in Middle Cretaceous times, prior to the deposition of the Chalk in the Upper Cretaceous. The Chalk is itself folded, and there is evidence that it was involved in structural movements in pre-Tertiary times, but the major movement is thought to date from the Mid-Tertiary. The problems of dating the fold and faults of the Bristol Channel area is considered by Jones, and he concluded his argument 'I have never been able to conceive of any reason why the folding which has so strongly affected the Mesozoic and Cainozoic strata of the south of England should suddenly cease at the western limit of the Cretaceous tract' (Jones, 1931, p 63). This would seem to represent a very reasonable summary of the geological arguments for Mid-Tertiary tectonic activity in the Mendip region.

Whilst it is clear that the post-Armorican structures are of minor significance as regards intensity (when compared to their Armorican equivalents), they are of importance to an understanding of the evolution of the present landforms of Mendip. Even minor structural effects would have exerted a marked influence on the evolution of the drainage pattern of the area, and the drainage pattern is of fundamental importance in shaping the landscape as we see it today. In the absence of geological deposits later in age than the Mid-Jurassic, it may well be that the unravelling of the later structural history can only be undertaken by considering the history of the landscape itself. Such a study of landscape evolution is known as geomorphology, and having set the geological scene it is to a study of the geomorphology of the region that we must now pass.

The geological maps published by the Institute of Geological Sciences for the Mendip region are at three scales. The smallest scale is the one inch to one mile (1 :63,360) New Series. Mendip is covered by five such maps and the key to the numbers and sheet boundaries is given in Fig 16. All of these, except for sheet 279, are currently available. Sheet 279 has not been reissued and can only be consulted in major reference libraries. However, it can be seen from Fig 16 that most of the sheet is in fact sea! The one inch New Series maps for the area are all 'solid and drift' editions. Mention should also be made of a 'special' one inch map that is

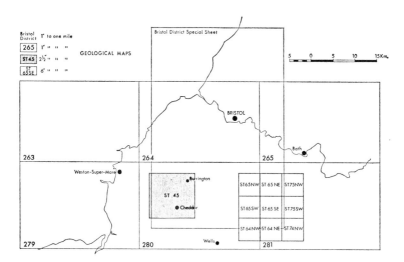

Fig 16 A key to geological maps of the Mendip area

available for the Bristol District. This includes portions of the maps mentioned above and the boundaries of this special sheet are also shown in Fig 16.

The Institute of Geological Sciences has also produced a two and a half inch to the mile map (1 :25,000) for the Cheddar area. This conforms to the sheet boundaries for the Ordnance Survey 1 :25,000, sheet number ST45, and covers 100sq km. Only a limited number of maps have been produced at this scale (for areas in the British Isles of particular geological interest).

Finally, for a limited area of eastern Mendip, maps at six inches to the mile (1 :10,560) have been published. These are uncoloured but contain a wealth of detail; the series is only published for those areas of the British Isles associated with coalfields. The sheet boundaries correspond to those of the most recent series of six inch Ordnance Survey maps, and each 100sq km map in the two and a half inch series is divided into four such six inch geological maps. For example, four maps comprise the two and a half inch sheet number ST65, and these are referred to as ST65NW (for the north-western quadrant), ST65SE (for the south-eastern quadrant) etc.

It is also possible to consult the unpublished six inch geology sheets for the remainder of the Mendip area in the library of the Geological Museum in South Kensington.

3

The Geomorphology of Mendip—
The Sculpting of the Landscape

D. I. Smith

Geology is fundamentally concerned with the composition of rocks and with the history of their formation. The nature and properties of the underlying rock form the raw materials from which the landscape is sculptured. A comprehensive knowledge of geology is therefore of prime importance to any explanation of the physical landscape of a region. The interpretation of the evolution of any particular landscape that we see today is a separate study known as geomorphology. This science can, for convenience, be divided into two main branches, both with the ultimate aim of constructing a history of the evolution of the landscape. The first branch is concerned with the establishment of a chronology. This objective, of necessity, requires knowledge of the ways in which rocks of differing lithologies are eroded under differing climates, the second aspect of geomorphology which has become known as a study of process. These two branches of geomorphology are in fact intimately related, and progress in the one can only be by application of information provided by the other.

CHRONOLOGY IN GEOMORPHOLOGY

The techniques available to the geomorphologist for the construction of a chronology for an area differ from those employed by a geologist concerned with the unravelling of the stratigraphical sequence. In geomorphological studies evidence is not only obtained from sequences of depositional material but also from the interpretation of those portions of the landscape that result from the erosional activity. Ideally, the material eroded from, for example, an escarpment would be deposited as a stratigraphical sequence, and the erosional and depositional forms could be correlated. The model situation, showing the erosion and its association with the corresponding deposits, is known as correlative method and is illustrated in Fig 17.

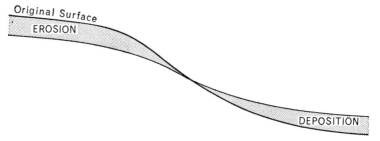

Fig 17 An idealised model for the correlation of erosional and depositional features

Unfortunately this ideal is not frequently found in the field. Often, as in the case for much of Mendip, attempts to construct a chronology are forced to rely heavily upon studies of the erosional forms exhibited in the landscape. Such a chronology is referred to as a denudation chronology.

The length of time involved in a geomorphological chronology can vary considerably from region to region, even within relatively narrow geographical confines. A convenient starting-point for such a chronology on Mendip is from Cretaceous times, when the normal stratigraphical methods cease to be meaningful as younger rocks are not represented in the area. Little can be said concerning this initial evolution of Mendip, but as we move through time the story, as preserved in the landscape morphology, becomes progressively clearer. Intimately involved with landscape evolution is the formation and modification of the caves and cave systems of the area. There is agreement that the region was buried under a very considerable thickness of Jurassic strata and the Cretaceous rocks alone probably reached a thickness well in excess of 150m. Sedimentation possibly continued through into the Tertiary era, but the palaeogeography of that period in the British Isles is far from clear, and estimates of the thickness of the strata deposited are little more than academic guesses. It must be stressed that despite the paucity on Mendip of rocks younger than the Upper Jurassic there is no doubt that the region was completely mantled by a great thickness of such rocks. The removal of these deposits and the fashioning of the present landscape represent the geomorphological problem to which we must now turn.

EROSION SURFACES

Little can be said regarding the earlier phases of removal, as no tangible field evidence remains. By analogy with other areas in southern Britain it is likely that the Mid-Tertiary orogeny had some limited effect and may have initiated a renewed period of erosion, although the removal of the mantling strata would have started well before that date. The methods employed by geomorphologists in Britain to elucidate the evolution of landscape where the correlative deposits are absent, depend largely on the recognition and interpretation of erosion surfaces. These can vary in size and morphology, but are all thought to represent pauses in the evolution of the landscape. In brief, erosion surfaces are areas that are nearly flat, and are thought to represent remnants of earlier landscapes. As such they are essential to the reconstruction of a denudation chronology. They are thought either to have been initially carved out of a landscape by marine action or to be fragments of fluvially eroded peneplains. Those considered to be marine would be fragments of wave-cut platforms, and ideally the remains of a backing cliff line would be discernible in the present landscape, with the possibility of the preservation, locally at least, of shells, sands and gravels of a marine type. In size, such erosion surfaces vary (particularly as regards width) from features that are best described as raised beaches, to more extensive flats of the kind associated with unconformities in the geological column.

Erosion surfaces which represent earlier peneplains are frequently referred to as sub-aerial in origin. In this case it is thought that a period of steady sea level allowed river erosion to reduce the landscape to an area of low relief or peneplain. A change in the relation of sea and land levels, referred to as a change of base level, brought about either by a fall of sea level or by the land mass undergoing uplift, causes the rivers to incise into their valleys and to initiate a renewed cycle of peneplain formation. The further incision of the rivers causes the watershed fragments of the earlier peneplain to remain as erosion surfaces. Such erosion surfaces enable a chronology to be constructed. Should the relationship of land to sea be unstable over shorter periods of time the river incision is more limited and the erosional flats resulting are recognised as river terraces. These limited periods of renewed river downcutting are known as phases of rejuvenation.

The recognition and interpretation of erosion surfaces in any given area, however, are normally fraught with difficulty. The flats in the landscape become modified by subsequent erosion, and with older erosion surfaces it becomes progressively more difficult to ascribe them to a particular mode of formation. In addition to the marine and sub-aerial origins outlined above, confusion can occur between truly erosional features, and flats in the landscape due to structural control. Structural flats of this kind are usually associated with resistant strata and have a very low dip. This difficulty is of limited significance on Mendip as most of the underlying strata is folded and therefore has a relatively high dip. Thus erosion surfaces that truncate the underlying strata are of particular value to the geomorphologist.

The Mendip landscape has one additional complication, which

occurs less frequently in other British areas: the problem of exhumed erosion surfaces. The possibility exists that portions of the landscape on Mendip formed in Jurassic, Triassic or even pre-Triassic times have been exhumed from beneath their cover of later strata. In this case, limited areas of the present-day landscape are really attributable to a period of development some 200 million years ago. Such fragments have emerged from beneath a cover of rocks that at some stage in the past could have been several hundred metres thick. Exhumed surfaces formed at periods after the Triassic may also be present, the most likely contender being portions of the marine-cut surface underlying the Rhaetic deposits.

Chronologies, based mainly upon studies of erosion surface remnants and drainage patterns, have been proposed for many parts of the British Isles. In general, there is agreement concerning the major features, which were outlined over thirty years ago by Wooldridge and Linton (1955) for south and south central England. They consider that the extensive hill summits and plateau areas of southern England that occur at, or a little above, 250m are attributable to erosion in the Miocene and early Pliocene (normally termed Mio-Pliocene), and therefore post-date the Mid-Tertiary folding. The next peg on which their chronology is hung is the erosion surfaces of limited width that occur near to 180m. They argue, cogently, that these surfaces are of marine origin, and indeed at certain sites in south-eastern England deposits of a marine nature, including shells, have been found. The shell remains are considered to be of early Pleistocene age, although initially they were ascribed to the Pliocene. Further erosion surfaces and associated terraces have been recognised by numerous workers to occur at about 120m and again near to 60m. In the London region these lower surfaces are associated with various glacial deposits, which enables a firmer date to be placed upon the age of their formation.

Wooldridge and Linton, and other workers in regions adjacent to Mendip such as Driscoll (1958) in south Wales, Balchin (1952) on Exmoor, and Brunsden (1963) for Dartmoor, consider that the erosion surfaces that they have proposed are, in general, progressively younger as one moves altitudinally down the sequence. Further, the erosion surfaces these workers describe occur at similar heights at widespread localities. This is interpreted as indicating that the erosion surfaces are related to a falling sea level, each fall of sea level initiating a renewed phase of rejuvenation and associated erosion surfaces and, additionally, that no further tilting or folding has occurred after the formation of the features. Diagrammatically the sequence of erosion surfaces can be portrayed as a staircase, each tread corresponding to a pause in the overall fall of sea level. There is some evidence that these major erosion surfaces are not only to be found throughout the British Isles but are of world-wide significance.

Erosion surfaces on Mendip

For the Mendip region, comparable studies are surprisingly sparse in number, although adjacent areas have been studied in some detail. Indeed there are only two studies which deal specifically with Mendip. The earlier study was by Trueman (1939) who outlined a possible tentative sequence for the Bristol area which he took to include Mendip. A more detailed study for part of Mendip has been presented by Ford and Stanton (1968). Trueman stated that his account was based upon observations made in the course of fieldwork devoted to other studies, and he made considerable use of relief cross-sections drawn to highlight 'flats' in the landscape. There is little doubt, however, that the erosion surface levels that he mentioned are well developed in the region, and he was adamant that they represent surfaces which truncate the strata, ie they are not structurally controlled features. He recognised the following main surfaces, and the Mendip localities that he gave are given on p 95:

260 – 230m	Summit level of Mendip
185 – 165m	Wells Rd, near Ston Eston
140 – 125m	Farrington Gurney and to the south-east of Wells near Nunney
90 – 60m	Compton Martin and West Harptree
30m approx	Bleadon Hill and Uphill Church

He ascribed a late Tertiary (probably Pliocene) date for the higher and older surfaces, although more recent work in analogous situations elsewhere would suggest a Pliocene or possibly slightly later date. Trueman avoided stating whether the majority of the surfaces were marine or sub-aerial. The 30m surface below Uphill Church, however, is an exception which 'is obviously a marine platform backed by old cliffs' (1939, p 421).

Criticisms of the map analysis undertaken by Trueman have been made in a more detailed study by Yates (1950). A detailed map and field study by Smith (1963) for south Gloucestershire and a large part of the Bristol Avon drainage basin agrees with the overall sequence of events outlined by Trueman but gave slightly differing altitudinal ranges for the major erosion levels.

The work of Ford and Stanton described in detail south–central Mendip, an area defined by the catchment of the dry valleys leading to the Cheddar and Ebbor Gorges. A Mendip 'Plateau' surface (hereafter termed the Plateau Surface) was recognised as lying dominantly between 250 and 260m (see Plate p 133) and a staircase series of levels was given for the south flank of Mendip. Ford and Stanton listed six erosion benches ranging in altitude from 21 to 205m, and an earlier study by Ford (1963) tentatively recognised a seventh bench at about 140m. The height ranges of the better-preserved remnants of these benches are given below in a table based on Ford and Stanton (1968, p 409).

205 – 230m	Chelm's Combe Bench and higher fragments
152 – 163m	Forecliffs Bench
137 – 144m	Knapp Wood Bench
95 – 104m	Wattles Hill Bench
70 – 80m	Warren Hill Bench
37 – 43m	Axe Bench
21m	70ft Bench

Ford and Stanton delimited the Plateau Surface and the benches by detailed field mapping, and the heights quoted are based upon field surveyed data. The paucity of studies of this kind on Mendip is due in large part to the lack of clear-cut erosional surfaces and benches, and Ford (1963, p 302) commented upon the Mendip south flank benches that 'it cannot be claimed that it is a clear-cut sequence' and later that 'the correlation [of the benches] is not a good one. No attempt to reconstruct a sequential palaeogeography from the correlative benches is merited, because they are so few and scattered.' Ponsford (1970), in discussing the work of Ford and Stanton, drew attention to similar benches to the east of Wells, some of which are partly covered by Triassic material, the inference being that possibly all the benches may be exhumed sub-Triassic features.

The dominant erosion surface of Mendip is undoubtedly the plateau itself, the relative flatness of this surface being perhaps the most outstanding single geomorphological feature. The dominance of the Plateau Surface has led to a number of authors ascribing varying ages and origins to the feature. Recent workers are divided between two major schools of thought: those who consider that the Plateau Surface represents an exhumed surface and those who consider it to represent a sub-aerial peneplain. Earlier workers thought the surface to be an exhumed Triassic desert surface whilst other writers, such as Reynolds (see Wooldridge, 1960, p 154) and Kendall (1955), suggested an exhumed sub-Liassic surface. More recently, Donovan (1969, *a & b*) postulated that the summit plain is largely an exhumed Mid-Cretaceous feature. Wooldridge (1960) and Trueman (1939) argued for a subaerial peneplain of probable Mio-Pliocene age. An origin as an exhumed sub-Triassic surface is thought unlikely, since in localities where the form of the sub-Triassic surface is preserved and available for study it is far from being a flat plain. Origins as a sub-Liassic feature are considered unlikely, as most writers follow Jones (1931) in recognising some degree of folding of the area in the Mid-Tertiary. Thus an origin for the Plateau Surface as an exhumed sub-Liassic surface is dismissed, as the topography does not correspond to the postulated fold form, ie the surface is, in part, cut across the postulated Mid-Tertiary folds. Similar arguments could be applied to an origin as an exhumed Mid-Cretaceous feature.

Ford and Stanton dealt with this problem in some detail and produce a plausible compromise solution. Basically, they agreed with Mid-Tertiary folding with an open domal form upon which the drainage was initiated, resulting in a sub-aerial erosion surface, which they suggest is late-Pliocene in date. They also suggested that fragments of a buried Rhaetic-Liassic surface 'were coincident in elevation with a wider north Somerset erosion surface' and were therefore incorporated into the overall Plateau Surface. Ford and Stanton considered that the Old Red Sandstone periclinal cores of Black Down, Beacon Hill etc, which rise above the Plateau Surface by about 30m, are essentially exhumed sub-Triassic features. The lower elevation of the limestone surface is due to solutional weathering of the limestone, both at the time of formation of the Plateau Surface in the late Tertiary, and in subsequent periods.

The balance of the evidence and views argue for a sub-aerial origin for the Plateau Surface in late Miocene or Pliocene times, although all workers recognise the possibility, in this area above all others of the limited contribution that exhumation of earlier surfaces could play in the landscape evolution. Indeed, Wooldridge (1960) states that '. . . the Bristol district is perhaps the chief example in Britain of such exhumation of buried landscapes'.

An early work by Davis (1899), outlining the concept of subaerial peneplains, suggested that one of the criteria in recognising such long-standing landscape elements was a deep, residual soil cover. Wooldridge and Linton (1955) demonstrated that where the Mio-Pliocene surface was cut on Chalk the soil depth was greater than on Chalk surfaces of a more recent date. Stevens (1959) substantiated this view in his work on the Chalk of northeast Hampshire. It is therefore worth noting that the Plateau Surface of Mendip, when it is developed on Carboniferous Limestone, is associated with a particularly deep soil type. This soil is known as the Nordrach Series and was described in detail by Findlay (1965) who stated that it 'is the most extensive soil on the Mendip Plateau'. The soil has a consistent depth of about a metre and is normally stone-free. It is possible that this deep soil results from the accumulation of insoluble residue from the solutional weathering of the limestone, and its depth is a reflection of the age of the Plateau Surface. This attractive hypothesis was not favoured by Findlay mainly on the grounds that 'to accumulate an average thickness of one metre of insoluble residue would require solution of much greater amounts of rock than seems possible on geomorphic grounds' (1965, p 48). Findlay favoured an origin for this material as wind-blown loessic material deposited in Pleistocene times. However, if the material is dominantly loessic, a similar cover should mantle the whole region and not show a preferential distribution upon the Plateau Surface.

THE PLEISTOCENE

In the British Isles deposits of Upper Tertiary age, comprising the Miocene and Pliocene, are very poorly represented, and this period of time has been likened to the stratigraphical equivalent of the Dark Ages of the historians. The period of time from the uppermost Tertiary strata to the present day is often referred to as

(*above*) A weathered piece of Black Rock Limestone, the silicified remains of crinoids stand out from the rock surface. The crinoid 'stems' are about one centimetre in diameter (*below*) Wookey Hole viewed from the south. The rising of the R. Axe is hidden by the trees in the foreground. The flat Plateau Surface of central Mendip occupies the middle and far distance

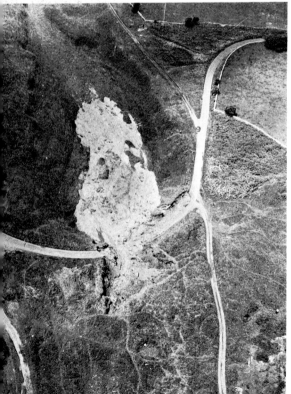

(*above*) The flooded peat lands of the Somerset Levels to the south of Mendip (*left*) Flood debris in Velvet Bottom, Charterhouse deposited by the floods of July 1968 which also destroyed the road bridge; the valley is normally dry. The area to the right of the photograph consists of waste from earlier lead-zinc smelting

the Quaternary, and in older texts is separated into a lower division, the Pleistocene, and an upper, Holocene or Recent division, These various classifications were outlined in the nineteenth century when the origin of the deposits was imperfectly understood. Indeed the Institute of Geological Sciences classifies superficial materials (gravels and the like) simply into Pleistocene and Recent. Such superficial materials are also referred to on British geological maps as 'drift'. The term 'drift' originated from the middle of the last century when these deposits were thought to represent material dropped from melting icebergs at the end of the Ice Age, the icebergs drifting at a phase of higher sea level loosely correlated with the biblical Flood.

A discussion of the nomenclature was given by West (1968), and in this text his suggested notation, that the term Pleistocene be used to include all post-Tertiary time, is followed.

The placing in time of the boundary between the Pliocene and the Pleistocene has given rise to much heated debate, little light, and an extensive bibliography, but in general terms the onset of the Pleistocene corresponds to a climatic deterioration which heralded the onset of the major glacial advances loosely referred to as the Ice Ages. Initially it was thought that the Pleistocene contained but one major ice advance, but the now classic studies of Penck and Brückner, at the turn of the century, established that there was a multiplicity of glacial advances and retreats, termed glacials and interglacials respectively. Later work has shown that each glacial contains minor oscillations of deteriorating climate, termed stadials. The corresponding term interstadials is used for short-term phases of climatic amelioration. Penck and Brückner worked in the northern Alps and suggested four glacials; and unfortunately attempts were made to apply a similar four-fold division to other glaciated areas, including the British Isles and North America. The trend over the last decade has been away from such rigid classifications, and the emphasis has been towards local glacial chronologies. The overall result is that attempts to correlate the old and new, local

D

and regional terms have led to confusion. There is no agreement between differing workers in the British Isles as to how many glacial advances did in fact occur.

Table 2 is an attempt to show the correlations of varying terms used by differing workers for the later phases of the

TABLE 2 *A correlation table for the various terms used for the later phases of the Pleistocene*

	Alps	North west Europe	Zeuner's Classification	British Isles
Glacial	Würm	Weichselian	Last Glaciation	Weichselian
Interglacial	Riss–Würm	Eemian	Last Interglacial	Ipswichian
Glacial	Riss	Saale	Penultimate Glaciation	Gippingian

Pleistocene covering the last two glacials. No attempt has been made to correlate the earlier phases of the Pleistocene, as agreement between the various schemes is so disputed. However, Table 3 illustrates a chronology for the whole of the Pleistocene

TABLE 3 *Stages of the British Pleistocene*

			Stage	Climate
	(Holocene)		Flandrian	t
	....	Upper	Weichselian	c g p
			Ipswichian	t
			Gippingian	c g p
(Quaternary)	Pleistocene	Middle	Hoxnian	t
			Lowestoftian	c g p
			Cromerian	t
			Beestonian	c p
			Pastonian	t
		Lower	Baventian	c p
			Antian	t
			Thurnian	c
			Ludhamian	t

c cold   g glacial deposits known
p permafrost known   t temperate

based upon proposals made by West (1968, p 230). This table applies particularly to the extensive Pleistocene deposits in East Anglia but is included here as it gives a good general indication of the climate that could have been expected to apply to Mendip.

Such Pleistocene chronologies are, in the main, based upon studies of the various glacial deposits found well to the north of a line from London to Bristol. It is interesting to note that Mendip is the only caving area developed on Carboniferous Limestone in the British Isles that was not glaciated on at least one occasion.

Glaciation in the Bristol region

The position of even the maximum Pleistocene ice advance in the Bristol region is not accurately known and most workers, until recently, considered it to lie many miles to the north of Bristol. Notable early exceptions to this general view included Lucy and Harmer. Lucy (1874) suggested that glacial deposits, specifically boulder clay, occurred in west Somerset in the vicinity of Minehead. Harmer (1907) envisaged a series of glacially dammed lakes of which the largest was termed Lake Trowbridge. The ice-front blocked the pre-glacial rivers and caused the ponding up of extensive lakes which eventually overflowed and excavated new gorge-like valleys. This origin was envisaged for the Limpley Stoke Gorge on the Avon south of Bath, and for the Clifton Gorge in Bristol. Drainage diverted along the Frome and '. . . thence into the gap between the Mendip Hills on the one side and the Wiltshire Downs on the other' (1907, p 484) was also thought to be a possibility.

Recent work by Mitchell (1960) and particularly by Hawkins and Kellaway (1971) has seriously questioned the normally accepted more northerly limit of the glacial advance. The views of Hawkins and Kellaway are firmly based on detailed fieldwork and there seems little doubt that at its maximum, glacial ice occupied the lowland area to the south of Clevedon. The new field evidence presented by Hawkins and Kellaway, and by Hawkins (1970), describes boulder clays, striated boulders and gravels of glacial origin, particularly in the vicinity of the village of Kenn and in and around Failand. The majority of the sections exhibiting this material are, however, in temporary exposures. The age favoured for these deposits is Chalky Boulder Clay which we can correlate to the Gipping glacial phase of West. Hawkins and Kellaway also draw attention to higher-level gravel deposits in the region, particularly those at Bathampton Down, for which they consider a glacial origin likely. If this interpretation of the higher-level deposits is correct they would represent evidence for deposition in an earlier glacial.

In addition to these deposits of glacial drift, various features of an erosional nature occur that could also be interpreted as of a glacial origin. The genesis of such features is more difficult to establish, but attention must be drawn to the deeply cut dry valley which runs from near Blagdon (498593) to Rickford (487593). The long-profile of this valley shows a distinct hump-backed form, whilst in plan it resembles meanders with a very large amplitude. Such a morphology is consistent with glacial melt-water channels described from more northerly parts of Britain, and Kellaway accepts this origin. This view would therefore move the limits of the Gipping ice margin at least as far as the northern edge of Mendip. There is a very considerable literature regarding the formation of this form of glacial melt-water channel (for a summary and bibliography see Sissons, 1967), and the overall conclusion is that they formed beneath the ice edge and were not simple marginal channels open to the atmosphere and thus marking the actual ice edge. In this case the maximum ice edge could possibly have encroached onto Mendip itself.

Hawkins and Kellaway produced a map (1971, p 288) showing the assumed direction of glacial flow between northern Mendip and Bristol. At the extreme southern edge of this map a melt-water channel is marked, the former flow of which was to the west. The channel would appear to commence in Burrington Combe, flow along the outcrop of the Lower Limestone Shales, near to the University of Bristol Speleological Society hut, and continue along the line of the valley that occurs to the south of Dolebury Warren (455590). This tantalising feature is not, however, described in the accompanying text, but by inference the glacial cover would indeed have encroached upon the higher parts of Mendip. The present authors do not consider this origin to be more than a speculative suggestion and it is nowhere near as convincing as the possible glacial channel described between Blagdon and Rickford.

Indirect effects of the Pleistocene glaciations

In the light of the above discussion it would be rash to make any categorical statements regarding an ice cover over Mendip itself. The Plateau Surface is best regarded as unglaciated unless firm evidence is put forward to the contrary.

Evidence for the actual encroachment of glacial ice on to the main mass of Mendip is lacking, but indirect effects of the Pleistocene glacials are of considerable importance. Such effects are embraced by the overall term periglacial and result first, from the influence of a climate considerably colder than at the present day and secondly, from modifications due to the marked oscillations of sea level caused by the growth and subsequent melting of the ice sheets. The world-wide volume of the major Pleistocene ice sheets at the glacial maxima was sufficient to lower the sea level by some 100–150m. This water was returned to the oceans during the interglacials when the remaining ice cover was probably less than that of the present. A broad definition of an interglacial is that the climate would have been at least as favourable as that found today in the area concerned.

The major climatic effects of the glacials on Mendip resulted in the formation of permafrost. Permafrost is found at the present day in arctic regions, and consists of a subsurface layer of soil or rock which remains frozen throughout the year. The importance of permafrost in a limestone region is that the ground-water circulation is likely to be substantially modified. If the permafrost is continuous, subsurface flow will cease. To establish that an area was underlain by permafrost at some occasion in its past is far from easy, but current geomorphological opinion supports the view that permafrost was present throughout Britain on one or more occasions in the Pleistocene. Table 3 which has been described earlier, is based on work in East Anglia and postulates five separate phases of permafrost for that area. It is difficult to give meaningful precipitation figures for the glacial phases but undoubtedly much of the precipitation would have been in the form of snow, and the spring melt would have resulted in extremely high discharge figures over limited periods of time.

Other periglacial effects that would have left their mark on the landscape are the intensive rock weathering, covered by the term frost shattering. Such weathering gives rise to sharp, angular fragments and is probably related to the number of oscillations of temperature above and below freezing point, and to the sparse nature of the vegetation cover during the cold phase. Frost-shattered material does not necessarily require true permafrost conditions, but is thought to be indicative of a climate colder than that now found in the area. The production of frost-shattered debris on Mendip was very considerable, and it would appear that the Old Red Sandstone was particularly susceptible. The depth of material of this kind on the slopes between the Twin streams in the Burrington area can reach thicknesses in excess of two metres. Frost-shattering effects of this kind in caves are limited to the entrance passages, as during any climatic phases the subterranean temperatures would have remained almost isothermal and, incidentally, approximate to the mean annual temperature of the surface. Tratman (1963*a*, p 33) comments on frost-shattered material of this kind in the Entrance Gallery to Goatchurch. Angular material indicative of frost-shattering can, however, be transported into the caves by stream action, and deposits of this kind give some general indication of their deposition.

A further periglacial effect is the enhanced rate of downslope movement of material. Such effects are known as mass movement, with the term solifluction used for movement under cold conditions. The paucity of a close vegetation cover, coupled with conditions of soil saturation at the time of the snow melt, is particularly suitable for this downslope movement of material to take place. The movement is markedly accelerated if permafrost is present, as this gives an impermeable base to the downward movement of the soil water and increases the saturation of the soil and rock mantle and promotes its tendency to 'flow' downslope. The material moved downslope under such conditions is frequently referred to as head, and for a discussion of this term and the problem of mapping head deposits see Dines *et al* (1940). Intensive frost action, although not necessarily accompanied by true permafrost conditions, also causes the contortion of gravel and head deposits, such a process being known as congeliturbation. It is also possible that deposits of wind-blown material, known as loess, may have been deposited during the colder climatic phases.

Sea level changes during the Pleistocene

The erosion surfaces discussed above, formed in late Tertiary and Pleistocene time, are usually taken to be indicative of an overall falling sea level relative to a stable land mass. Such changes of sea level are referred to as eustatic. In addition to this postulated overall fall, the explanation of which is obscure, there were further oscillations of sea level—glacio-eustatic effects— brought about by the formation and melting of the extensive Pleistocene ice sheets. The picture is thus of a fall from a shoreline at about 180m in the earliest Pleistocene to the present sea level, upon which each glacial and interglacial and, to a lesser degree the major stadials and interstadials have superimposed a separate rise and fall. The amplitude of this superimposed effect for a full glacial cycle amounts to a change of sea level of perhaps 150m.

The details of these sea level changes on a world-wide scale were given by Fairbridge (1961), and a summary for the British Isles by West (1968). A recent account of the details for the Bristol region was given in Hawkins (1970). The salient features for the present study are to establish the approximate altitude of sea level in relation to Ordnance Datum for the various phases of the Pleistocene. Ford and Stanton (1968) related the erosion benches they described to a tentative chronology (p 424) and suggested heights for the high interglacial and interstadial sea levels. It is perhaps unfortunate that the chronology used for comparative purposes is that evolved for the Mediterranean, and that they do not comment on the elevation of the glacial and stadial low sea level stands.

Details of the low sea levels are less easy to obtain, as the key areas are below present sea level. However, the estimate for the sea level corresponding to the Gipping Glaciation of about −50m OD put forward by Mitchell and Orme (1967) can be considered acceptable. The following interglacial (the Ipswichian) sea level is thought to have attained an altitude of about +20m OD. This is a general elevation for Britain, and locally ApSimon and Donovan (1956) have described marine deposits at this level from Weston-in-Gordano, some 3km to the south of Portishead, which are dated as Ipswichian.

The last glaciation, the Weichselian, has naturally left a clearer landscape record than the earlier Pleistocene glaciations, and it is possible to describe the sea level changes in more detail and to recognise the more important of the stadial episodes. The late Weichselian glaciation, which is dated with some accuracy by radio-carbon techniques to about 20000 BP (before present), is considered by a variety of authors to have corresponded to a sea level at about −120m OD. Fig 18 which is based upon the work of Milliman and Emery (1968), shows that the present sea level is only slightly higher than that for the Mid-Weichselian interstadial. The last phase of sea level change,

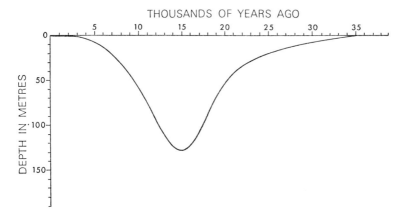

Fig 18 Sea level changes for the past 35,000 years (after Milliman and Emery, 1968)

known as the Flandrian, has given a rise in sea level of some 40m in the last nine thousand years. This rise in sea level is still continuing as the world's remaining ice sheets slowly melt, and whilst the contemporary rate of rise is small compared to that of the early Flandrian, the complete disappearance of the remaining ice sheets would cause a glacio-eustatic rise of about 50m. Local deposits corresponding to this period of time and continuing into an archaeological chronology can be found at Brean Down (295588), and are described in detail by ApSimon, Donovan and Taylor (1961).

The clay and peat deposits which form the Somerset Levels immediately to the south of Mendip (see Plate p 100) were formed during the Flandrian. The pre-Flandrian landscape to the south of the western part of Mendip is now at about −30m OD. The relatively rapid phase of sea level rise, the Flandrian Transgression, caused the deposition of blue-grey clays to commence in this area at about 8000 BP, and this form of sedimentation continued until about 6500 BP. The top of the clay now lies at approximately Ordnance Datum throughout the area. A

D*

sequence of fresh organic deposits composed of various forms of peat continued until about AD 250 when a layer of grey silty clay was deposited. The top of this clay is at about 6m OD and it reaches a thickness of about 4m. This second layer of estuarine material is not thought to indicate an increase in the rate of sea level rise and could be due to changed tidal conditions in the Severn Estuary. The details of the peat stratigraphy have been studied in detail by Godwin and his co-workers (see, for example, Godwin, 1955 and 1960) and are of particular interest due to the prehistoric trackways buried within the peat.

PLEISTOCENE FEATURES ON MENDIP

The detailed evolution of the caves will be dealt with in a later chapter, but it cannot be divorced from the chronology and effects of the Pleistocene. It has been argued that the initial major surface form of Mendip (the Plateau Surface) dates from the Mio-Pliocene, and it is therefore reasonable to assume that cave development, except under special circumstances, cannot have occurred at an earlier date. As with the relics of the exhumed erosion surfaces, it is possible that fragments of caves dating back even to pre-Trias times may be locally preserved, and the evidence for these will be reviewed later.

The formation of the majority of the caves will have occurred in Pliocene and, particularly, Pleistocene times and will have been affected by the climatic variations and sea level changes associated with that period. There has been a tendency in British geomorphological studies concerned with cave evolution to relate the development of the caves to changes in the levels of the water-table. These water-table levels are then correlated to changes in base level, which for Mendip approximate to changes in sea level itself. It will be seen in chapters 5 and 6 that the authors have grave reservations as to the relationship of caves to water-tables in areas of Carboniferous Limestone but, if some relationship is to be allowed, a full understanding of the base level changes is necessary.

Ford and Stanton (1968) and Ford (for example, 1963 and 1971), albeit guardedly, relate cave evolution to water-table and base level changes. Valuable though these studies are, they do not discuss the effects of the *low* sea level stands, but consider a sequence of falling sea levels with periods of relative stability at each phase. This approach only considers a particular portion of the evolutionary story. It is clear that the amplitude of the glacio-eustatic rise and fall of sea level would have caused some of the caves formed at low sea levels (glacials and stadials) to have been either flooded with sea-water—at subsequent phases of high sea level (interglacials and interstadials)—or to have continued to flow as submarine springs at these high sea-level phases.

Evidence can be found from many parts of the world that groundwater in limestone regions can resurge well below present sea level, and the unfortunate meeting of the Severn Railway Tunnel with submarine Carboniferous Limestone strata, containing a powerful flow of fresh, calcium-rich water, illustrates this aspect (Drew, Newson and Smith, 1970). It is likely that the origin of this submarine drainage, which takes water from Carboniferous Limestone areas in south Wales, was initially related to a low glacial sea level.

Further details of the evolution of caves and cave systems will be left for consideration in chapter 6.

Dry valleys and gorges—the overall problem

In nearly all the world's limestone regions, excepting where permafrost is present, a recurring feature is that the surface valley systems are dry, except perhaps in times of exceptionally heavy precipitation. British limestone areas fall firmly into this category, and the limestone surface of Mendip contains a well integrated pattern of dry valleys. Geomorphological discussions of British limestones suggest three possible hypotheses to explain these dry valley systems. Briefly these are :

(1) The erosion of the dry valleys dates from the earliest local

phase of drainage evolution when the limestone acted as an impermeable barrier to downward percolation; in brief, this can be termed origin by progressive solution.

(2) The valleys were eroded during periods of permafrost when subterranean drainage became impossible.

(3) General water-table lowering occurred due to the recession of limestone escarpments.

Progressive solution : The initial phases of drainage evolution on limestones are comparable to those found on other lithologies. As solutional erosion of the limestone continues, the joints and other lines of weakness within the rock will be opened up and the secondary permeability progressively increased (see, for example, Smith, 1971). This is particularly true for the development of drainage on massive limestones. Precipitation falling on the developing soil of the area will cease to join the surface drainage network by interflow through the soil material and will, instead, drain directly through the soil into the solutionally formed fissures of the bedrock itself. The surface stream-flow will gradually decrease until all the precipitation drains directly into the bedrock. The only exception will be at times of extremely intensive rainfall when the subsoil fissures are not sufficiently large to cope with the discharge. The effect of rare surface flow after prolonged heavy rain can be seen in the Plate on p 100. This hypothesis for dry valley formation has the added attraction that it is not dependent on any particular water-table concept. Some introductory geomorphological text-books give the impression that the progressive development of sub-surface drainage is dependent on the surface drainage being engulfed by stream swallets associated with the actual stream courses. Stream swallets are only of prime importance on Mendip where the discharge from non-calcareous catchments crosses on to the limestone itself.

Permafrost : There is no question that limestones situated in regions with continuous permafrost do have a surface drainage system that is comparable to that of networks of nearby non-calcareous strata. The extensive massive limestones in Cornwallis and Somerset Islands in the Canadian Arctic at about latitude 70°N are in a region of continuous permafrost, and all the drainage is on the surface. The pattern of the drainage and the gorge-like valleys are astonishingly similar to the now dry valleys of Mendip. However, it is fallacious to argue that the limestone dry valley systems in lower latitudes therefore originated under permafrost conditions. This could be true for Mendip, but limestone dry valley systems are known from virtually every climatic region, and no palaeoclimatologist would argue that permafrost conditions extended beyond the regions that are now situated in the temperate climatic zones.

Scarp recession : This ingenious hypothesis was initially suggested by Fagg (1923) in an attempt to explain the dry valleys of the Chalk areas in south-eastern England. Recession of the Chalk scarp lowered the junction with the Chalk and the underlying impermeable Gault Clay, and this caused the water-table to fall. It is possible that this is a reasonable theory for the region for which the concept was formulated, but it requires a special geological structural pattern and is not of wide application.

Dry valley and gorges on Mendip

Basically, the pattern of the dry valleys on Mendip is thought to have originated by the first of the hypotheses outlined above. The dry valley system would have been reactivated as a surface drainage system during phases of permafrost formation, and to that extent the genesis is a multiple hypothesis. The literature concerning one particular aspect of the dry valleys of Mendip is especially voluminous. This aspect is the now dry, gorge-like valleys of which Cheddar (see Plate p 133), Burrington (p 134) and Ebbor represent the major examples.

The contrast between the gorges and the dry valleys which are developed on the Plateau Surface itself is most marked. It is therefore reasonable to expect the two differing valley morphologies to differ in age and formation. Little further can be said regarding the dry valleys of the plateau other than that their initial origin is related to the formation of the erosion surfaces on which they are found, and that they were reactivated as surface streams at various phases during the Pleistocene when continuous, or possibly discontinuous, permafrost conditions prevailed. Many of these valleys are partially filled with superficial deposits which could well be termed periglacial head. The Plate on p 133 shows the valley infill exposed in the East Twin Valley.

Many and varied origins have been put forward to explain the genesis of the gorges. Indeed, a history of these views reflects the evolution of ideas regarding the geological formation of the scenery as a whole. In the eighteenth and nineteenth centuries, the gorges, especially that at Cheddar, were explained as resulting from catastrophic happenings associated with earthquakes and like phenomena. The latter half of the nineteenth century saw the emergence of the two main hypotheses that are still debated today. The first school ascribes the gorges to cavern collapse, with varying degrees of subsequent fluvial modification. The second school stresses that the drainage network of Mendip and the gorges are interlinked, and the overall morphology is indicative of formation by normal surface stream action. An additional complication considered in some of the studies is that, in part, the gorges and valleys represent exhumed sub-Triassic features.

Cavern collapse: It would appear that the earliest advocate of this hypothesis was Dawkins (1862). His studies were mainly at Wookey Hole and Ebbor, and it is possible that the evolution of the valley of the River Axe immediately below Wookey Hole differs from that at Cheddar and Burrington; however, he extended his views, in a footnote, to include a wider area. His ideas are best illustrated by a quotation :

I do not see the reason why the change of insoluble carbonate into soluble bicarbonate of lime, by which swallow-holes and parts of caverns are perpetually being enlarged, should be limited in its effects, if infinite time be granted, and why it should not have been the chief agent in forming the ravines so common in all limestone districts (1862, p 121).

It is interesting to note that over a century ago Dawkins had a very sound knowledge of the processes of limestone solutional erosion.

Woodward (1891) and Winwood and Woodward (1891) also inclined towards a cavern collapse theory, although the approach is a little more guarded. For example, Woodward (1891, p 493) stated '. . . many of the great fissures in Mendip, originating along joint-planes or lines of fracture, have so enlarged as to form caverns and ravines; the latter in some cases having resulted from the former'. Woodward also pointed out in a delightful piece of geological prose that the form of Cheddar Gorge was considerably affected by the geological structure.

'in the case of Cheddar it will be seen that the dip of the strata has exercised much influence on the shape of the cliffs—what may be called the conservative side standing up boldly and precipitously and exhibiting but little change in the course of years—whilst the other side, the dip slope, may be said to be exceedingly liberal (1891, p 493).

The paper by Winwood and Woodward (1891) is, in fact, the account of a Geologists' Association field excursion to Mendip, and gives a précis of the field discussions that arose concerning the differing views as to the origin of the gorge. Here, Winwood and Woodward suggest that Lamb Lair could, in the process of time, become unroofed to form a gorge comparable to Ebbor or Cheddar, and that they considered Cheddar Gorge to be not a single unroofed cave but a 'series' of such caverns.

Callaway (1902) was particularly impressed by the zig-zag course of Cheddar Gorge (see Plate p 165) and thought that this joint-controlled form could only have been formed by subterranean streams as 'such a stream must have followed joints for they are the only conceivable channels' (1902, p 69). Few modern geomorphologists would accept this view, and many surface streams have courses that are joint-controlled.

Whilst recent workers have sometimes allowed for the possibility of limited modification due to cavern collapse, Stride and Stride (1949) were probably the last writers to give this possible origin prime place in stating that the 'gorges and combes . . . can only be explained by the work of phreatic rivers' (1949), p 13).

The cave collapse theory for the evolution of the gorges has been refuted by many recent writers. The nature of the problem necessitates that most of the arguments are based upon the size and form of the gorges when compared to those of known Mendip caves. Attention is drawn to the disparity in volume between the gorges and the larger known Mendip caverns such as GB and Lamb Lair. Ford and Stanton (1968) stressed the difference in the long-profiles of the gorges and valleys on the one hand, to those of the stream cave passages. The former are 'the diametric opposite of that typical of known Mendip caves, in which the streams descend steeply to, and below, the water-table' (1968, p 415). Additionally, Ford and Stanton point out that the gorges, especially Cheddar, have cut vertically down through pre-existing cave passages. The meandering nature of the gorges was considered by Tratman (1963*a*) to be typical of surface streams and of a form not commonly found in cave stream passages.

Individually, some of these arguments can be countered by reference to specific examples, but in total they render a cave collapse hypothesis untenable except as a modifying factor on a local scale. The surface stream origin gives a better overall account of known facts. However, cavern collapse, albeit on a local scale, is the only reasonable explanation for the valley immediately downstream of the Wookey Hole resurgence (see

Reynolds, 1929*b*), and Ford and Stanton argue that Ebbor Gorge is, in part, an unroofed cave.

Surface stream origin: The majority of the workers subscribing to a sub-aerial origin for the gorges and valleys of Mendip, place some emphasis upon the role played by permafrost in causing the streams to flow on the surface, and also stress the importance of spring snow melt under previous colder climatic conditions. This is the case with the earlier studies of Morgan (1888) and Reynolds (1927 and 1929*b*), despite the fact that the previous existence of permafrost conditions in southern Britain has only become widely accepted in the last twenty years. Indeed, the word 'permafrost' was only coined in the early 1940s, and despite comments that it is etymologically unsound, it is now firmly entrenched in the scientific literature. However, Reynolds leaves no doubt as to the conditions he envisaged for the formation of limestone gorges in Britain:

> . . . a more probable explanation for most dry valleys is that they are the work of ordinary river erosion during glacial and early post-glacial times when, owing to the underground water being still frozen, the limestone was impervious and surface streams could exist (1929*b*, p 118).

These earlier accounts suggesting a permafrost cover were based on little direct evidence, but Clayden and Findlay (1960) drew attention to the fan-like gravel deposits that occur sporadically around the periphery of Mendip, showing a relationship to the entrance of the major gorges and valleys. These gravel, or, more specifically, gravelly head deposits are poorly exposed, and were encountered in the course of field by field soil mapping. The low-angled fan deposits associated with the mouth of Burrington Combe exhibit a clear morphological feature in the field. The form of the feature can be well seen from vantage points south of Burrington (eg from 482604). The composition and distribution of the gravels have been further described in

detail by Findlay (1965). There is little doubt that these deposits
are water-lain and not produced by the direct action of
solifluction. The included material is, however, only poorly
sorted and the coarse debris is particularly angular for a fluvial
deposit. The deposits to the north of Mendip contain a large
proportion of Old Red Sandstone material whilst those to the
south are mainly composed of limestone. The fresh form of the
fans, and the possible correlation with the frost-shattered material
in the Brean Down sequence (ApSimon *et al*, 1961), suggest a
late Glacial age of about 20000 BP. It is possible that other
scattered patches of gravelly head, capping low ridges adjacent to
the better-preserved fans, may be of a similar origin, representing
earlier Pleistocene permafrost conditions. Fig 19 shows the
distribution of these periglacial gravel fans, and is based upon
the work of Findlay (1965, p 32).

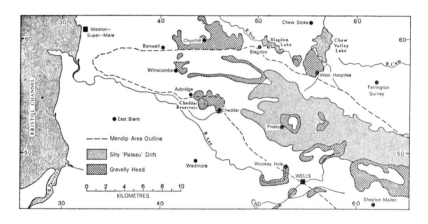

Fig 19 Distribution of periglacial drift deposits in the Mendip
region (after Findlay, 1965)

In discussing the development of Burrington Combe (see Plate
p 134), Tratman (1963*a*) drew attention to the exposures of

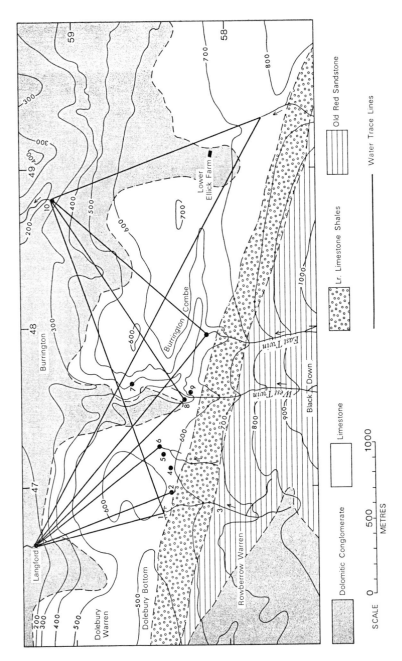

Fig 20 The relief, bedrock geology, surface and subterranean drainage of the Burrington Combe area. Contours are in feet. *Key*: 1—Read's Cavern; 2—Bos Swallet; 3—Hunter's Brook; 4—Drunkard's Hole; 5—Rod's Pot; 6—Bath Swallet; 7—Aveline's **Hole**; 8—Lowest sink for West Twin Stream; 9—Goatchurch **Cavern**; 10—Rickford Rising

Dolomitic Conglomerate that can be found in the lowest north–south section of the gorge and again in the vicinity of Lower Ellick Farm (490580). An accessible exposure of Dolomitic Conglomerate near the mouth of the Combe can be seen almost opposite the Café (476590). In this case the present valley has clearly taken advantage of a pre-existing Triassic valley which, in part, it has exhumed from beneath its ancient cover. At Lower Ellick Farm the line of the present valley cuts across the line of a similar Dolomitic Conglomerate-plugged valley. To this limited extent the Combe is an exhumed feature, but for most of its length it has cut along the strike of the Carboniferous Limestone. Tratman considered that the most likely explanation of the gorge is by headward erosion of a surface river, perhaps initially sited in its lowest section on the older Dolomitic Con-glomerate-filled valley. The relationship of Burrington Combe to the Dolomitic Conglomerate is shown in Fig 20.

Ford and Stanton (1968) discussed in some detail the develop-ment of the Cheddar and Ebbor Gorges. Ebbor Gorge is comparable to Burrington Combe in that the lowest portion of the valley also exposes Dolomitic Conglomerate. The evolu-tionary sequence for Ebbor is thought to have been attenuated by the subterranean drainage being diverted to its present outlet at Wookey Hole. Ford and Stanton presented detailed surveyed sections of the long-profiles of the Ebbor and Cheddar gorges, and attribute the valley segmentation to 'waves of retro-gressive erosion entrenching the valleys into the Plateau, keeping step with the intermittent exhumation of the south flank' (p 414). The grandeur and relatively large size of Cheddar is consequent upon it having the largest catchment area.

Thus the dry valleys are considered to have developed by normal fluvial processes whilst the gorges represent overdeepened, rejuvenated sections of the drainage network formed under periglacial conditions. The major phases of rejuvenation are thought to have occurred during cold phases of the Pleistocene, especially when permafrost was well developed. Locally, the drainage lines may have taken advantage of earlier drainage systems established during or before the Trias and long buried by deposits of Dolomitic Conglomerate, but in most cases even these were re-excavated only during the Pleistocene.

Closed depressions

Dry valleys are one of the recurring world-wide features of limestone landscape; another widespread form is the closed depression. There is no question that the size and morphology of such features can vary between wide limits, and it is probable that the various forms of closed depressions can originate in differing ways. Coleman and Balchin (1959) listed some fifty terms that have been used to describe closed depressions. The terms listed are in a variety of languages and, to add confusion, foreign terms are used far from their original source areas by authors who have but a sketchy idea of the forms to which the terms were first applied. In this account verbal semantics will be avoided by using the neutral term closed depression proposed by Ford and Stanton (1968).

It is possible to ascribe closed depressions to three possible causes. They can have formed initially as stream sinks, and have become inactive though retaining a closed depression form. Secondly, they could be collapse features into cave chambers and passages or, thirdly, they could have originated due to solutional activity working down from the surface. This three-fold classification is clearly little more than a framework to clarify the argument. An account of the terminology and sequences of morphology and infill to be expected with each of these origins is given in Coleman and Balchin (1959).

Three groups of workers have specifically discussed the closed depressions on Mendip; namely Stride and Stride (1949), Coleman and Balchin (1959), and Ford and Stanton (1968). All agree that, to some extent, examples can be found that fall into each of the three classes described above. However, it is also true to say that each pair of workers concluded that the bulk of the depressions were due to a single origin, and each pair supported a different origin!

Stream sink hypothesis: The Stride brothers stressed the importance of the stream sink hypothesis. In this case the inactive depressions are interpreted as earlier stream sinks where either the stream migrated up-valley as new sinks became available, or the depressions mark the boundaries of patches of impermeable cover material that have been removed by subsequent erosion. They recognised that features such as Wurt Pit (558539) and Sandpit Hole (531498) are due to cavern roof collapse and considered that new depressions are no longer forming and that the present phase is one of modification.

Collapse hypothesis: Coleman and Balchin undertook a field programme on Mendip and mapped about a thousand depressions. Their conclusions were firmly given and they recommended 'the abandonment of the solution hypothesis and the acceptance of collapse to account for the vast majority of Mendip depressions, the remainder being stream sinks' (1959, p 304).

Closed depressions resulting from collapse or solution can look very similar, but fundamentally the collapse features diminish in size (after their initial function) as they infill, whilst the solution features get progressively wider and deeper. A number of lines of field evidence in favour of collapse are given. Of those based upon field criteria the salient point is that where evidence from excavation is available it would appear that the debris infilling the depressions does become progressively coarser with depth. Specifically, the evidence from Hunter's Hole (549500) is cited. It is unfortunate that nowhere in the paper is the possible confusion with features resulting from previous periods of lead-zinc mining discussed. Mining was widespread in Mendip for about two thousand years and a wide variety of techniques have been employed, features of undoubted mining origin are shown in the Plate on p 134. Some depressions undoubtedly occur due to the sinking of the capping placed over disused vertical mining shafts, whilst further confusion arises as in many cases mining took advantage of natural depressions.

Surface solution hypothesis: Ford (1963), and Ford and Stanton (1968) have, over a number of years, assembled a considerable amount of data concerning the closed depressions of Mendip. Their view on the closed depressions is 'that the great majority are dolines percées (de Martonne, 1926), created by solution working down from the surface, and deepened by breakdown of the rotted rock walls at the top of the pipe or fissure which drains them' (1968, p 417). They stress the difficulty in mapping depressions, of distinguishing those of undisputed natural origin, and suggest that there are more than five hundred closed depressions. They consider about 90 per cent of the natural depressions are aligned along dry valley floors and that the frequency is inversely proportional to the gradient of the long-profile of the valley floor. This valley concentration reflects the concentration of surface flow, but should not be confused with the stream sink mechanism outlined by the Stride brothers. Ford (1963) considered the problem of the age of the formation of these features. Firm evidence is lacking but, in general terms, a continuous permafrost layer would militate against the forma-tion of surface depressions, whereas phases of discontinuous permafrost, ie large lenses of permafrost separated by unfrozen material sometimes known as talik, would concentrate both the surface and subsurface flow into the unfrozen areas which would greatly enhance the formation of closed depressions. Such talik conditions would prevail in the various Pleistocene climatic phases which were cold but not so severe as to give continuous permafrost. Ford suggested that the Younger Dryas phases at about 10000 BP would fall into this category. It is also likely that during the build up and particularly during the breakdown of a continuous permafrost cover, that talik-like conditions would also prevail.

Mendip subsurface hypothesis: The present authors agree in general with the suggestions of Ford and Stanton. In detail, the following mechanism, based largely upon an unpublished account by F. H. Nicholson (1962), is thought to provide the most likely explanation for the majority of the closed depressions. Field observations, and published speleological accounts of cave digs in depressions, make it clear that the views put forward by Coleman and Balchin for Hunter's Hole (549500)—that the material is progressively coarser as one digs down through the fill—is misleading. The entrance shaft has indeed been strongly attacked by solutional activity, and loose boulders are frequent, but with increasing depth the still loose blocks show no sign of movement. The bottom of the entrance shaft is narrow and in solid rock, and thus formation of the overlying depression cannot have resulted from any form of major collapse. This pattern is repeated with local variations in most of the depressions that have been excavated; chambers with solid rock walls and roofs with no sign of collapse underlie the surface depressions. A side elevation is given for Hunter's Hole in Fig 21.

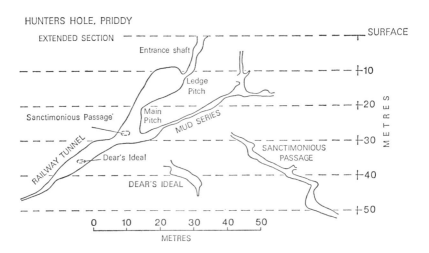

Fig 21 A side elevation of Hunter's Hole

HOLLOWFIELD SWALLET, PRIDDY

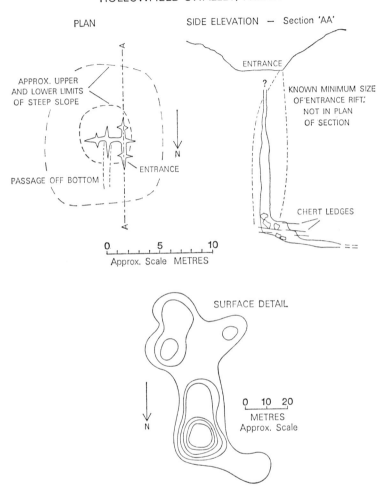

PLAN

SIDE ELEVATION — Section 'AA'

A

ENTRANCE

APPROX. UPPER
AND LOWER LIMITS
OF STEEP SLOPE

?

KNOWN MINIMUM SIZE
OF 'ENTRANCE RIFT'
NOT IN PLAN
OF SECTION

N

ENTRANCE

PASSAGE OFF BOTTOM

CHERT LEDGES

A

0   5   10

Approx. Scale METRES

SURFACE DETAIL

0   10   20

METRES
Approx. Scale

N

Fig 22 Surface detail, plan and side elevations of Hollowfield
Swallet. The surface form is shown by form lines and is not
accurately surveyed

Coleman and Balchin (1959, Fig 3, p 302) produced a detailed map of the depressions at Priddy Hill (528519). This map extract has been criticised in that there is no doubt that many (some would say nearly all) of the depressions included are artificial or modified by mining. The map includes Hollowfield Swallet (519526) and this again cannot be due to simple collapse. The rift which at the surface is about 30cm by 75cm. The walls of the rift are lined with fossils standing proud of the surface and providing incontrovertible evidence of solution at least, on a local scale. The shaft and the narrow, nearly horizontal, passage forming the lower part of the cave are cut in solid rock, and indicate that the very considerable volume of the surface depression cannot have evolved according to any hypothesis which invokes major collapse. The plan and sections for Hollowfield Swallet are illustrated in Fig 22. With minor local variations this pattern is repeated in most of the depressions that have been excavated. It could be said to hold for the caves at Vee Swallet (544538), Red Quar Swallet (561519), Alfie's Hole (550500), Easter Hole (580494), and Whitsun Hole (581494), all of which are sited in depressions. The last of these in fact takes a small stream and illustrates well the problem of distinguishing in the field between true stream sinks with a more or less perennial flow, and depressions that act as local drainage centres for a more limited period of time, or those that are completely dry.

The genesis of depressions of this kind is considered to be due to solutional activity acting on lines of weakness in the limestone, of which joints and bedding planes are usually prominent. It will be seen later that solutional erosion in limestones is particularly concentrated in the immediate subsurface zone. Such solution will, in time, enlarge certain joints to the extent that water flow becomes very much easier than in neighbouring joints which have not been enlarged to quite the same extent. The initial concentration of solutional activity will tend to be located at the line of intersection of the two planes of weakness; often at the intersection of two joint planes. Theoretical considerations of the critical width for this 'faster' flow to occur are considered in White and Longyear (1962), and Atkinson (1968). However, once certain joints or joint intersections become enlarged, the subsurface water movement tends to be funnelled towards that

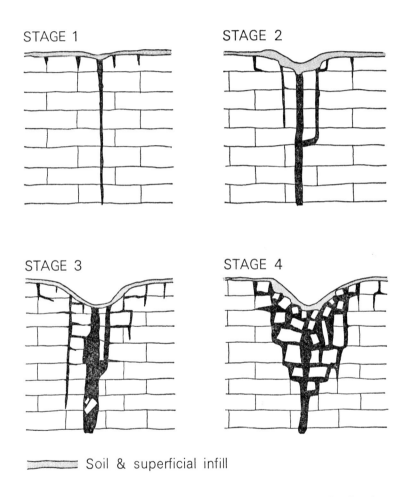

STAGE 1   STAGE 2

STAGE 3   STAGE 4

▬▬▬▬ Soil & superficial infill

Fig 23 Stages in a suggested evolutionary sequence for the development of surface depressions in Mendip

flow path. The enlargement process then becomes self-perpetu-
ating and may be further aided by local surface flow at times
of heavy precipitation—a form of flow similar to that of the more
normal stream swallet type. The solutional process, therefore,
works from the surface downwards, and the form of the
depression is aided by local collapse. Such collapse is not into
voids resembling cave passages or chambers, but into much
smaller cavities associated with the solutional process immediately
underlying the depression. The process is perhaps best illustrated
by reference to Fig 23. This evolutionary sequence is considered
to fit the field evidence, and would overcome the complications
of assuming, for example, that Hunter's Hole is a simple collapse
form. A variety of closed depression forms on the Plateau Surface
are shown in the Plate on p 167. Furthermore, the tendency for
the alignment of surface depressions along valley lines would be
expected, as this would represent a zone with concentrated subsurface flow.

This proposed origin does not account for all closed depressions and, without modification, does not offer an explanation
for the closed depressions that occur on non-calcareous strata
overlying the limestone. Whilst perhaps relevant to many of the
Mendip depressions it certainly should not be applied indiscrimin-

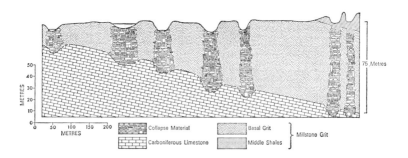

Fig 24 A geological cross-section illustrating the origin of closed,
surface depressions found on the Basal Grits of the Carboniferous
of South Wales (after Thomas, 1963)

ately to other limestone regions. The work of Thomas (see, for example, 1963) in south Wales demonstrates beyond doubt that large scale features due to collapse occur in that area. Occurrences of geologically distinctive rock types have been let down through vertical distances which in some cases exceed 200m (see Fig 24). It is perhaps worth noting that the rock stratigraphically overlying the Carboniferous Limestone in this case is composed of a particularly massive quartz conglomerate known as the Basal Grit. The water on the surface of the Basal Grit migrates, through joints, into the underlying limestones where solution commences and the subsequent collapse is into the solutional voids at this contact. Where a massive bed such as the Basal Grit occurs, the evolutionary sequence suggested in Fig 23 can be modified to that illustrated in Fig 24. It is worth noting that Wurt Pit (558539) is mainly developed in the siliceous rocks of the Harptree Beds, and its genesis may have been similar to that outlined in Fig 24.

Finally, it must be stressed that Mendip is a far from ideal location for the study of surface depressions, due to the influences of man, especially those early modifications associated with the lead and later the zinc mining (Gough, 1967).

Closed basins

The features described above as closed depressions, have attracted the attention of a number of workers, but only Ford and Stanton have drawn attention to related forms which they termed closed basins. They defined closed basins as 'basins of interior drainage feeding one or more closed depressions located at or about the lowest point of the basin floor' (1968, p 417). The closed basins are much larger in areal extent than the closed depressions, varying between 0.04 and 1.20sq km in area. Seventeen such basins are known in the south central Mendip area, and their distribution is shown in Fig 25 which is entirely based on the work of Ford and Stanton. The closed basins have low-angle slopes which are normally soil covered and frequently have a flat floor composed of a clay fill. The floors of the depressions are rarely more than about 15m lower than their perimeter, and generally the perimeter itself is notched by a col. The size and amplitude of these features is often sufficient for their presence to be detected on the 1:25,000 Ordnance Survey maps. Examples can be found on the south-east portion of the Cheddar sheet (number ST45). Although the detailed study by Ford and Stanton was limited to south-central

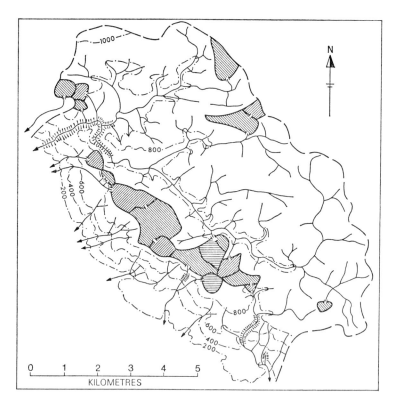

Fig 25 The location of closed basin features in south central Mendip (after Ford and Stanton, 1968). Contours are in feet

Mendip this is undoubtedly the major area for the occurrence of closed basins on Mendip.

The closed basins differ from the closed depressions not only as regards size, but also in respect of the position they occupy in the landscape. They are typically seen today on the Plateau Surface itself—in contrast to the concentrated areas of the closed depressions which show a close association with the narrower dry valley floors. In detail, Ford and Stanton suggested that their formation was similar. They saw the evolution commencing with the occurrence of a closed depression in the headwater sections of the valley system. The closed depressions at such a site 'cause the upstream parts of the surface channel to become entrenched towards the depression floor'. Later solution and downslope movement of material under the action of soil creep, grades the basin to the central sink.

Some of these closed depressions have flat floors developed on clay deposits, and it is thought that they may have formed in association with permafrost conditions. The permafrost rendered groundwater discharge from the basins impossible, and water was ponded up. The water overflowed from the basins and cut the notches that can still be recognised as dry cols. Clay settled out in the ponds and further added to the already impeded subsurface drainage. The relatively fresh form of the flat clay floors argues for a late Weichselian age. The closed depressions found in most of the closed basins are due to relatively recent subsidence of the clay infill into the underlying bedrock shafts.

Ford and Stanton discussed the form of evolution of Cross Swallet (516500) and Nod's Pot (476549) in particular detail. In the former case not only is there a clay floor, but there is also a well marked corrosion terrace cut into the limestone some 5m below the level of the overspill col. This striking feature is not shared with the other closed basins, and demands some particular hydrological explanation. The closed depression in the clay floor of Nod's Pot has been the site of an extensive cave dig, and is remarkable in that the shaft has been dug to a depth of about 25m without encountering solid bedrock.

There is no doubt that further studies of these closed depressions would be of considerable geomorphological interest, and the clay infill may reveal evidence indicative of the late Pleistocene climate.

Page 133

(*above*) Cheddar Gorge photo-
graphed from the south and
showing the deep incision of the
valley cut into the Plateau
Surface (*left*) Head deposits of
probable periglacial origin
forming an infill in the East
Twin valley

(*above*) The lower section of Burrington Combe viewed from the north. The valleys of the East and West Twin streams can be seen in the background cut into the slopes of Black Down (*below*) Mined, 'gruffy' ground at Shipham

4

The Erosion of Limestones on Mendip

D. I. Smith

The occurrence of underground water flow in limestones is a product of the solubility of the rock. Where such solutional activity is concentrated along a limited number of pathways these may become sufficiently enlarged to rank as caves. Thus a study of the process and rate of solutional activity has a key role to play in speleological studies. Such studies have been undertaken in detail on Mendip over the past ten years by a number of workers, and have two main aims. There are those primarily concerned with the establishment of the rate at which erosion proceeds at the present day at various sites on and within Mendip, whilst others attempt to explain the reasons for the variations.

Most writers concerned with the erosion of limestone focus their studies on the chemical erosion, often to the total exclusion of other forms of erosion. It should be remembered that the underground water flow on Mendip has many similarities to normal surface river flow and a brief review of the transport in such networks will be given.

THE TRANSPORT OF MATERIAL BY RIVERS
Rivers, surface or subterranean, act as transporting networks carrying away the weathered material produced in the area which

E

they drain. Very little of their load is actually eroded from the river channel itself. Thus, if we are interested in the rate of erosion in an area, an analysis of the total load transported by the rivers enables an estimate to be obtained for the rate of erosion operative in the catchment.

The load carried by rivers is normally considered to be of three main types: material can be transported solely by solution, or as bedload, or as suspended load. In practice there are difficulties in applying such a division to any given river since material is present as bedload at periods of relatively low discharge, and therefore low flow velocity, becomes suspended load at times of high discharge and increased velocity. Further, the dividing point between true solutional load, and very fine suspended load moving in the form of colloids, is difficult to establish. The tripartite classification is, however, a useful basis for the consideration of material moved by fluvial processes.

Determinations of the quantities of the bed load or suspended load transported by rivers in limestone areas are infrequent. Indeed, quantitative data for the amount of transported bedrock can be dismissed as totally unknown, since no studies appear to have considered material moved in this way. That bedload transport exists in subterranean drainage systems is clear to every caver since coarse material occurs in many cave passages, and is clearly undergoing fluvial transport. Additionally, coarse-grained material is frequently seen at resurgences in limestone areas and the only explanation, in the majority of cases, is that this material passed through the cave system as bedload to emerge eventually at the springs.

For cave streams, information regarding suspended sediment is also sparse. Indeed, one of the few limestone areas for which data of this kind is available is Mendip, and detailed results are given by Newson (1970, 1971, *a* & *b*). These results form the basis of this account. Suspended sediment is determined by collecting a sample of stream water and then filtering the sample to separate the particulate material. The distribution of suspended sediment in the stream cross-section is not uniform, and greater concentrations of sediment occur near the base of the stream. Thus a depth-integrated sample is collected. Depth integration in this sense means that the sampler is lowered and raised through a vertical profile until a sample of the required volume is obtained. The details of the sampler and method are given in Drew, Newson and Smith (1968). The sampler is subsequently filtered through a filter-paper or membrane. Membranes will retain sediment in excess of about one micron in diameter. From the volume of the sample and the weight of the filtered material, it is possible to obtain a value for the suspended sediment present. Such values are normally expressed in terms of parts per million (hereafter ppm) concentration, which in equivalent terms is milligrammes per litre. A detailed account of the method for surface streams is given in Gregory and Walling (1971).

Suspended sediment concentration is extremely dependent on stream velocity, which is itself related to discharge. The suspended sediment content varies in surface streams as approximately the square or the cube of the discharge. Thus, for a meaningful estimate of suspended sediment load, measurements must be repeated at the same site under a variety of discharge conditions until a rating curve is established. Newson (1971b) has presented such a curve for Cheddar in which the suspended sediment concentration is plotted against stream discharge. Fig 26 (Smith and Newson, 1974) shows the suspended sediment and solute rating curves for the risings at Langford and Rickford.

SOLUTIONAL EROSION AND TRANSPORT

Despite the importance of suspended and bedload transport, it is the solutional aspects of erosion that have claimed the major attention in limestone areas. Again we have the two-fold aim of assessing the rate of solution and the nature of the processes responsible. The intensity of study of the solutional erosion of limestone for Mendip is quite exceptional. The first detailed

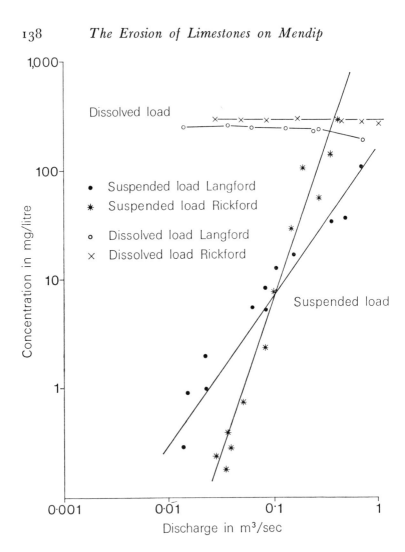

Fig 26 Rating curves for the concentration of suspended sediment and solute concentration for the risings at Langford and Rickford

results of this kind were presented by Smith and Mead (1962) and the subsequent history of research has been one of intensification of sampling, both as regards the number of samples from individual sites and the number of sites sampled. Changes in technique have also occurred, and many of the techniques were first developed on Mendip before their application to other regions. Thus the work described below should be considered as a review of the many papers available; where possible every attempt has been made to draw general conclusions rather than to present extremely detailed results. The methods employed are similarly dealt with in an outline fashion, although references are given to detailed accounts. Many of the techniques are not very demanding in chemical expertise or the availability of expensive equipment.

In an account of the solutional erosion of limestone it is necessary to have some basic understanding of the processes involved in order to fit the observed data into context.

THE SOLUTION OF LIMESTONE

In chapter 2 it was pointed out that most limestones, and certainly most of the limestones represented in the Carboniferous Limestone stratigraphy of Mendip, are extremely pure carbonate rocks. Many of the limestones are essentially composed of calcium carbonate, whilst in others varying degrees of dolomitisation have occurred (shown by the presence of the double carbonate of calcium and magnesium $(CaMg(CO_3)_2)$. This relatively straightforward rock chemistry has resulted in the solution of limestone being discussed in terms of simple chemical equations.

The equation usually employed to discuss the solutional erosion of limestone is :

$$CaCO_3 + CO_2 + H_2O = Ca(HCO_3)_2.$$

This is a simplification of the field situation, as it considers the limestone to be solely composed of calcium carbonate (the mineral form of which is calcite) and the water to be 'pure' rather than containing the additional constituents associated with 'natural waters' : the dissolved calcite is then present in the form of calcium bicarbonate in true chemical solution. Despite the obvious field complications, nearly all workers concerned with the study of limestone solution consider this equation to present a valid generalisation of the processes involved under field conditions. The equation can be broken down into a number of sub-stages and these are discussed by Smith and Mead (1962).

If we consider that this equation gives a good representation of the basic chemistry of the solution process, the next question to ask is how much calcium carbonate can be dissolved in water at differing temperatures and with differing concentrations of the carbon dioxide present in the atmosphere in contact with the water?

EFFECTS OF TEMPERATURE AND CARBON DIOXIDE VARIATIONS

It has long been known that at any given temperature (and assuming constant atmospheric pressure) the amount of gas that will dissolve a liquid is proportional to the percentage of that gas in the atmosphere. This relationship is known as Henry's Law. It has also been shown that the amount of gas dissolved decreases with increasing temperature. This effect is considerable in that a rise in temperature of some 30°C will cause the carbon dioxide content to fall by about 50 per cent. A conversion table is given below to convert the solubilities at 10°C to other temperatures. The temperature of 10°C has been chosen as unity as this closely approximates the temperature of limestone groundwater found in the United Kingdom.

Temperature °C	0	10	20	30	40
Factor	1.28	1.00	0.78	0.64	0.43

The amount of calcium carbonate that can be dissolved depends ultimately upon the carbon dioxide content of the atmosphere in contact with the solution. On a global scale, the carbon dioxide content of the atmosphere is about 0.033 per cent by volume, and there is very little latitudinal variation. At a temperature of 10°C a mixture of calcium carbonate and water in contact with a normal free air atmosphere, will attain a saturation value of about 74ppm $CaCO_3$. Since most naturally occurring waters on Mendip and in most other limestone areas contain considerably more than 74ppm $CaCO_3$, the problem resolves itself into finding a suitable source for the carbon dioxide.

The determination of the calcium saturation values for differing carbon dioxide levels is based upon a number of sources, the details of which can be found in Smith and Mead (1962), and Picknett (1964). It is stressed, however, that these saturation values are for solutions in contact with a continuous supply of air with a constant carbon dioxide content; it is therefore an open system. The relationships in this case are shown in Fig 27

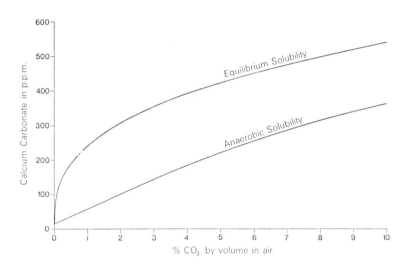

Fig 27 Saturation figures expressed in terms of calcium carbonate for waters at 10°C in open and closed systems

and are labelled 'equilibrium solubility'. The opposing situation, of a closed system with a fixed content of carbon dioxide *not* in contact with a continuous supply of air, is also shown in Fig 27 and is termed 'anaerobic solubility'.

It is also necessary to consider the time taken for the water to reach a saturation value. This is a complex problem and depends fundamentally on the rate of exchange of the carbon dioxide across the atmosphere/liquid boundary, and the calcium across the rock/liquid interface. With still water conditions both these exchange rates are slow, and it may take many days or weeks to reach saturation values. However, if the water is in motion the rate of exchange of carbon dioxide across the atmosphere/liquid boundary is greatly increased. A discussion of this effect was given by Weyl (1958). Roques (1969) also considered this problem, and stated that the exchange of the calcium across the rock/liquid interface is much slower than that of the carbon dioxide across the atmosphere/liquid boundary. Roques, from experimental and theoretical evidence, considered that in a system similar to that of a natural cave passage, the equilibrium time could be in the range of 200 to 250 hours. Studies of this kind are of importance when studying the formation of caves since, if the saturation value was reached in a very short time, the solutional activity of the stream would be totally expended *before* the water had the opportunity to reach an underground environment.

The intensive study of the calcium and magnesium content of waters associated with limestone areas is in large part due to the relative ease with which these ions can be determined in natural waters. Studies prior to the late 1950s were undertaken using soap solution to determine hardness, but since that date an improved titration method using EDTA (ethylene-diamine tetra-acetic acid, disodium salt) has been employed. The details of the procedure for this titration for natural water samples, and a discussion of the possible inferring ions are given in Smith and Mead (1962), and Douglas (1964), while chemical texts such as Schwarzenbach and Flaschka (1969) present fuller details of the chemistry involved.

A short explanation regarding the terminology employed in papers using this technique is necessary. The results are normally presented in terms of calcium hardness, magnesium hardness, or total hardness. The units used are generally parts per million $CaCO_3$ (hereafter ppm) for calcium hardness and ppm $MgCO_3$ for magnesium hardness; total hardness is the sum of the two. The quantity expressed in ppm is exactly comparable to milli- grammes per litre. It has become a convention in work on limestone solution to present the result in terms of calcium carbonate. It must be stressed that this in no way suggests that calcium is transported in the form of calcium carbonate. The titration for calcium hardness in fact measures the concentration of the calcium ion (Ca^{++}), and this is converted into the equiva- lent amount of calcium carbonate that would need to be dissolved to obtain the level of calcium found. It is probable that the calcium is actually transported in solution as calcium bicarbonate. Essentially this calculation assumes, purely for convenience, that all the calcium was derived from the solution of calcium car- bonate. A similar situation holds for magnesium hardness, although in this case the values are expressed in terms of the equivalent concentration in ppm $MgCO_3$. Total hardness is the sum of the two, again in terms of ppm $CaCO_3$. A full guide to the terminology and methods of determination is given in Stenner (1969, 1970 and 1971).

AGGRESSIVITY

It is of interest in limestone solutional studies to establish if the water sample is, in fact, saturated in respect of calcium carbonate. The field samples can be in equilibrium, supersatur- ated, or undersaturated. The water in the undersaturated case is said to be aggressive, that is it still has the potential to take up additional calcium before reaching its equilibrium value. A number of methods have been proposed to establish whether or not a given sample is aggressive. The methods and their short- comings are reviewed by Stenner (1969).

E*

Ideally, what is required is a determination of the aggressive carbon dioxide content of the solution; but this is difficult to determine accurately even under laboratory conditions, and impossible under field conditions. The first methods used relied upon the measurement of the pH (hydrogen ion content) of the sample and the determination of its calcium content. The former should be made in the field and the latter can be undertaken in the laboratory. The pH and the calcium content could then be compared with standard graphed relationships to establish if a given sample is aggressive or not. The first set of standard curves for pH and calcium content at a variety of temperatures, was that of Trombe (1952). Picknett (1964) re-determined the values given by Trombe, and presented a corrected curve for use at 10°C. Picknett also improved the technique by incorporating the saturometer technique, first outlined by Weyl, (1961) so that it became possible to assess the degree of saturation in percentage terms.

There are, however, two major handicaps with methods using pH curves. First, pH must be measured accurately in the field, and this involves the use of a portable glass electrode pH meter. Such instruments are somewhat temperamental under field conditions and it is doubtful if they are sufficiently sensitive or reliable for detailed work (see Roques, 1969, p 144). Secondly, the curves of pH against calcium content on which the observations are plotted, are determined under laboratory conditions with 'pure' water and impurity-free calcium carbonate. At best, such methods used in the field are likely to give only a broad indication as to whether the samples are aggressive or not; it is thought that determinations of the degree of aggressivity using these methods is unrealistic.

Stenner (1969, 1970) described a further method for the measurement of aggressivity for natural waters. This method does not involve the measurement of pH, or rely upon comparisons with results obtained by laboratory determinations on pure calcite solutions. It is in fact a direct measurement of aggressivity for the sample under study. Stenner undertook rigorous, controlled tests on the method to establish its validity, and subsequent application by other workers has demonstrated its value for the determination of aggressivity.

In outline, the samples are collected in duplicate. One sample is artificially saturated at the time of collection by the addition of a small quantity of calcium carbonate in such a way as to minimise the effects of the loss of carbon dioxide between collection and analysis. The other sample is not treated with calcium carbonate. On return to the laboratory both samples are analysed for their calcium content. If the sample is, in fact, aggressive the calcium value of the artificially saturated sample will exceed that of the untreated sample. In the case of the samples being supersaturated, the untreated sample will have a higher hardness value than the saturated sample.

The description of the processes of solution, the determination of calcium and magnesium hardness and aggressivity, are relevant to any study of limestone solution. They have been included here as background to the field results discussed below, since many of the methods were first applied in the field on Mendip.

FIELD RESULTS OF SOLUTIONAL LIMESTONE STUDIES ON MENDIP

It is estimated that since 1960, in excess of 10,000 water samples have been collected from Mendip and analysed for their calcium and magnesium content. Further, these samples were specifically collected for the purpose of limestone solutional studies. There is little doubt that this intensity of study far exceeds that of any other comparable limestone region. It does, however, cause difficulties when attempting to present an overall picture of the results.

In general terms it is possible to consider that the solute content of natural waters varies with the following five factors.

1 *Site*. This is a general description of the type of locality from which the sample was collected. For the purposes of description these sites can be classified into four major types. (i) *Surface*

stream sites: Normally sampled at the point at which the stream disappears underground. These could also be termed swallet sites. (ii) *Cave sites*: These are capable of further sub-division and include samples from the main streamway, from drips, or from underground streams without clear swallet feeders. (iii) *Soil water sites*: These samples are taken from soils overlying the limestone and are sampled at differing depths with the soil. (iv) *Spring or resurgence sites.*

2 *Discharge.* Each site should be sampled under varying discharge conditions to investigate the variation of solute content.

3 *Time.* The time factor is an attempt to consider possible variations in solute concentration that are not due to discharge variations. The most important time factor would be that of a seasonal nature. In practice it is difficult to distinguish seasonal trends from those due to discharge.

4 *Lithology.* Comparable sites associated with differing limestone lithologies may well be expected to exhibit differing solute concentrations. The variations in calcium and magnesium content of the water in respect of the degree of dolomitisation is probably the main factor.

5 *Climate.* Within a region the size of Mendip, climatic variations are unlikely to have any measurable effects. The climatic factor is of importance when comparing the results with those of other regions within the United Kingdom or on a world scale.

Site factors

(i) *Swallet sites*: A wealth of data is available for a large selection of swallet streams from all parts of Mendip. The initial sampling was described by Smith and Mead (1962) and gives details of samples collected over a period of twelve months for the Tyning's Swallet stream feeding GB Cave. A tentative 'model' figure for the calcium hardness values of differing Mendip sites was presented by Smith and Nicholson (1964), and this was critically reviewed by Ford (1966) who presented additional data for the Tyning's Swallet stream, together with values for the

major swallets feeding the St Cuthbert's and Swildon's Hole
system.

Since this initial work, the results of intensive sampling for
fourteen swallets in East Mendip for the period 1964–7 has been
presented by Drew (1970*a*). Newson (1970) has published results
describing similar analyses for the swallets in the Burrington area,
and Atkinson (1971) sampled eleven swallets in central Mendip
on a weekly basis for a period from October 1969 to September
1970. Additional detailed studies for GB and St Cuthbert's
Caves have been presented by Stenner (1966, 1970).

All these studies agree on two major points. First, there is
considerable variation from swallet to swallet as regards the
mean hardness values and secondly, all the swallet streams show
major variations which are, in a general sense, inversely related
to discharge conditions.

Fig 28 shows the total hardness values for the swallets at
Tyning's (the major swallet feeding GB Cave), Longwood and
Swildon's and their relationship to prevailing discharge condi-
tions.

It is difficult to give a detailed explanation for the variation
in hardness from swallet to swallet. Such variations are undoubtedly related to the lithological and soil differences in the
surface catchments of the swallet streams. Some of these catchments encompass only a limited area of limestone whilst in others
the proportion of limestone is large. The limestone bands within
the Lower Limestone Shales are of importance as well as
calcareous–rich strata within the Old Red Sandstone succession.
Additionally, the variations in the rate of water movement
through the soils within the catchments is of significance.

In addition to the calcium hardness of the swallet waters it is
of interest to know to what degree the water is saturated in respect of calcium carbonate. The first attempts to study this
relationship were by Ford (1964*a*), but the techniques and
apparatus available at that time enabled only generalised
comments to be made regarding the degree of saturation. The

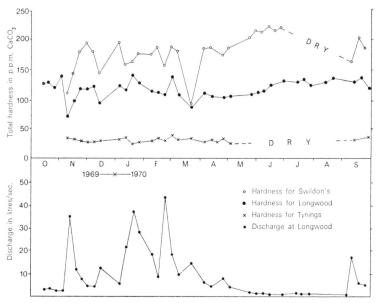

Fig 28 Variations in calcium hardness for the swallets at Tyning's, Longwood and Swildon's; the discharge for the Longwood Stream is also shown (from Atkinson, 1970)

water at Tyning's and St Cuthbert's swallets was in fact aggressive, while that at Swildon's was saturated. Drew (1970*a*), employing the saturometer methods proposed by Picknett (1964) for fourteen swallets in east Mendip, presents his results in terms of percentage saturation figures. The overall range of values for the fourteen sites was from 73 to 99 per cent saturation, with the majority of the figures falling within the range 78 to 90 per cent.

Stenner (1970) and Atkinson (1971) made extensive use of the saturation technique described by Stenner. Stenner presents a diagram showing the variations in aggressiveness for the Tyning's Swallet stream in terms of ppm $CaCO_3$ which shows the stream to be consistently undersaturated. Fig 29 is based upon

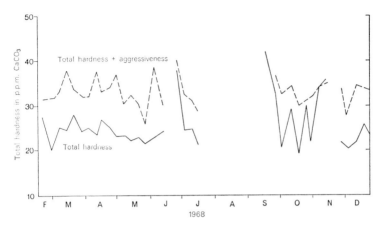

Fig 29 Variations in total hardness and aggressiveness for the
Tyning's Swallet stream (from Stenner, 1970)

Stenner (1970, p 285). Atkinson presents mean saturation figures
for the eleven swallets sampled during his work. These mean
values vary between -2ppm and $+13$ppm $CaCO_3$, indicating
the aggressive nature of most of the swallets. The negative values
indicate supersaturation. The two streams that are, from the
mean values, supersaturated (namely Manor Farm and Swildon's)
have mean total hardness values that are in excess of 200ppm.
(ii) *Cave sites* : In considering cave sites it is possible to distinguish
cave streams fed by swallet streams as a specific category. However, it is difficult to further classify cave waters into other
meaningful sub-divisions. Once the swallet water has entered the
cave, often to become the main streamway, additions of water
from cave stream tributaries and cave drips complicate the field
situation. By definition, none of the cave tributaries will have
distinct swallet sources and are generally composed of water that
has percolated down through the soil into the bedrock and then
become concentrated into small pipes and joints, finally appear-
ing as a cave tributary stream. Similarly cave drips vary markedly
in size—from the slow regular drops falling from a stalactite to

those that resemble an incipient stream showering down into the cave passage from an aven. Ford (1966), delightfully described the cave drips as 'drip and trickle water'. These problems of classifying underground sampling sites are important if, for example, attempts are made to assess the rate at which solutional activity is eroding the actual cave passage. This problem was stressed by Smith and Mead (1962, p 200): 'The direct solutional activity of the main stream is considered to be responsible for only a small part of the increase in the calcium carbonate content of the main stream. Attempts to measure directly the solutional activity of underground streams should carefully assess the part played by tributary streams and roof drips.'

Numerous studies have shown that there is a relatively large increment in the calcium content of cave streams between the swallet and the lowest accessible point in the cave. The amount of this increase in terms of concentration varies, particularly in respect of discharge. This increase for the main streamway in GB Cave between swallet and cave end is shown in Fig 30, which is based upon a similar diagram in Smith and Mead (1962). Subsequent work by Ford (1966) for GB Cave and St Cuthbert's and Swildon's demonstrated a similar large increase between swallet and cave end but stressed that the absolute calcium values were different in other caves. Ford also stated that drip and trickle increments were quantitatively of little significance, and that the rapid increase of the calcium content progressively down the streamway was due to rapid initial solution by the streamway water itself. As the intensity of study and sampling increased, this conclusion was disputed by Stenner (1970) who demonstrated that the increments in hardness along the GB streamway were not explained by direct solutional uptake of calcium by the stream water, but were almost entirely the result of the admixture of tributary water with a higher calcium content. Fig 31 is based upon Stenner's work, and also shows the earlier results of Ford.

Several workers have analysed samples collected from cave

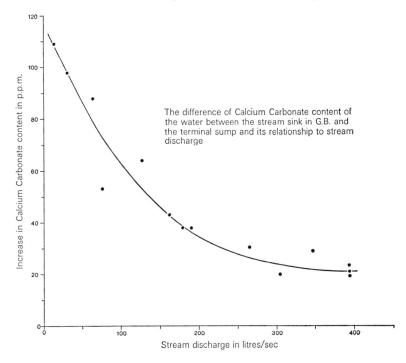

Fig 30 Relationships of discharge to calcium hardness increase for the main streamway in GB Cave

drips in a number of caves, at differing depths below the surface and under varying discharge conditions. In general, and exceptions are not difficult to find, the hardness values are in excess of those obtained from swallet streams and frequently in excess of the hardness values for the streamway. The figures presented by Atkinson (1971) are the most comprehensive in respect of the number of caves sampled. Atkinson sampled thirty-eight sites in five caves. The caves were Swildon's, Twin T's Swallet, Contour Cavern, Reservoir Hole and Cuckoo Cleeves. The majority of the Swildon's sites were sampled on two occasions. The overall mean total hardness was 187 ppm although if the

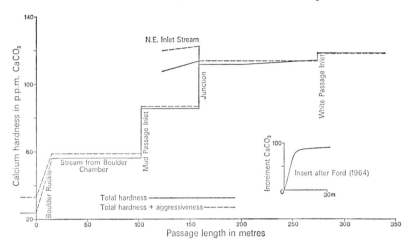

Fig 31 Variations in hardness and aggressiveness for the main
    streamway in GB Cave (from Stenner, 1970)

anomalously low values obtained from Cuckoo Cleeves are
omitted the mean is 241 ppm.

Repeated sampling of individual cave drip sites over a pro-
tracted period with considerable variations of discharge was
described by Smith and Mead for four sites in GB Cave. They
suggested that individual drips showed relatively little variation
of hardness with discharge, and that from the results then available there would appear to be 'a rough correlation between
the calcium carbonate content of the water from the drips, and
the distance from the ground surface to the point where the
water falls from the cave roof'. Ford (1966) also collected samples
in GB Cave and found that for a particular drip site the variations in calcium hardness over a period of eight days was as
great as 50 ppm. Newson (1970, p 49), from detailed studies of
drip sites in East Twin Cave and Read's Cavern, found that
variations in calcium content depended on the type of drip but
that the range of the variations between drips was small.

Atkinson's work confirmed the relationship of the calcium hardness of the drip sites to the depth below the surface. The work was extended in that Atkinson also found that the carbon dioxide content of the cave atmosphere increased with depth and, by inference, the increase of hardness was associated with this enhanced carbon dioxide value. The aggressivity of cave samples is usually slightly negative, indicating a small degree of supersaturation.

The results outlined above are for cave drips, but from a descriptive viewpoint these grade into what may be termed cave tributary sites. The only essential difference is that the former are normally dripping from the roof of a cave while the latter represent a concentration of percolation flow to give a distinct cave stream. As might be expected, the cave tributary sites exhibit hardness values and variations intermediate between the cave streamway and drip sites. Diagrams showing the hardness values found for sites of this kind can be found in Smith and Mead (1962, p 201), and Stenner (1970, p 287).

(iii) *Soil water sites* : Fewer observations for the solute concentration of soil water have been made on Mendip than for other sites. Results are presented by Newson (1970) for the Burrington area and by Atkinson (1971) for a number of sites in the Cheddar catchment. The sampling method employed was to insert lengths of perforated plastic tube into the soil and to collect the sample from water that had drained into the tube. The tubes vary in length and the perforations can be arranged to sample soil water at differing depths.

Variations in soil depth, texture, and composition, present sampling problems and, additionally, the solute concentration can be expected to change in response to rainfall and the overall soil moisture conditions. Newson investigated the solute concentration in a soil profile overlying the limestone after a period of heavy rain. Two factors emerged : first, an increase in calcium content with depth in the profile, and secondly a tendency for the solutes to assume an equilibrium value after a period of about twenty-four hours. The results are illustrated in Fig 32 which is based upon the work of Newson (Fig 26, 1970).

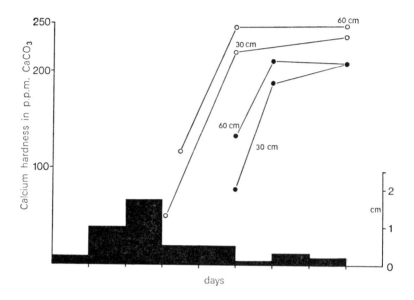

Fig 32 Calcium hardness for soil water in relation to soil depth and rainfall (from Newson, 1971)

Atkinson collected regular samples for the Cheddar catchment from thirty soil tubes, at various depths, over a period of about a year. The overall mean was 53ppm $CaCO_3$ and with little seasonal variation. Additionally, Atkinson calculated a value for the potential hardness of his samples and found these to be about 150ppm $CaCO_3$ during winter, but rising to nearly 300ppm during the summer. Fig 33, based upon Atkinson (Fig 8.13, 1971), shows the mean hardness soil values (an average obtained from all thirty sampling sites) and the calculated potential hardness for the same sites.

(iv) *Spring sites* : Detailed studies of the hardness of spring sites have been undertaken for a large number of Mendip springs over the last ten years or so. Initial results were given by Smith and Mead for Rickford, Langford, Cheddar and Wookey.

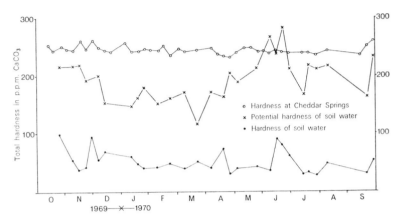

Fig 33 Actual and potential hardness for soil sites compared to the measured hardness at the Cheddar springs (from Atkinson, 1971)

Intensive studies were undertaken by Newson (1970) for Rickford and Langford, and for Cheddar and Wookey by Atkinson (1971). Similar detailed work in east Mendip for St Dunstan's rising and various springs in the Ashwick area were described by Drew (1970a). In addition to these risings, less detailed work has been undertaken for springs at Compton Martin and Banwell (Drew, Newson and Smith, 1968).

The mean total hardness values obtained for the risings at Cheddar, Wookey Hole and Rodney Stoke are 245, 272 and 291ppm respectively and the ranges (expressed in percentages of the mean) are 13, 18 and 11 per cent. These variations, expressed in terms of the standard deviation for the three risings, are 6.9, 6.4 and 9.0ppm. Rickford rising yields a mean total hardness of 269ppm, and that for the rising at Langford is approximately

200ppm. The variations exhibited by Rickford are comparable to the south Mendip risings described by Atkinson, while Langford shows very much larger variations in hardness. Total hardness values for Langford can vary from nearly 250ppm under extremely low discharge conditions, to less than 150ppm with flood flows. The results, presented by Drew (1970) from studies in eastern Mendip, tend to show higher calcium hardness values than those described above, and also the range in hardness with varying discharge conditions is greater. The values for the spring at St Dunstan's Well East give a mean calcium hardness of 182ppm (with a standard deviation of 27ppm) and a range of between 113 and 248ppm. For St Dunstan's West the corresponding figures are 243ppm (standard deviation of 46ppm) and a range of 220–320ppm. Observations on the springs in the Ashwick valley show even greater differences from the overall picture found for central and western Mendip. Ashwick Lower rising, for example, has a mean calcium hardness of 320ppm (standard deviation of 34ppm) and a range of 280–380ppm, while Ashwick High rising situated nearby has a mean of 278 ppm and a range of 255–340ppm. All the figures presented by Drew are solely in terms of calcium hardness.

All the workers interested in the analysis of hardness figures from risings on Mendip have stressed that the variation in hardness with discharge is considerably less than the variation encountered at the swallets. But the hardness variations at the risings, although much smaller than those for the swallets, are also related inversely to discharge. The difficulty is in explaining why differing spring sites showed differing degrees of variation with discharge : for example, the small variations at Rickford compared to the much greater variations for the neighbouring spring at Langford, or the variation between the springs on the south flank of Mendip compared to those of eastern Mendip. It is now clear that much of this variation can be explained by considering the proportion of the spring discharge that is composed of swallet water. The greater the swallet contribution, the larger the variations in hardness at the spring. Newson (1971) presented a graph showing the relationship between hardness (plotted as a coefficient of variability) and the average swallet contribution as a percentage of the spring discharge. Fig 34 is based upon this work.

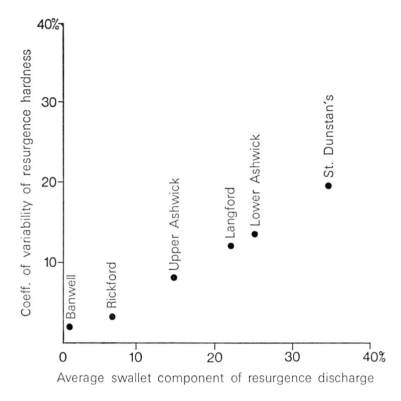

Fig 34 Relationship between resurgence hardness and the contribution of swallet waters (from Newson, 1971)

The other major difference between swallet and rising water, relates to the aggressivity. The first attempt to measure aggressivity at spring sites was by Drew who used the Picknett–Weyl saturometer technique, which involved the use of a field pH meter. This method does not achieve the accuracy of the Stenner method used in later studies, but the data presented by Drew (1970) demonstrates that the springs in eastern Mendip are very near to saturation, and that undersaturation occurs at times of high discharge. An example of the results, in this case for the double rising at St Dunstan's Well, is given in Fig 35 and is based upon Drew (Fig 4, 1970). The results are plotted on the graph produced by Picknett (1964).

Atkinson undertook regular sampling to establish the degree of saturation at Cheddar, Wookey Hole and Rodney Stoke, and found that the mean values were $+2.4$, $+6.9$ and -6.0ppm respectively. Thus, under average conditions, the risings are very near to a saturation balance, with Cheddar and Wookey Hole very slightly undersaturated. Similar figures are found for the springs occurring on the northern flank of Mendip. If we confine our attention to average values collected over an extended period of time, the saturation results demonstrate a state of near balance for the risings.

In discussing hardness and aggressivity it is also of interest to consider short-term fluctuations associated with periods of high discharge. Newson (1971b) discusses the effects of floods on the total hardness, aggressivity, and suspended sediment for the Rickford and Langford risings. Fig 36 shows a marked decrease in hardness for Langford compared to a very minor effect at Rickford, which reflects the greater proportion of swallet water at the former. The pattern of these variations is also found at other risings.

2 *Discharge*

Changing discharge conditions are of major importance in determining the variations in solute concentration at differing sites. The relationship is such that it is impossible to describe site factors without reference to discharge, and these relationships have been considered in the preceding section.

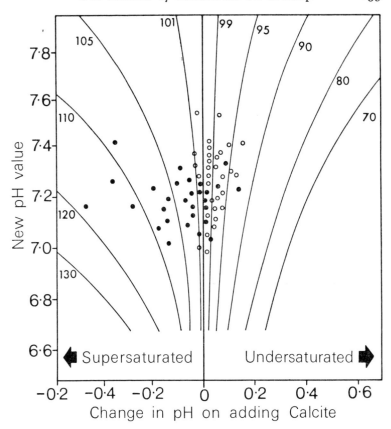

• St. Dunstan's East ○ St. Dunstan's West

Fig 35 Percentage saturation for the springs at St Dunstan's Well (from Drew, 1970)

3 *Time*

It is extremely difficult in practice to distinguish the effects of time from those of discharge as regards solute values. The time factor of major interest is of a seasonal nature. Variations in

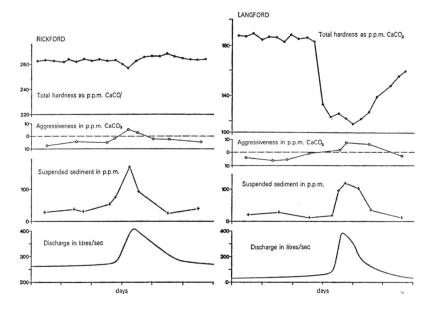

Fig 36 Values for total hardness, aggressiveness and suspended sediment concentration for a flood hydrograph at Rickford and Langford risings (from Newson, 1971)

surface temperature, and the consequent effects on the production of carbon dioxide in the soil—from a variety of biogenic sources—are of importance, and have been stressed by Pitty (1966) in comparable studies in Derbyshire.

The hardness of the swallets and risings does not appear to show any clear or marked variations of a seasonal nature, and this lack of relationship was discussed by Smith and Mead (1962). Atkinson (1971), from his detailed study of central Mendip, could find little difference between winter (October to March) and summer (April to September) for the hardness values at the springs or swallets. Similarly, observations by other workers on Mendip do not appear to find any seasonal variation of hardness figures for swallets or springs other than those linked to discharge effects.

Indeed, the only sites at which seasonal factors appear to be important are those associated with soil water. The only detailed results of this kind were collected by Atkinson. He finds that the mean figures of calcium hardness for summer and winter are 49 and 57ppm respectively. The difficulty of collecting representative samples would suggest that these figures should not be used to infer that winter soil values are significantly higher than those for summer, but that the two 'seasons' are essentially similar. The only marked seasonal variation is found when potential soil hardness values are calculated. These show a marked peak in early summer and most probably correspond to the 'spring burst' effect noted by Pitty for Derbyshire; the increase being due to the increased production of biogenic carbon dioxide. However, it must be stressed that from the Mendip work there is no clear link between this increase in potential soil hardness and the actual hardness values obtained from any of the sites sampled.

4 *Lithology*

Theoretical and laboratory based studies of the solubility of limestones containing varying amounts of magnesium carbonate would suggest that such lithological variations should be reflected in the calcium to magnesium solute values obtained from water samples. Only limited—and inconclusive—studies of the solubility of the Mendip limestones have been undertaken in a laboratory context. However, most of the workers mentioned above have measured both calcium and magnesium hardness values for the sites from which the water samples have been collected. Variations in the ratio of magnesium to calcium do occur between differing sampling sites, but the evidence available suggests that for an individual sampling site the ratio of magnesium to calcium remains constant regardless of variations in discharge.

The greatest problem in relating solute values to bedrock composition is the relative paucity of bedrock analyses. Atkinson (1971) has reviewed this problem in detail for south central Mendip and concludes his statistical treatment by stating that there is 'no significant difference between the samples of bedrock analysed and those of dissolved limestone at a 95 per cent confidence level'. This is in accord with the less detailed observations of other workers on Mendip. For example, the rising at Banwell has the highest magnesium values of any of the major Mendip risings, and its catchment also contains the largest proportion of Carboniferous Limestone mapped as dolomitised.

This is a field of study in which further work would be of value, but as a working hypothesis based upon the limited information available for Mendip and, indeed, for other limestone areas, the statement by Smith (1968) that calcium and magnesium are dissolved in amounts comparable to their proportions in the bedrock, would form a convenient starting-point. In limestone areas where the calcium and magnesium are not present as carbonates but as sulphates, a more complex relationship would be expected.

5 *Climate*

Within a region the size of Mendip, climatic variations do not have any measurable effects. In fact it is possible that climatic controls on limestone solution are of considerably less significance than many earlier workers suggested. For example, the springs associated with the Jurassic oolitic limestones to the north of Bath, which for our purposes are identical in climate to Mendip, all exhibit greater concentrations of calcium and magnesium than comparable sites on Mendip. On the other hand the corresponding solute concentration values for similar sites in Jamaica, with a very differing climatic regime, are lower than for Mendip. As additional results become available from differing climatic regions it is becoming clear that climatic factors alone

TABLE 4 *Generalised variations of total hardness for Mendip sites*

Site	Variation in total hardness in ppm CaCO$_3$	Effects of variations of discharge	Seasonal effects	Saturation status
Surface stream at swallet	Usually in range 20–200, varies according to nature of surface stream catchment	Very marked effects, these show a general, inverse relationship to discharge	Not distinguishable from effects due to discharge	Undersaturated except where hardness is high, in excess of about 200ppm
Cave sites (i) Main streamway	40–250, depends largely on the proportion of swallet-derived water	Marked but less than for surface streams	As above	Variable, frequently slightly under-saturated except at times of low discharge
(ii) Streams not directly fed by surface streams	80–260, varies in relation to degree of hydraulic connectivity to the overlying surface	Less than for main streamway	No seasonal effects	Generally in approximate equilibrium except at times of very high discharge
(iii) Drips	50–260, site variations in part related to depth below ground surface	Effects generally small	No seasonal effects	In equilibrium or slightly over-saturated
Soil water	Observations usually for saturated soil conditions. Values generally less than 100, increase with depth down the soil profile	Not applicable	Possibility of slight seasonal effect for saturated soils	Calculated *potential* hardness is in excess of actual hardness values particularly at times of 'spring burst'
Springs	Mainly in the range 220–260. Some springs in excess of 300 and others show greater range	Effects usually limited in the range of 10–20% of the mean value. Variation related to the proportion of discharge that is derived directly from swallets	No seasonal effects	In equilibrium or slightly over-saturated

are of limited importance in explaining differences in solute variations. It is equally true to say that the explanation of these differences is still very far from clear.

TOWARDS A MODEL AND AN EXPLANATION

In order to present the large amount of information accumulated from Mendip on the calcium and magnesium hardness and measures of aggressivity, the data has been presented in terms of differing sites, and the importance of discharge conditions has been stressed. From the data it is possible to outline a model situation in an attempt to explain the variations described and to suggest the key factors responsible for the solution process.

The salient points of the varying sites discussed are given in Table 4.

An earlier attempt to portray this data in diagrammatic form was given in Smith and Nicholson (1964) and was subsequently criticised by Ford (1966). Since that date additional information, particularly of aggressivity and carbon dioxide content, has been obtained and a revised diagrammatic model is given in Fig 37.

The earlier work stressed the importance of carbon dioxide in the solution process, particularly drawing attention to the part played by the enhanced carbon dioxide content of the soil atmosphere. In outline, the precipitation falls on to the ground surface, and the proportion of this water not lost by evapotranspiration percolates down through the soil reaching equilibrium with the carbon dioxide within the soil atmosphere. The water is therefore aggressive with respect to the limestone bedrock, and it is this carbon dioxide-enriched water that is responsible for the solute figures found. The aggressiveness progressively decreases as the water follows its path through the groundwater circulation, to give fully saturated waters at the risings. The major inadequacy of this simple model is that the information available on the soil atmosphere stresses that the soil carbon dioxide content should exhibit variations related to seasonal differences in the biogenic production of the carbon

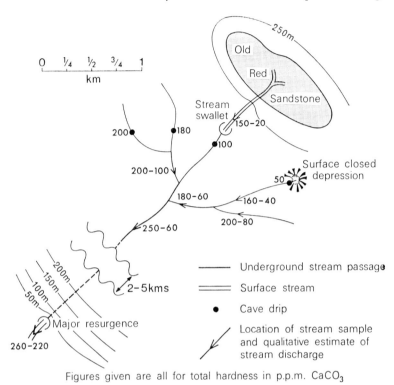

Figures given are all for total hardness in p.p.m. $CaCO_3$

Fig 37 Hardness values for a hypothetical model Mendip cave

dioxide, but the hardness values at the risings do not exhibit this variation in terms of hardness.

A further point raised by Smith and Mead was that the carbon dioxide in the soil atmosphere and in the bedrock below may not be in free contact with the air above the soil, in which case the anaerobic values shown on Fig 27 would apply, and not those marked as equilibrium solubility.

Atkinson (1971) has made direct measurements of the carbon dioxide content of the soil atmosphere and has calculated the potential hardness of the soil water, illustrated in Fig 33. This too, is insufficient to explain either the amount of calcium and magnesium found at the risings, or to account for the lack of seasonal variation. Atkinson also described observations made on the carbon dioxide content of cave air, and found that where these observations were made close to joints occurring in the cave walls, the carbon dioxide was markedly higher than for the air generally circulating in the cave. Similar results have been described by Ek and his co-workers from caves in Belgium and Poland (see Ek *et al*, 1969), and Stenner (1970) has drawn attention to similar phenomena in GB Cave. It is therefore suggested that additional solution may take place in the joints of the limestone mass far below the soil zone. This solution would result from carbon dioxide produced by biological activity associated with organically rich material infilling the joints. Thus, in addition to the enhanced carbon dioxide content of the soil atmosphere, which shows a seasonal variation, there is a further supply of carbon dioxide, generated at greater depths in the limestone mass, produced from organic material leached down from the soil above. This is perhaps best termed 'ground air' to distinguish it from the soil atmosphere. Tentatively, the calculated quantity of this ground air would be sufficient under anaerobic conditions to give the hardness figures observed at the risings. An additional fact of importance is that since this organic material is situated deep in the limestone, the temperature conditions would be isothermal, and therefore the supply of carbon dioxide would not normally be expected to show any seasonal variations. This hypothesis is difficult to verify by direct observation but could usefully act as a basis for further work.

RATES OF EROSION

The quantitative discussion of solutional and mechanical erosion on Mendip so far has been in terms of the concentration of solutes or particulate load. Mention must be made of the rate at which the limestone is actually eroded, both in terms of the

(*above*) Closed depressions on the Plateau Surface of Mendip, near to the Miner's Arms. The view is to the south with the summit of North Hill in the background. A Roman road can be seen running diagonally across the photograph (*below*) The Great Chamber in Banwell Stalactite Cave

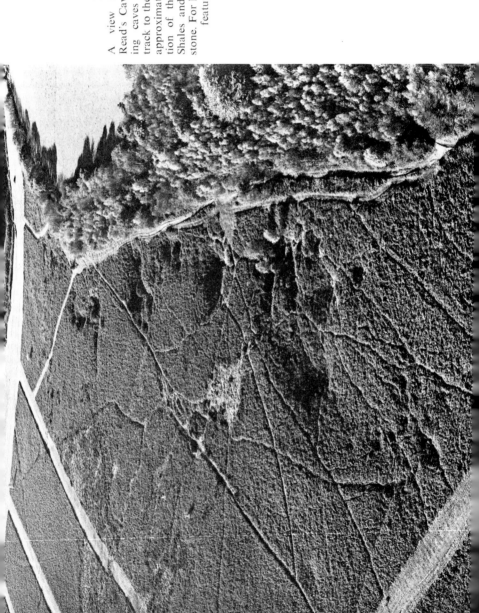

Page 168

A view to the west over Read's Cavern and neighbouring caves and swallets. The track to the right of centre runs approximately along the junction of the Lower Limestone Shales and Black Rock Limestone. For location of individual features see Fig 20

total amount of material removed from the Mendips as a whole, and also of the rates of removal from specific sites.

The material removed as particulate load has only been studied in any detail by Newson (1969, 1970 and 1971*b*), and the rates of removal of material in suspension are subject to such extreme variations between periods of low and high discharge that any precise statement is liable to be misleading. The best overall comment that can be made at present is that the particulate load removed from the area as a whole is estimated to be 10–20 per cent of the solutional load (Smith and Newson, 1974).

Estimates of the overall rate of solutional erosion from limestone areas have been given in the literature for a number of years. The first worker to apply this method in any detail was Corbel, who produced solutional erosion figures for many differing lithological and climatic regions. The figure for the overall erosion rate for Mendip was given by Corbel (1957, p 322) as 40 cubic metres per square kilometre per year (hereafter m³/km²/yr). This figure can alternatively be expressed in terms of the equivalent thickness of limestone that would be removed, as a slice from the surface of the limestone, by solution; in this case the answer would be 40mm of surface lowering per thousand years. The surface lowering equivalent is only intended as a value for use in a comparative sense and in no way should it be considered as a direct measurement of surface lowering.

The estimate given by Corbel was based upon indirect estimates of the discharge obtained by a general consideration of the precipitation and evapotranspiration loss, and upon a limited number of observations of the hardness of the spring waters. The mean calcium hardness value used by Corbel was 200ppm $CaCO_3$, the magnesium values were ignored.

The work of Corbel created an impetus for further studies of this kind. A later estimate for the Cheddar catchment, based upon a larger number of hardness determinations but also relying

F

upon meteorological data for the discharge, was presented by Ford (1963); the figure was between 38 and 45m³/km²/yr.

There has been a reluctance amongst most Mendip workers to produce such estimates, although as the detail of study has increased such estimates have been given. Direct measurements of discharge are necessary, and the concentration of solutes should clearly include values for both calcium and magnesium, carefully weighted for any variation in respect of changing discharge. Drew (1967) gives three values for eastern Mendip based upon detailed observations at differing spring sites. The discharge values in this case are direct, and Drew discusses the errors that may occur in using the less precise, meteorologically derived, run-off data. The values obtained are 50–64m³/km²/yr for the St Dunstan's Well catchment, 101–102m³/km²/yr for Ashwick Lower, and 84–88m³/km²/yr for Ashwick Lower.

Newson also produced estimates for the solutional erosion of parts of Mendip by using discharge data related to the hardness values obtained. His estimate for the Cheddar catchment is 22.8 m³/km²/yr (very considerably less than the figure given by Ford, 1963) and that for the joint Langford–Rickford catchment on the north flank of Mendip is 28.7m³/km²/yr. The figures are further detailed to separate material removed by the percolation water as opposed to the discrete channel flow. The percolation figures are 20.5 and 25.2m³/km²/yr for the Cheddar and Langford–Rickford catchments respectively.

Finally, Atkinson (1971) gives a further set of figures for the southern central Mendip catchments, the value for the overall solutional erosion rate being 81m³/km²/yr for the year 1969–70. Additionally, Atkinson apportioned out the amount of solutional erosion at each of the sites discussed above. It is suggested that over 60 per cent of the solution takes place at the junction of the soil and bedrock, and a further 35 per cent of the erosion within the bedrock mass itself. It is interesting to note that less than 0.1 per cent of the total solutional load is obtained from the actual cave passages.

5

The Limestone Hydrology of the Mendip Hills

D. P. Drew

The caves of the Mendip Hills cannot be studied independently of the present-day surface and subsurface hydrology to which they are genetically related with varying degrees of directness. Before examining the hydrology and caves of the Mendip area, a brief summary of the various theories that have been advanced to explain the behaviour of water in massive limestones and speleogenesis may be useful in order that their applicability to Mendip may be assessed.

The hydrology of areas of massive limestone has only been seriously studied since the beginning of the twentieth century. Several major and incompatible theories put forward early in the century have remained current to the present day. All workers agree that the solubility of limestone is of fundamental significance in the evolution of limestone areas, and further, that initial and secondary geological structure, together with climate, act as major controls on the subterranean landscape development. Information as to the frequency of primary and secondary fractures in limestones, the initial degrees of openness and the ability of fractures to transmit water is largely absent, and hence most theories of limestone hydrology are compounded from largely indirect evidence (for example, water tracing and solution data) together with limited exploration of accessible conduits.

The initiation of flow within these conduits is essentially a study of fluid dynamics and carbonate solution chemistry and has been discussed by Davis (1966) and Atkinson (1968). The processes of limestone solution are outlined in chapter 4 and thus this resumé will be concerned largely with the flow-paths followed by groundwater in limestones, and the processes of cavern development.

The two major theories of groundwater conditions in karst are essentially those of Grund (1903) and Katzer (1909); both theories being developed to explain features of the Yugoslavian karst. The difference between the two theories is essentially that Grund maintained the existence of a continuous piezometric surface[1] within the limestone which extended down to an underlying impermeable base, this being analogous to the conventional water-table postulated for porous rocks. Precipitation, infiltrating at the surface, moves rapidly and largely vertically to the zone of saturation, and thence laterally along the steepest hydrologic gradient to the springs. Grund called the gravity-zone water (vadose) 'Karstwasser' and the main body of groundwater (phreas) 'Grundwasser'.

Katzer, a practical caver, doubted the existence of a continuous water-table in limestone areas, and introduced the concept of localised groundwater flowing from sink to rising in discrete conduits.

These two theories have remained the major points of difference between karst hydrologists. In general, the theoretical approach, and especially that of engineering geologists, has been that of Grund, whereas practical speleologists, for example Martel (1921) in France, using the data from their underground explorations, have tended to favour Katzer's views.

Cvijič (1918) introduced a major compromise theory, invoking a discontinuous water-table together with a regional base level governed by underlying impermeable rocks. In the 1930s two

1 The piezometric surface, or water-table is the upper limit of the saturated zone within the rock.

American geographers propounded the first comprehensive theories of cavern development. W. M. Davis (1930) based his work on studies in North America, and largely accepted the views of Grund. He suggested that the majority of caves develop as a result of deep phreatic solution and only become accessible when the water-table is lowered. Davis described this as the two-cycle theory of cave development, in contrast to the one-cycle theory which postulated a purely vadose origin for caves. Gardner (1935) and Malott (1938) re-emphasised the case for a vadose origin for caves. Swinnerton (1932) suggested a zone of maximum cave development in the immediate sub-water-table zone, where maximum lateral movement of water occurred.

Theories of groundwater flow in limestone areas were codified especially by Rhoades and Sinacori (1941) who, in a mathematical study, proposed that a marked concentration of flow occurred near resurgences, and that 'master conduits' were developed by headward erosion from the rising at the level of the water-table.

More modern views have tended to be orientated to one or other of the earlier workers' conclusions. Mandel (1965) re-affirmed the views of Rhoades and Sinacori that solution channels develop in an upstream direction from the risings, and that gradually, one favoured spring captures all the groundwater in a limestone massif. He suggested that the development of a limestone drainage system should be regarded as the transformation of a more or less isotropic aquifer into a markedly anisotropic one. He further suggested that variations in lithology and structure in the carbonate rocks are of secondary importance compared with the flow of water towards hydraulic lows. Thrailkill (1968) supported the contention that cave development is localised in the shallow phreatic zone, and suggested that the major reason for this is that the effects of mixture corrosion (Bögli, 1964) will be at a maximum in this zone. Howard (1964) evolved a mathematical model of cave development and again suggested a mechanism (similar to that put forward by Rhoades and Sinacori) to explain maximum cave development in the shallow phreas.

An important symposium on cave development, based largely on a study of the limestone areas of the Appalachians (Davies, 1960), drew five major conclusions about cave development in folded limestones. First, that cave passages generally develop parallel to the strike and have a uniform slope independent of the regional dip. Secondly, that caves commonly have passages on several horizontal levels, and that these levels correlate regionally between caves. Thirdly, these levels correlate with gravel benches on the major surface valleys of the region. Fourthly, that the major occurrence of caves is adjacent to the large valleys. Finally, that cave passages decrease in size and increase in number with increasing distance from major surface valleys. Sweeting (1950), working in Yorkshire, drew similar conclusions as to the relationship between valley side benches and cave levels, whilst Woodward (1961) suggested that caves are formed very rapidly in response to the water-table adjustments that accompany stream piracy.

The stages of cavern development suggested are: fairly random solution at depths below the water-table to produce an unintegrated network of tubes and pockets. Secondly, the integration of some of these tubes into mature caves at the top of the water-table during a period when the piezometric surface was at a steady height and uni-directional flow was constant. Thirdly, deposition of clastic fill as the water-table falls; and finally, a relative uplift of the cave above the saturated zone, and later modification of passages by calcite deposition, erosion by secondary streams, and collapse.

The idea of Katzer and Martel of flow in discrete conduits, and the absence of any coherent piezometric surface have been re-emphasised by Maurin and Zötl (1959) working in the Dachstein Alps of Austria, by Sweeting (1958) in Jamaica, and by Drew (1966) in Jamaica and the Mendip Hills. These conclusions are largely the result of the examination of evaluated flow-lines within specific regions. The fact that vadose streams appear to cross one another within the limestone massifs, without mixing occurring, and then proceed to separate risings, militates against the conventional notion of a water-table. White and Longyear (1962) made the same argument from the theoretical standpoint, and argued that the analysis of limestone hydrological systems should be couched in terms of hydraulic gradients rather than regional water-tables. White (1969) and Rauch and White (1970) paid special attention to the effects of structure and lithology on the evolution of cave systems. In an examination of the caves of the Nittany Valley area in central Pennsylvania, they concluded that cave development was markedly localised in a few members of the Mississippian limestone succession. The cavernous limestones appear to be those with low dolomite and clay fractions, and a high micrite grain fraction. Coarse limestones and dolomites were found to be less cavernous.

Fig 38 illustrates, diagrammatically, the lines of groundwater flow in limestone according to the theories of W. M. Davis, Swinnerton, Hubbert (1940) and Rhoades and Sinacori respectively. Fig 38c shows equipotential lines with flow normal to them, as occurs in isotropic aquifers.

Fig 39 illustrates approximate flow paths within a limestone aquifer, under various hydrological conditions, according to Thrailkill (1968). Fig 39 is a section through a small aquifer having uniform supply of water to the water-table; in nature this would approximate to a very porous limestone, or a region of massive limestones with even, frequent fracturing and an absence of water derived from other rocks; the Axbridge-Crook Peak area of western Mendip for example. Under these conditions the piezometric surface will approximate to an equipotential surface, and flow-lines will be almost vertical just beneath the water-table. The water is presumed to discharge at an effluent stream. Fig 39b is of a small aquifer containing a single discrete source. In this case the equipotential surfaces are normal to the piezometric surface in the upper phreas, and

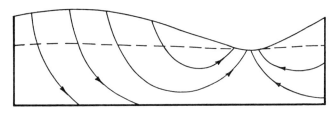

(a) After Davis (1930)

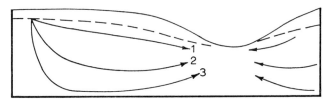

(b) After Swinnerton (1932)

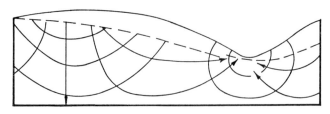

(c) After Hubbert (1940)

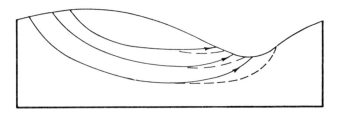

(d) After Rhoades and Sinacori (1941)

Fig 38 Flow-lines in limestone aquifers

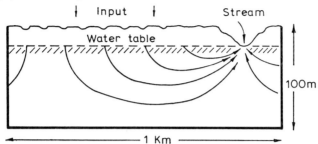

(a) Uniform Input

Input   Stream

Water table

100m

1 Km

(b) Single Discrete Input.

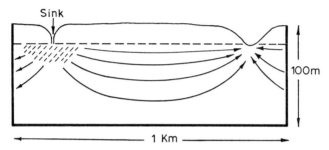

Sink

100m

1 Km

(c) Multiple Discrete Inputs

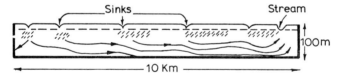

Sinks   Stream

100m

10 Km

(d) Multiple Irregular. Discrete Inputs

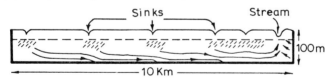

Sinks   Stream

100m

10 Km

Zones of solution

Fig 39 Flow-lines in limestone aquifers under various hydrological conditions (after Thrailkill, 1968)

F*

flow is thus concentrated parallel to the water-table. Fig 39c shows the effect of several discrete water inputs in an area. Water, sinking near to an outlet, tends to flow directly towards the outlet and close to the water-table, whereas water from more remote sinks follows deeper paths. Fig 39d, perhaps most accurately reflects actual conditions within a majority of limestone aquifers, there being multiple irregularly spaced inputs to the groundwater system. Water from the larger sources is gradually forced deeper by water arriving from points downstream of these major sinks.

The main conclusion to be drawn from the disparate theories of limestone hydrology and cave genesis is that no one all-embracing theory appears possible to explain the regional diversity of limestone drainage types. The great majority of the theories advanced have been based on specific regional studies and thus the conclusions drawn, whilst possibly valid for that particular region, are not necessarily applicable elsewhere. Similarly, many of the theoretical studies of groundwater motion in limestone, are rooted in analogies to engineering formulae for groundwater flow in porous media, and this analogy may lead to misleading oversimplification. Regional differences with respect to climate, lithology, structure, and age may be the determining factors in the development of any particular karst drainage system. It is apparent in the study of the caves of the Mendip Hills that no one of these theories is adequate to explain the pattern and areal distribution of the caves.

HYDROMETEOROLOGY

The Mendip Hills consist largely of four major rock types: the Old Red Sandstone, the Lower Limestone Shales, the massive Carboniferous Limestone, and isolated outcrops of Jurassic rock. Within this disparity of rock types, Carboniferous Limestone is, areally, the dominant formation, and the Mendips may be considered to be a karst area, exhibiting many of the classic features of this type of landscape.

Of the total area of the hills (approximately 300km^2) only some 10 per cent is directly drained by surface streams, and of these, the majority occur in eastern Mendip where the Jurassic cover is most extensive and continuous. The only major surface streams on the Mendip plateau are the River Yeo on western Mendip, occupying the eroded Blackdown pericline, the River Sheppey on south-central Mendip, and the Nunney Brook and Whatley Combe stream on eastern Mendip, the last two being tributaries of the Mells and, ultimately, the River Avon.

The mean drainage density of the hills is 0.3km of perennial channel/sq km. This mean figure disguises considerable regional disparities; for example, western Mendip has virtually no surface streams whilst the east, especially on the northern flank, has a full complement of surface drainage. Drainage densities in regions adjacent to Mendip, and having similar precipitation and ruggedness indices, commonly exceed values of 2.0 or 3.0km of perennial channel/sq km. The total length of surface streams on the Mendip is approximately 90km. Of the over 400 known caves or stream sinks and risings on the hills, the majority are unrelated to present-day drainage systems. There are some 77 active stream sinks and some 41 resurgences. This ratio of approximately one rising to two sinks is very high compared with other karst areas of Britain. For example, in Yorkshire, risings tend to be large and widely spaced with some 10 to 20 feeders to each resurgence.

There is an absence of reliable long-term meteorological data from the Mendip Hills and, until recently, assumptions about the climate in the area had to be made by extrapolation from stations several kilometres distant and located in topographically dissimilar areas. Since 1966, fully instrumented automatic meteorological stations have been in operation at Downhead on the Beacon Hill pericline, and at Chew Stoke, some 8km north of the Mendip Hills. The Mendips function as a major orographic barrier to the prevailing moist westerlies and, therefore, precipitation on the plateau is considerably higher than on the surrounding Somerset Levels, and normally ranges between 850 and 1,250mm per annum. The precipitation is commonly in the form of a gentle, prolonged drizzle; violent precipitation is rare and generally confined to high summer. Hanwell and Newson (1970), discussed the major flood of July 1968 on the Mendip Hills, suggested that for a precipitation of 130mm within 24 hours, the return period is within the order of 60 to 110 years. With the establishment of the two automatic meteorological stations on and near Mendip, accurate computation of evapotranspirative losses has become possible. Previously, the nearest station from which data could be computed was that at Filton near Bristol, which registered a mean potential evapotranspiration loss of 40 per cent.

Fig 40 shows the precipitation at Downhead for the year

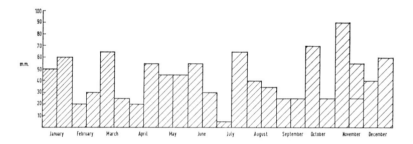

Fig 40 Precipitation at Downhead, Mendip for 1969

1969. Total precipitation during this year was some 1,035mm. Data from the Chew Stoke station shows very little difference either in total amount or in serial distribution. The precipitation is fairly evenly distributed throughout the year, with a noticeable maximum during the late autumn and early winter. Fig 41 shows the moisture balance at Downhead for the same year. Evaporative losses were computed on a daily basis and amounted to 548mm for the entire year. Thus the balance of 578mm constitutes an effective precipitation of some 55 per cent. Incoming precipitation exceeds evapotranspirative losses for the majority of the year, and a deficit only occurs from late June to late September. This would appear to be fairly representative of normal hydrometeorological conditions within the area, and thus there are, on average, only two months of the year during which the streams are fed entirely by base flow. However, soil and groundwater storage on the plateau would appear to be very limited, as the great majority of swallet streams become dry after a few weeks without rain.

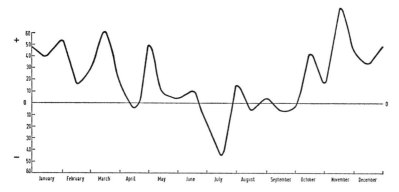

Fig 41 Moisture balance at Downhead, Mendip for 1969

The major rock types that have hydrological significance on the Mendips are the Carboniferous Limestone (together with the Dolomitic Conglomerate which, geohydrologically, appears to function very similarly to the limestone), the Lower Limestone Shales and the Old Red Sandstone. The sandstone appears to be a poor aquifer, possibly because of the extensive infilling of primary pore spaces by silica and calcite, but there are wells on this rock which appear to yield adequate water supply, and this is especially the case on the eastern Mendip. Virtually all the springs feeding the sinking streams of the hills rise on the Old Red Sandstone outcrop and thus have commonly been regarded in the literature as overflow springs, marking the inter-section of the water-table within the sandstone with the land surface. There are, however, serious drawbacks to this idea. Tratman (1963a) in a study of the hydrology of the Burrington area stated that the numerous springs rising from the sandstone portion of the Black Down pericline are derived from superficial deposits rather than from the sandstone itself. These superficial deposits have been proven to be in excess of 3m deep in places. Tratman suggested that the springs dry up too rapidly during a drought period to be derived from a sandstone aquifer, and also that they emerge from too great an altitude on the sandstone. Furthermore, on several areas of Blackdown, the higher springs are the last to dry up during a period of drought, and this is the reverse of what would be expected were they true water-table overflow springs. An attempt by the Bristol Waterworks Company to derive water from an adit driven into the Old Red Sandstone of Blackdown Hill was largely unsuccessful, again suggesting that water storage within the sandstone is limited. The porosity of the sandstone is approximately 6 per cent compared with 0.2 per cent for the Carboniferous Limestone and 10 per cent for the Oolite of the Cotswold Hills nearby. Drew (1968) attempted to correlate flow in the swallet streams of eastern Mendip to water levels in wells on the Old Red Sandstone of the northern flank of the Beacon Hill pericline, for the summer of 1966. Very little correlation was apparent and the wells showed little change in level in response to precipitation. Thus, it may be argued that the majority of the flow in the sinking streams originating on the Old Red Sandstone is derived from slow throughflow from the superficial deposits of the surrounding slopes.

The Lower Limestone Shale has proved to be a very variable aquifer, some boreholes being completely dry whilst other areas yield large quantities of water. For example, the large stream sinking by Longwood swallet is apparently derived from the central members of the Limestone Shale. In addition, the transmissivity of the Limestone Shale seems to vary areally, and whilst in some regions the shales may act as an impermeable barrier to groundwater flow, in other areas they may transmit water from the sandstone aquifer through into the Carboniferous Limestone, perhaps via faulted zones.

Little is known of the effects of the superficial cover of Jurassic rocks on the hydrology of the area, and for the most part they will be ignored in this study. The major aquifer of the hills is the Carboniferous Limestone, occupying the greatest area and absorbing the great majority of the precipitation which falls on it. Surface run-off is rare except in the most violent storms on the limestone. The majority of the allogenic streams derived from the sandstone, sink at, or close to, the Lower Limestone Shale– Black Rock Limestone boundary as swallets (sinks), to emerge again as springs at the base of the flank of the hills (commonly at the point at which the limestone plunges beneath the younger, unconformable strata surrounding the upland).

The catchment areas for the various swallet streams are generally small; for example, Longwood swallet (the largest) has a catchment area of some 5.6km^2, the Stoke Lane catchment some 4.2km^2, that of Swildon's Hole 2.9km^2, GB 1.3km^2, St Cuthbert's 1.2km^2, and Eastwater 0.7km^2. Except under flood conditions, the swallet streams appear to be misfits within their catchments, the majority of precipitation apparently percolating directly to groundwater rather than first gathering in the stream channel. On eastern Mendip, there appears to be an inverse relationship between the amount of run-off (per unit of precipitation input) and the percentage of the catchment floored by limestone. Much of the water which reaches the ground is apparently funnelled into discrete sinks (commonly not open holes) via throughflow within the soil. Atkinson (personal communication) has measured rates of throughflow of the order of 5–25cm/hr within the soil overlying Carboniferous Limestone on central Mendip. Weyman (1970), studying throughflow within the East Twin Valley catchment of Burrington Combe, found that no overland flow occurred even following substantial precipitation and that storm flow was discharged from the B horizon of the soil, reaching a peak some 24 hours after the rainfall maximum, and ceasing within five days without rain. Base flow to the stream is supplied by the BC horizon, and remains constant for periods up to 40 days without recharge, with a slight peak some five to six days after a storm. Hanwell and Newson (1970) demonstrate that, under normal conditions, the contributing area of a typical swallet catchment is very small (under 10 per cent). In a study of the Swildon's Hole catchment, the direct relationship between increased precipitation, increased contributing area, and increased lengths of active channel is demonstrated.

Fig 42 (after Hanwell and Newson, 1970) shows the channel

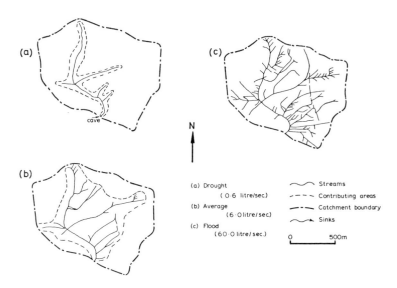

Fig 42 Swildon's Hole catchment under varying discharges

network and contributing areas under conditions of extreme flood, normal flow, and drought, within the Swildon's Hole catchment (area 1.2km²). In extreme flood conditions the whole basin will contribute to stream flow, water flowing in all available conduits, including furrows, land-drains and footpaths. Under this discharge situation, the sinking stream has in the order of

700 first-order tributaries and becomes a fifth-order stream, the basin as a whole having a drainage density of some 47km/km².

Under conditions of average flow, the contributing area declines to about 50 per cent of the total catchment area, whilst under drought conditions the effective contributing area is only some 14 per cent and drainage density declines to 0–1km/km².

Fig 43 (after Hanwell and Newson, 1970) shows the regression

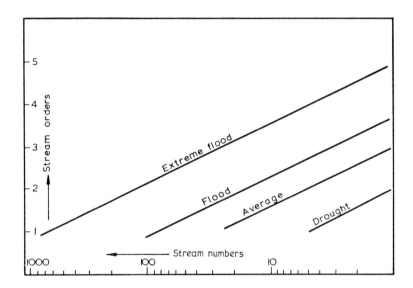

Fig 43 Graphical representation of Swildon's Hole channel networks

of number of streams of a given order, plotted against stream order; under conditions of average flow, flood flow, and drought. The regression lines are parallel, suggesting a progressive diminution of the flow network and contributing area with decreasing discharge.

The situation outlined for the Swildon's Hole catchment seems likely to be representative of many of the swallet stream catchments on Mendip, though probably not for the points of input not demarcated by a sinking stream. The great increase in the contribution of direct run-off to the swallet stream and, therefore, the concomitant rapid increase in discharge, is of some significance in the interpretation of cave development in the area, especially in relation to underground clastic deposits, and in hydrological terms such events would appear to be relatively common.

CAVE HYDROLOGY

Figures 44 and 45 show the distribution of caves over the Mendip Hills. The caves are designated as isolated caves (Fig 44), old sinks and risings, and normally-active sinks and risings (Fig 45). The distinction made between isolated caves and old sinks and risings is largely arbitrary and unrealistic, in that the majority of caves —unless they represent intersected remnants of old systems— will have functioned either as sinks or risings at some time in the past, and thus the category isolated caves should more realistically be regarded as caves, the hydrological function of which is no longer readily apparent.

Fig 45 shows sites which can be identified with some certainty as being fossil inputs or outputs to the karst groundwater system. There are some 180 caves classified as isolated. Fig 44 illustrates the considerable degree of localisation of these caves. The major concentrations are associated with the three large dry gorges of Mendip; Burrington Combe in the north-west, Cheddar Gorge in the south-west, and Ebbor Gorge on south-central Mendip. Apart from these three concentrations, secondary clusters are apparent in the extreme western area of the hills and on the extreme north-eastern edge of the range. It is important to note that these distributions *do not* represent the locations of all Mendip caves, but simply all those caves with an open entrance. Thus the true pattern of cave distribution may differ considerably from that shown on the map. Again, the clusters of caves associated with the major dry valleys may not be representative of the true situation in that the dry valleys may have intersected

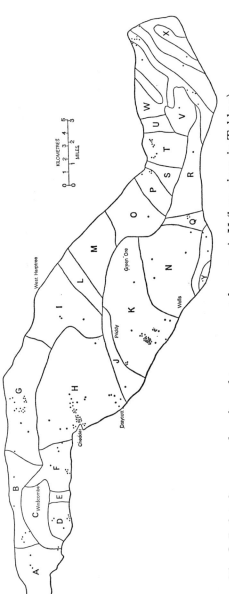

Fig 44 Isolated caves and major subterranean catchments, A–Y (key given in Table 7)

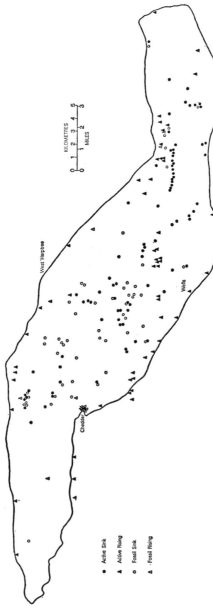

Fig 45 Fossil and active sinks and risings on Mendip

many old cave systems during their period of active downcutting, and thus similar intensive networks of subterranean tunnels may exist elsewhere on the plateau. However, there appears to be a distinct genetic correlation between the major resurgences of the Mendip Hills and the major surface dry valleys. Thus, it may be that for a long period these gorges have been the focus of cavern development on the hills.

Fig 45 exhibits a similar concentration of fossil risings close to the flank of Mendip and, in the case of Cheddar, also associated with the gorge. The fossil sinks which may be identified with reasonable certainty, closely follow the pattern of present-day active sinks, excepting that they are displaced somewhat further from the shale–limestone boundary than are currently active sinks. The paucity of sinks on western Mendip is probably due to the difficulty of identifying them positively, whereas the equally pronounced absence of fossil features on eastern Mendip may probably be attributed to the relatively youthful stage of karstification attained in that area.

Fig 45 shows active or intermittently active sinks or risings and this distribution is perhaps the most significant in interpreting the hydrology of the Mendip Hills. In general, the position of the sinking streams faithfully reflects the geology of the area— the great majority of the sinks being close to the shale–limestone boundary. This is especially true of central Mendip, though on the North Hill pericline there is a noticeable concentration of sinks on the southern and eastern flanks of the hill. Again, there is a considerable difference between eastern and western extremities of the Mendips. There are no known sinks west of Langford rising, whereas eastern Mendip has an abundance of sinking streams, most especially the long line of closely spaced swallets feeding the St Dunstan's Well and Ashwick Grove risings. This concentration on eastern Mendip of sinking streams, again may reflect the relative immaturity of the landscape in this area, and it may be that with time, stream capture will diminish the number of active sinks. Mean flow in swallet streams is generally very small (within the order of 1–3l/sec). The major exception to this being the stream sinking at Stoke Lane Slocker.

The distribution of springs is rather more difficult to explain than that of swallets. The general distribution is shown on Fig 45 and the distribution according to size of spring is shown on Fig 47 (see also Table 5). The springs are grouped in orders of magnitude according to discharge. Category 1 includes springs with discharges in excess of 250l/sec; there are only three such springs on the Mendip Hills, those at Cheddar, at Wookey Hole, and St Andrew's Well. Category 2 includes streams with discharges between 50 and 250l/sec; there are twelve such springs; for example St Dunstan's Well, Banwell, and Gurney Slade. Category 3 springs are those having discharges of between 25 and 50l/sec. There are only two such springs, those at Axbridge and Honeyhurst. Category 4 springs are those with very small discharges of less than 25l/sec. It is possible to explain the location of some of the springs in relation to local geological conditions. For example, St Dunstan's Well is located at the point where a lateral fault brings the grits of the Carboniferous Quartzitic Sandstone Group into contact with the limestone, thus blocking the westward flow of water. Others may be located in distinct hydrological lows for an area for example, Gurney Slade and Banwell, whilst the largest of the springs (excepting St Andrew's Well) are located in or close to the outlet of major surface dry valleys. The smallest springs (category 4) are often intermittent, and sometimes little more than seepages. It is difficult to suggest reasons for the particular location of the majority of these smaller springs, and many of them may have very limited catchments within the surficial deposits of the adjacent slopes (for example Compton Martin springs and Halfway spring). Table 5 lists the risings of the Mendips together with their mean discharges, magnitudes, altitudes, and grid references.

Fig 46 shows six-hour unit hydrographs for the two Mendip risings at St Dunstan's Well and Wookey Hole (mean discharges are 153l/sec and 789l/sec respectively). The discharge axis is not

TABLE 5 *Mendip risings data summary*

Rising	Magnitude	Elevation (m)	Average Discharge (l/sec)	Grid Reference
Ashwick Higher	2	182	79	649478
Ashwick Lower	2	170.5	79	652479
Axbridge	3	19.7	26	431546
Banwell	2	9.8	184	399592
Barnet's Well	4	21	1.05	477506
Barrow Well	4	75	5.3	538573
Cheddar	1	24.6	947	466539
Chewton Mendip	2	154.1	158	600531
Combe Lodge	4	90.4	2.6	497591
Compton Martin	4	170	10.6	546566
Cross Springs	4	9.2	8.0	416547
Darshill	4	100	11	609439
Dulcote	4	60	11	565445
Dunnett Spring	4	6.6	11	401547
Easton	4	51	1.1	515481
East Well	4	45.9	16	415567
Egford	2	82	63	756481
Garrowpipe	4	206.2	22	549549
Glencot	4	44.1	22	523470
Gurney Slade	2	192.8	68.4	631495
Halfway	4	30	2.7	467523
Hollybrook	4	62.1	5.3	508467
Holwell	4	126.2	22	739451
Honeyhurst	3	10.5	40	477503
Langford	2	42.6	53	466593
Ludwell	4	19.7	22	359592
Rickford	2	65.6	158	485594
Rodney Stoke	2	59	53	487503
Rookery Farm	4	64	1.1	521582
Rookham Spring	4	188.5	8.0	547482
Rowpit	4	3.3	16	472502
St Andrew's Well	1	49.2	421	552459
St Dunstan's Well	2	159.3	153	659479
Scadden's Lane	4	54.1	5.3	491502
Seven Springs	2	147.5	105	710453
Sherbourne	2	99.3	68	586550
Spencer's Spring	4	49.2	1.6	488501
Vigo Wood	4	180.3	4.0	546482
Westbury	4	72.1	5.3	503493
Whitehole	4	162.3	10.6	680480
Wookey Hole	1	66	789	532480

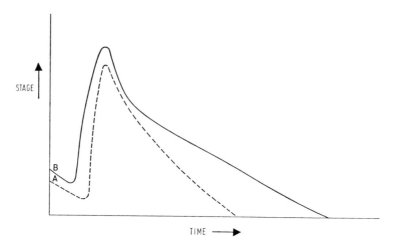

Fig 46 Six-hour unit hydrographs for Mendip risings

drawn to scale, in order to facilitate comparison. The unit hydrograph for St Dunstan's well (A) shows a very rapid response to
precipitation, a sharp peak, and a fairly rapid recession curve to
base flow conditions. This hydrograph is typical of that for a
surface stream and may be a result of the fact that the St
Dunstan's Well outflow is largely supplied by swallet water which
is quickly transmitted through the subterranean conduits.
Wookey Hole rising has a considerably smaller percentage of its
water supplied by swallet feeders, and its hydrograph (B) shows
an equally sharp rise in response to precipitation as that for St
Dunstan's Well, but the rate of decrease of discharge on the
recession limb is much slower, and the stream stays above normal
flow level for many days following heavy precipitation. The
hydrograph for other sites, for example the Wishing Well in
Ashwick Grove, shows virtually no response to any but the most
intense precipitation—like that of streams with a catchment
area on highly porous rock, for example chalk. Thus, although
the Wishing Well is known in part to be fed by swallet water,
it seems likely that the majority of its discharge is derived from

slow-moving percolation water. The major risings of the area will be considered in further detail in the chapter section dealing with speleogenesis.

Figure 47 shows the active risings of the Mendip Hills, graded according to magnitude of discharge; sinking streams which have been traced to their rising are also shown on the map. The flow-lines are diagrammatic. Tracings have been carried out within the area over a period of many years, using many different methods of varying degrees of efficiency. Only those traces which are almost certainly correct are shown on the map. The majority were established using lycopodium spores as the tracing agent, whilst the majority of the remainder were established using conventional dye techniques. The forty streams traced thus far all emerge at one or other of eleven risings. With the exception of the rising at Whitehole, all the risings with known feeders are of magnitudes 1 or 2. Major risings with no known surface feeders include those at Banwell, Litton, Chewton Mendip, and Egford, these being the major north flank risings.

Before catchments can be established with any certainty for major risings, it will be necessary to develop sophisticated water-tracing techniques to trace percolation water, especially within the basins having no sinking streams within the catchment. The catchments will be examined in turn.

Perhaps the simplest pattern is exhibited by the risings of east Mendip—especially those at Ashwick Grove, at St Dunstan's Well, and at Seven Springs, where all the possible feeders have been traced. Each of these risings is fed by numerous small streams draining from the flanks of Beacon Hill and sinking at or close to the shale–limestone contact.

There is a sharp division between the catchments of St Dun-stans' Well and the two risings in the Ashwick Grove valley. However, there are two discrete resurgences at St Dunstan's Well at the same height and only some 2m apart horizontally. The water from these two sources differs in respect of hydrologic regime, of chemistry, and, in part, of origin, although it is not

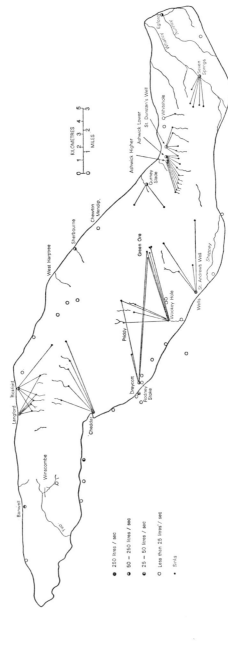

Fig 47 Underground flow-lines and spring magnitudes

possible to differentiate separate catchments for the two sources on the ground. The two resurgences at Ashwick Grove are some 330m apart, and are separated vertically by some 12m. All drainage to the Lower Ashwick rising lies between the Withy-brook fault in the east and the Oakhill fault in the west, whilst the Higher Ashwick catchment lies entirely to the west of the Oakhill fault with the exception of Stout Slocker.

Rates of flow for underground streams in the area, range from between 154 and 525m/hr, though the majority lie between 245 and 280m/hr. Treating the catchments as individual units rather than considering separate swallet streams, there is an increase in mean rate of flow of swallet water from east to west across the area. The stream draining to Whitehole rising has a flow rate of 197m/hr, streams draining to St Dunstan's Well have an average flow rate of 216m/hr, streams draining to Lower Ashwick have a mean flow rate of 256m/hr, and streams draining to Higher Ashwick a mean flow rate of 292m/hr.

There seems to be no correlation between the sink to rising gradient and the flow rate, and similarly no correlation between increasing flow rate and decreasing swallet to rising distance. Therefore, the trend to increasing flow rates with distance west-wards is presumably related to better-graded flow channels and thus, perhaps, to the geological structure. Within this area, the rising to which an individual sinking stream drains, appears to be that having the steepest hydraulic gradient for that particular stream. Some eleven of the sixteen traced flow-lines are established along maximum hydraulic gradient lines. Only when the difference between the hydraulic gradient of two adjacent risings is less than $0.6°$ for a particular sinking stream, do factors other than hydraulic gradient appear to become dominant in deciding the flow path. This relationship, however, does not hold true on other catchments of the Mendip Hills.

The other major catchments on the north flank of the hills to which many sinking streams have been traced are those of the two large risings at Rickford and Langford. All swallets tested within this area, with the exception of Ubley Hill Pot which flows only to Rickford, drain to both risings, though rates of flow are commonly very different for the two risings. Rickford spring, at an altitude of 65.5m, is the largest rising, with a mean discharge of 158l/sec. Langford, at an altitude of 42.6m, has a mean discharge of approximately 53l/sec. The flow pattern in this area is complex, with four of the streams bifurcating and draining to each of the risings. Bifurcation probably occurs relatively close to the point of engulfment, as the times of travel from a particular sink to the two risings are often very different. For example, water sinking at Read's Cavern reaches Rickford rising some 2,300m away, in about 4 hours, but takes between 42 and 46 hours to reach Langford rising only some 1,000m away. Flow rates to Rickford rising are some 303m/hr and only some 221m/hr to Langford. Within these catchments hydraulic gradient does not seem to be a major control in deciding the outlet point for sinking streams, and with the exception of Ubley Hill Pot the route of maximum hydraulic gradient is not followed preferentially. Thus, despite the fact that it is at a higher altitude than Langford rising, Rickford would appear to be the more maturely developed resurgence, possessing better-integrated and better-graded subterranean conduits. It may be that one rising is in the process of capturing the drainage of the other in this area. It is impossible to distinguish individual catchments for the two resurgences, as tracer dye placed on the limestone midway between the two risings, emerged at both springs.

The largest catchment and the largest spring on the hills is that of Cheddar, located at an altitude of 24.6m. The catchment extends at least as far to the north-east as Pine Tree Pot, but the only other sinking streams traced to it are those originating on the southern flank of the central Black Down pericline (Manor Farm, Blackmore, Longwood, GB). Flow rates are only known for Longwood and Manor Farm, these being some 184 and 216m/hr respectively. The waters from Pine Tree Pot and Blackmoor swallet are known to take 4–5 days and 3–4 days respectively to reach Cheddar. However, the two latter tests were undertaken during periods of low discharge, whereas the first group of swallets were tested under conditions of relatively high flow. In all cases, the rising at Cheddar possesses the steepest hydraulic gradient for each of the sinks.

The flow pattern to the risings at Rodney Stoke and Wookey Hole is extremely complicated, and although it is possible to delimit, with reasonable confidence, a distinct catchment area on the surface for Wookey Hole, this is not the case with Rodney Stoke. Wookey Hole, at an altitude of 66m is Mendip's second largest resurgence, draining much of the southern flank of North Hill and part of Pen Hill. Rates of flow to this resurgence are very variable; for example, the swallets draining off North Hill in the Priddy area (for example, Swildon's Hole) have flow rates of between 141 and 282m/hr, whereas water from Pen Hill takes from between 9 hours (Easter Hole) and 78 hours (Zoo Swallet) to traverse a similar distance to the rising at Wookey Hole. As with the Rickford–Langford drainage, the different times of travel for tracer from swallet to resurgence for the Wookey Hole feeders suggests that the swallet paths are separate for much of their length. Water sinking at Hillgrove Swallet, Whitsun Hole Swallet, Zoo Swallet, and Rock Swallet, emerges from the small springs at Biddlecombe before sinking once more to reappear at Wookey Hole. In order for the water to reach Biddlecombe from these swallets, it must cross the Old Red Sandstone outcrop to the east of Pen Hill thus, presumably, draining under the sandstone. Rodney Stoke rising is relatively small (discharge 53l/sec) and hydrologically very variable—it runs dry during extreme drought. The rising is at an altitude of 59m (some 7m lower than that at Wookey Hole). Superficially, Rodney Stoke would appear to be a moderate-size rising, collecting drainage from the flanks of Mendip adjacent to it. It may, in part, function as such a rising; for example, it takes drainage from Brimble Pit Swallet on the edge of the flank of the hills almost vertically above the spring. However, the other streams traced to Rodney Stoke suggest that its catchment area cannot, in part at least, be separated from that of Wookey Hole and that the two resurgences are connected, albeit tenuously.

Part of the water sinking at Hillgrove Swallet, Waldegrave Swallet, and Whitsun Hole, drains to Rodney Stoke as well as to Wookey Hole. To do this, water from these swallets must cross the flow-lines from the sinks of the Priddy area—and do so without any mixing of the waters, as there is no evidence that the Priddy swallets drain in part to Rodney Stoke. Flow rates from Hillgrove to Rodney Stoke have not been established with any certainty, though Waldegrave Swallet takes 24 hours to reach Rodney Stoke. This is comparable with flow rates for other swallets in the area.

Possibly the most unlikely swallet traced to Rodney Stoke is Waldegrave Swallet, located in the Triassic Conglomerate which rests directly on the Old Red Sandstone in the saddle of the North Hill pericline near the Mineries. Water from this swallet flows both to Rodney Stoke (in under one day) and also to Wookey Hole (in less than two days). The routes followed by the water are problematical; for the flow to be in the limestone, the underground route would have to loop around the western limb of the North Hill pericline. Atkinson (1970) suggested that the flow may split soon after the stream sinks, and that water may flow via the Stock Hill fault towards Wookey Hole and via the Priddy fault towards Rodney Stoke, thereby directly transversing the sandstone core of the pericline. (The flow of water from Hillgrove and Whitsun Hole to Biddlecombe may, in similar manner, cross the Old Red Sandstone outcrop via the Biddle fault.)

The only other resurgence (Gurney Slade apart) with known feeders is that at St Andrew's Well, located just beyond the scarp of the Mendip Hills in the city of Wells. This catchment appears to be reasonably simple and obvious to delimit on the ground—collecting water from the eastern flanks of Pen Hill. Known feeders of this resurgence are the sinks at Biddlecombe, at Haydon Drove, at Golf Course, and at Thrupe Swallet. In no case are exact flow rates known. Balch (1937) remarks that a *fluorescein* test proved that it took some 49 hours for water to travel 1.4km to the rising. St Andrew's Well is the third largest rising of the hills with a discharge of 421l/sec. It is at an elevation of some 50m above sea level.

WATER BUDGETS

Figure 43 constitutes an attempt to delimit rising catchment areas on the basis of established flow-lines and topographical and geological data. It is not possible to delimit catchments for all the Mendip springs and thus, only some twenty-five underground catchment areas have been designated. Table 6 lists the catchment names together with other smaller risings incorporated within that catchment to produce one hydrological unit. The table also lists the approximate area for each catchment, and the known feeders to the major rising of that catchment. Catchment C, the area between catchments Y and N, and the unnumbered areas at the extreme eastern end of the hills are all presumed to be drained by surface streams.

That the watershed lines computed by this means are unrealistic will become apparent later—it does not seem possible to establish with any degree of certainty the existence of distinct surface watersheds corresponding to the subterranean drainage divides. The three major springs of the Mendip Hills are located within the central portion of the southern flank of the hills, whereas the major north flank risings are concentrated at the extreme east and west ends. Within the central Mendip area at least, it may be possible to infer the position of the longitudinal east–west watershed separating northern and southern flowing water. For example, the watershed between the Rickford and Cheddar catchments must lie between Ubley Hill Pot and Pine Tree Pot. It seems likely that this major divide lies very close (within one to two kilometres) to the northern scarp of the hills

Major Catchment Name	Other Risings Included	No	Area (km²)	Area Revised by output (km²)	Known Feeders	Trace Time (hrs)
Ludwell	—	A	11.4	—	None	—
Banwell	—	B	8.9	9.9	None	—
East Well	—	C	8.3	—	None	—
Dunnett Spring	—	D	3.9	—	None	—
Cross Springs	—	E	11.6	—	None	—
Axbridge	—	F	8.0	1.54	None	—
Rickford–Langford	Combe Lodge Rookery Farm	G	21.3	10.8	Bath Swallet	—
					East Twin	4–15
					West Twin	15–17
					Read's Cavern	4–42
					Ellick Farm	4
					Ubley Hill	4
Cheddar	Barnet's Well Halfway Honeyhurst Rowpit	H	38.0	55.2	GB	48
					Longwood	20
					Manor Farm	20
					Pinetree Pot	120
					Blackmoor	96
Compton Martin	Barrow Well	I	18.8	1.87	None	—
Rodney Stoke	Garrowpipe Scadden's L Spencer's Spr	J	6.63	3.33	Hillgrove	500–1700
					Waldegrave	24
					Whitsun Hole	500–1700
					Brimble Pit	48
					Easter Hole	500–1700
					Zoo Swallet	500–1700
					Rock Swallet	500–1700
Wookey Hole	Easton Glencot Hollybrook Rookham	K	30.7	46.2	Easter Hole	11
					Eastwater	16
					Hillgrove	19
					Rock Swallet	98
					St Cuthbert's	11

Catchment	Code		Catchment area	Feeder	Flow time
Sherbourne		—		Whitsun Hole	19
				Zoo Swallet	8
Chewton Mendip		—		None	—
St Andrew's	L	3.59	5.2	None	—
	M	8.52	11.1	Biddlecombe	72
	N	23.2	23.2	Golf Course	48
				Haydon Drove	72
				Thrupe Swallet	—
Gurney Slade	O	—	11.5	Binegar	—
				Emborough	8.5
Ashwick Higher	P	—	2.6	Little London	7.0
				P1	8.0
				P2	8.0
				Pigpen	6.0
				Stout	—
Darshill	Q	—	1.6	None	—
Windsor Hill	R	—	11.1	None	—
Ashwick Lower	S	—	2.6	Blakes Farm	5
				Larkshall	4
				Midway	4
				Oakhill	5.5
St Dunstan's	T	—	5.8	Springfield	5
				Brickdales	4
				East End	6
				Midway	2.5
				Stoke Lane	8
				Withybrook	5
Whitehole	U	—	2.4	Pitten Street	4.5
				Bottlehead	21
Seven Springs	V	—	5.2	Broken Pipe	—
				Dairyhouse	12.5
				Downhead	7
				Heale	17.5
Egford	W	—	15	None	—
Holwell	X	—	2.3	None	—
Dulcote	Y	—	0.9	None	—

TABLE 6 *Major Mendip catchments, catchment areas, feeders, flow times*

G

on central Mendip, but may lie closer to the southern flank on both western and eastern Mendip. That this should be the case is borne out by the relative discharges from the north and south flank risings in central Mendip. Catchment areas for risings such as those at Litton and Chewton Mendip can only be established with reference to local topography and discharge. The large rising at Banwell (altitude 9.8m, discharge 184l/sec) must drain almost the entire northern limb of the Blackdown pericline west of the A38 road, and its catchment area is thus fairly closely defined by geological and topographical structure. It is noticeable that the south flank risings all appear to draw on water from the area to the north and the east of the rising; this is especially pronounced in the cases of Rodney Stoke and at St Andrew's Well. Risings on the north flank of the hills, however, with the exception of Rickford–Langford, tend to draw their water from west of the rising.

Using the available data for precipitation, evapotranspiration, and discharge at the risings, it is possible to compute a water budget both for the whole of the Mendip Hills and for specific catchments. The budget can be made for the individual years for which this data is available in detailed form. The budget is of necessity crude, and liable to considerable error, but is worth compiling in order to obtain some rough idea of whether input and output discharges are comparable within the area. Such a budget was compiled for the year 1969 for the entire Mendip Hills; it was found that outflow from the risings comprised only some 67 per cent of the effective precipitation input. The methods of computation were designed to underestimate input, rather than overestimate it, and thus it seems probable that the water budget for the Mendip Hills is indeed unbalanced, and that not all of the water percolating into the limestone massif reappears at the springs at its base. However, the limitations of the method and the possibility that water emerges over a very long period rather than within the year of input should be borne in mind. It is, however, possible that a portion of the water is removed from the hills as deep flow within the limestone beyond the point at which it dips beneath the outlying younger strata, though should this be so, the point of outlet of such water is not apparent. It is possible that the water does not remain in the limestone but permeates into the overlying younger strata within a short distance beyond the Mendip scarp. This may be the case in the zones immediately adjacent to the mouths of the major dry valleys of Mendip, where there are known to be extensive deposits of periglacial sands and gravels. There is some evidence, both direct and indirect, to suggest that deep flow from the Mendip Hills does occur. The borehole at Honeyhurst, on the levels south of Draycott, yields water (possibly from the Carboniferous Limestone) the source of which is almost certainly the hill behind the well. Similarly, the boreholes at Egford (close to Frome) have a considerable discharge from the Carboniferous Limestone, and insofar as is known this water did not discharge within the local area prior to the sinking of the boreholes. Direct exploration under water in the risings at Cheddar indicates the presence of a passage continuing below the level of the present risings which again may take some of the flow from this catchment out beyond the Gorge at depth. Balch (*op cit*), writing about western Mendip, also suggested the possibility of deep flow:

> The whole of the ancient and dry swallet caves of the Sandford, Banwell, Hutton, Uphill, Loxton, and Crook's Peak area tell of vanished lines of drainage carrying important streams, and all escaping below the present moor level, where the secondary beds effectively hide them. They keep the old buried beaches charged with water, and these have in several places yielded good supplies for domestic purposes.

The existence of deep water flow below sea level within the Carboniferous Limestone has been proven in the area adjacent to Mendip. Drew, Newson, and Smith (1970) investigated the

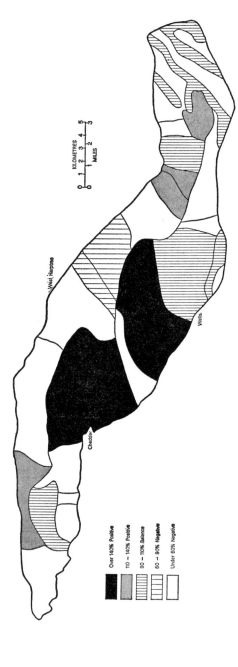

Fig 48 Rising output as a percentage of precipitation input, catchments as on Fig 44

origin of the Great Spring encountered whilst drilling the railway tunnel beneath the River Severn in 1888. Discharge from this spring was established at 860l/sec (comparable with the discharge at Cheddar rising). Before the tunnel was excavated, it seems likely that this fresh water discharged further down the Severn Estuary. The source for this spring would seem to be local and probably comprises some twenty square kilometres of Mountain Limestone on the Welsh side of the River Severn. The water appears to flow in a large, well developed conduit in the limestone. There is also further evidence of a Severn-oriented karst system, in that fresh water is known to emerge from the floor of the estuary around the islands of Steepholme and Flatholme. However, there is no evidence that these sources are connected to the Great Spring in the Severn Tunnel. Thus, there is some evidence that deep flow within the Carboniferous Limestone is possible, and it may be an explanation for the unbalanced budget of the Mendip Hills.

Figure 48 represents an attempt to compute water budgets for each of the major catchments of the Mendip Hills, the catchments being defined as in Fig 43. Catchments in which output is 90 to 110 per cent of input are regarded as being balanced; catchments in which output is more than 110 per cent of input have a positive balance; catchments in which output is less than 90 per cent are said to have a negative balance. Clearly there is no justification for allowing a catchment to have a positive balance, but such catchments are shown in this manner for convenience on the map. With the exception of the area drained by surface streams, only two catchments exhibit a good balance between input and output—those of St Dunstan's Well and St Andrew's Well—and in both of these cases it is possible to delimit the possible catchment area with considerable preciseness on the ground using geological, topographical, and hydrological evidence. The majority of the remaining catchments show a strongly negative water budget, indicating either that the true catchments are much smaller than those delimited, or that

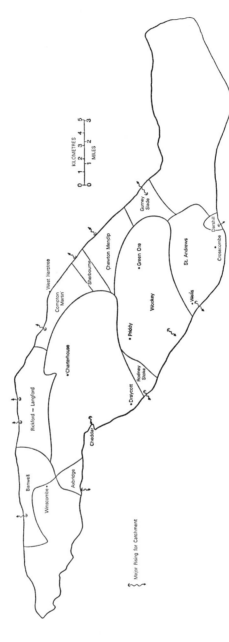

Barnwell

Winscombe●

Axbridge

Rickford — Langford

Charterhouse●

Cheddar

Draycott●

Rodney Stoke●

West Harptree

Compton Martin

Shetbourne

Priddy●

Chewton Mendip

Green Ore●

Wookey

●Wells

St. Andrews

Gurney Slade

Crosscombe

Darshill

KILOMETRES
0 1 2 3 4 5
0 1 2 3
MILES

Major Rising for Catchment

Fig 49 Central Mendip catchments adjusted by discharge balance

these are the zones from which there is considerable loss of water via deep flow. The most extreme example is that of the area around Windsor Hill, where there is no apparent outlet for the water entering the catchment area. Only two catchments exhibit positive budgets (both in the order of 150 per cent) and these are the two major risings of Cheddar and Wookey Hole. The input-output balance for each catchment is shown in Table 7.

Using the data from the water budget analysis, an attempt has been made to redraw the watershed lines for the central Mendip catchments (it is not possible to do this on eastern and western Mendip where part of the drainage is on the surface) and wherever possible, to adjust catchment area to more closely fit the discharge at the rising. This revised catchment map is shown in Fig 49 and the revised catchment areas using this method of analysis are given in Table 6. It can be seen that the effect of this readjustment is to increase greatly the areas of the Wookey Hole and Cheddar catchments, and to reduce correspondingly the catchment areas for the north flank risings with the exception of Banwell. The divide between water flowing to Cheddar and Wookey Hole on the one hand, and water flowing to the north flank rising in the other, is now very close to the northern scarp of the hills. Also, the catchments for both Cheddar and, to a lesser extent, Wookey Hole are extended considerably to the east of their previous position although, especially in the case of Cheddar, there is no topographical evidence to suggest that the watershed extends east of the rising. Atkinson (1971) using more detailed data found that inputs and outputs balanced for the central Mendip catchments taken in isolation.

The relative insignificance of water sinking at discrete points on the surface in the entire hydrological budget of the Mendip Hills, is apparent from a consideration of the small percentage of total output at the risings represented by allogenic water. Allogenic water is defined as that derived from rocks other than the Carboniferous Limestone, eg the Old Red Sandstone. Fig 50 shows percolation water (percolation water is defined

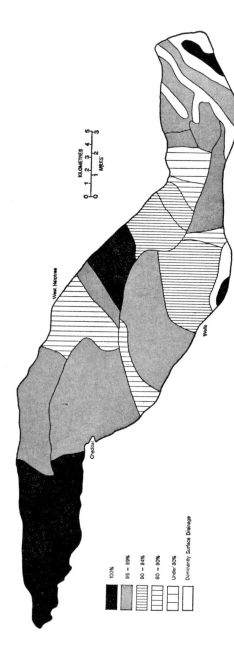

Fig 50 Percolation water as a percentage of outflow of catchment

as that part of the effective precipitation which enters the ground
by direct seepage and thence proceeds directly to groundwater
rather than by first accumulating in a surface stream) as a
percentage of the total outflow mapped by major catchments
of the Mendips. For the Mendip Hills as a whole, percolation
water comprises some 95 per cent of the total output at the
risings and, therefore, an even higher percentage of total input.
The lowest value for percolation water is that at St Dunstan's
Well (74 per cent), and this is accounted for by the presence of
the very large Stoke Lane Slocker stream as a major feeder of the
well. In general, the highest percolation percentage values are
for the extreme west and east portions of the hills, and for
western Mendip, for example, all water issuing at the rising
is of percolation origin, there being no swallet sinks.

TABLE 7 *Water budgets/percolation components, major Mendip
catchments*

Catchment	No	Input/Output x100 (%)	Percolation Water (%)
Ludwell	A	10	100
Banwell	B	112	100
East Well	C	104	100
Dunnett Spring	D	15	100
Cross Spring	E	37	100
Axbridge	F	18	100
Rickford–Langford	G	53	95
Cheddar	H	145	98
Compton Martin	I	11	86
Rodney Stoke	J	49	89
Wookey Hole	K	148	96
Sherbourne	L	72	98
Chewton Mendip	M	78	100
St Andrew's Well	N	99	93
Gurney Slade	O	32	94
Ashwick Upper	P	115	90
Darshill	Q	35	81
Windsor Hill	R	0	98
Ashwick Lower	S	124	89
St Dunstan's Well	T	106	74
Whitehole	U	28	99
Seven Springs	V	110	94
Egford	W	23	98
Holwell	X	49	100
Dulcote	Y	23	100

G*

Table 7 lists percolation components as a percentage of total discharge for each of the major catchments. As was suggested earlier, there appears to be some relationship between the percentage of percolation water at a rising and the hydrological characteristics of that rising. Springs fed entirely by percolation water tend to react to precipitation in a slow and subdued fashion (for example Sherbourne spring), whereas springs in which allogenic water comprises a sizable percentage of discharge, tend to be 'flashier' in their behaviour and react to precipitation more nearly as does a surface stream. St Dunstan's Well is the most marked example of this type of spring.

The overwhelming importance of percolation water in the hydrology of the Mendip Hills suggests that the results of the study of swallet streams and their associated caves are highly unrepresentative of the behaviour of the majority of the water entering the limestone aquifer. Virtually nothing is known of the behaviour of percolation water within limestones : whether for example, it enters the limestone over wide areas, or whether input is concentrated into solutional surface depressions via throughflow before entering the limestone. If the latter is the case, then the water may behave in much the same way as does true swallet water, excepting that it will take longer to reach the resurgence.

Equally little is known of the transit time for surface to rising of percolation water, though experiments by Drew (1970) in the St Dunstan's Well catchment, using the dye Pyranine Conc, indicated that dye placed in a dry depression on the limestone plateau behind St Dunstan's Well, some 60m vertically above the spring and 250m horizontally distant, took between two and three weeks after precipitation to reach the rising. The importance of the percolation component in any given limestone catchment will presumably be closely related to the degree of hydraulic homogeneity and isotropy of the local rock structure. In general, an inverse relationship between heterogeneity and anisotrophy with respect to porosity and the proportion of percolation water will be likely. However, the limestone drainage system is dynamic, and the situation will change through time as the system modifies itself and matures. The significance of the percolation water content in relation to speleogenesis in the Mendip area will be further considered in chapter 5.

In summary, it is apparent that none of the conventional views of limestone hydrology, taken individually, is adequate to explain what is known of the underground drainage system of the Mendip Hills. The overall pattern is that of the majority of the precipitation entering groundwater via direct percolation, and only a small percentage of total inflow sinking in discrete points at the surface. Groundwater output is strongly localised at a few major springs, suggesting that underground catchments may indeed exist. The presence of the numerous small springs (magnitudes 3 and 4) may possibly be explained simply in terms of their functioning as outlets for local drainage in the regolith and superficial deposits. That underground flow-lines and catchments are not simple is shown by the numerous underground crossings of swallet streams without apparent mixing occurring, together with the many example of streams splitting and resurging at more than one spring, the Wookey Hole, Rodney Stoke, and Rickford–Langford catchments providing the best examples.

Generally, there is a very low degree of coincidence between surface and subterranean basins, and rarely are there any apparent surface or geological features to indicate catchment separation. In attempting to 'explain' the drainage patterns on Mendip, it may be essential to examine the geomorphological and hydrological history of the region, rather than present-day conditions. For example, hydraulic gradient does not seem of prime importance in deciding the underground route of a stream. It may be possible to explain the concentration of major risings on the southern flank of central Mendip in terms of the base level for underground water (the altitude of the contact between Carboniferous Limestone and more recent deposits) being lowered more rapidly on the south flank than on the north flank, the River Severn presumably being the regional control of the base level for this part of south-west England. It may be noted, however, that the major south flank risings, especially Wookey Hole and Rodney Stoke, are not significantly lower in altitude than those of the north flank (especially Rickford–Langford).

On eastern Mendip, this trend is reversed and the best developed drainage systems and major risings are on the north flank. Again, this may be in response to relatively recent downcutting by the River Mells, which flows on or close to the northern edge of the limestone outcrop and is a tributary of the Bristol Avon. The Mells appears to act as a local base level in this area.

CONCLUSIONS

The concept of a true regional water-table in the limestones of the Mendip area is open to some doubt, and what evidence there is tends to militate against such a feature. The major risings are at significantly different altitudes, though horizontally very close to one another, and should a piezometric network surface exist, it would possess a considerable gradient. Secondly, the presence of a water-table requires that in a non-porous rock such as the Carboniferous Limestone of this area there be a multitude of interconnected fissures open to sustain such a surface—the zone of saturation of Grund. Evidence as to the existence of such a network is largely lacking. The existence of streams in the limestone massif crossing without mixing occurring is difficult to explain if a large unified body of groundwater is held to be present. Thus, although it is perhaps not possible to abandon entirely the concept of a water-table in the Mendip Hills, such a rigid concept is somewhat at odds with the experimental evidence gathered as to the hydrology of the area. Stanton (1969b) allowed for the existence of a modified version of the conventional water-table on Mendip. He points out that in the known swallet caves, gradient is controlled by the level of the resurgence for some 90 per cent or more of the sink to rising distance;

that is, streamways are graded to their resurgences. Stanton observes that :

> the picture that emerges is of a drainage system composed of many complicated channels, most of which are well graded to the resurgence. Their downstream, low-gradient, tracts will all lie in or near an imaginary somewhat irregular surface that rises very slowly in all directions upstream of the rising.

This approach emphasises the regionality of base control on flow within the Mendip Hills, and it may indeed be true that, in a sense, each major resurgence has its own water-table level or base level to which the streams in that catchment grade. This, however, need not imply that the zones between discrete active cave passages need be saturated and, therefore, there need be no conventional water-table surface. These various theories of limestone hydrology will be further examined when the origin and development of caves is discussed.

6

The Caves of Mendip

D. P. Drew

D. P. Drew

THEORIES OF SPELEOGENESIS

The caves of Mendip show a wide variety of morphology, of degrees of complexity, and of hydrology, implying that there is no one simple cave-forming mechanism to account for the origin and development of them all. In addition, the extent of exploration varies from cave to cave. Some apparently, have been explored over the greater part of their extent but the majority are only known for perhaps 1 to 5 per cent of their total length. Similarly, the research work carried out varies enormously from cave to cave and from catchment to catchment, and only four of the major caves have been studied at all intensively with respect to speleogenesis. This chapter is not intended to serve as a guide to the caves of Mendip, as such a function is more than adequately performed by Barrington and Stanton (1972).

Many of the views put forward as to the development of the Mendip caves are at variance with one another, and hence in this summary an attempt will be made to outline the various views propounded and to provide a synthesis. The majority of the theories pertaining to cave origin and development on Mendip have tended to Swinnerton's view that cave development is very closely related to the excavation of surface topography, and in particular to local base levels. This view appears in many guises. For example, Trueman (1939) suggested that there might be a relationship between the Mendip caves and the old erosion levels he postulated for the Mendip Hills. Balch

(1937) regarded the impermeable Mesozoic rocks that lie against the southern flank of the hills as being a major control on the level of cave development near the resurgences. Warwick (1962) proposed a modified Swinnerton concept for cave development, and suggested that some of the major resurgence caves, especially those associated with the large dry valleys, were controlled by external downcutting; but he suggested that caves such as Gough's have a more complex origin than this. Warwick also remarked on the comparatively small degree of vadose modification of the majority of the swallet caves and suggested that this was because of the relatively small discharges of the sinking streams. (He compared them with the caves of Yorkshire which show very extensive vadose development.) Glennie (1954) regarded the flow in the Mendip limestones as being, to a degree, artesian. He suggested that the water flows to a level below that of the outlet and is forced upwards by hydraulic pressure to break out, in places, from beneath a cover of impermeable rocks. He cites Gough's cave—a long bore passage apparently terminating in a series of tight rifts—as being an example of such a cave. This is basically the mode of cavern development proposed by Rhoades and Sinacori (1941).

The Stride Brothers (1949) again stressed the phreatic nature of Mendip caves, assuming that speleogenesis occurred under the conditions postulated by W. M. Davis and that groundwater circulation occurred and is occurring at great depths below the 'water-table'. The Strides correlated the presence of major clastic sediment deposits at an altitude of about 150m OD in some of the major central Mendip caves with the presence of an old water-table at that level; presumably this was the zone of intensive sedimentation as the flow became phreatic at this point. They found similar deposits in the caves of western Mendip at an altitude of about 65m, and again suggested a water-table origin.

The most intensive study of the caves of Mendip, and in particular Swildon's Hole, GB Cavern, St Cuthbert's, and the risings at Wookey and Cheddar, was made by D. C. Ford (1963–1971). He made detailed morphological, geological, and hydrological investigations in each of these systems and attempted to fit the data into an overall model of cave development for the Mendip Hills. He suggested that there were examples of caves formed predominantly under vadose conditions (GB cave), under water-table control conditions (Swildon's Hole), and under deep phreatic conditions (St Cuthbert's Swallet). He attempted to link these three modes of genesis in a single model by suggesting that cave passages follow a linear water-table which they have created, though they will make deep loops below it before returning to the level. He stated that the amplitude of this phreatic loop will reduce as the number of tiny groundwater conduits which may be utilised to guide principal passages, increases. He regarded St Cuthbert's Swallet and Wookey Hole as being portions of single phreatic loops, and Swildon's Hole and the Cheddar caves as consisting of several loops. He suggested that the three overall controlling development criteria for the Mendip caves studied were: the available groundwater discharge, the hydraulic gradient, and the efficiency of overground discharge of run-off. Ford again returned to the concept of external base level controls on cave development, and attempted to correlate vertically separated passage series in caves, with old Pleistocene base levels on the flank of the Mendip Hills. These various theories, together with other specific cave studies, will be examined in greater detail when the individual caves are studied.

Various attempts to classify the Mendip caves, either genetically or generically, have been made, though these appear to have little practical value in advancing the understanding of the development of the caves. One such classification, that of Gilbert (1960), will be briefly outlined (see Table 8). This classification is in part genetic (caves of engulfment being differentiated from caves of resurgence) and in part purely morphological (open rifts and rock shelters). He remarked that caves of type 1D,

TABLE 8 *Classification of Mendip caves* (after Gilbert, 1960)

Number	Type of cave	Example
I	Caves of engulfment:	
a	Active streamway	Swildon's Hole
b	Abandoned streamways	Goatchurch Cavern
c	Abandoned swallets	Rod's Pot
d	Vertically developed	Lamb Leer
2	Caves of resurgence:	
a	Active resurgences	Wookey Hole
b	Abandoned resurgences	Gough's Hole
3	Open rifts	Rhino Rift
4	Rock shelters	Sun Hole

vertically developed caves of engulfment, are uncommon on Mendip due to the relatively steep inclination of the strata, though Rhino Rift, near Charterhouse, shows extensive vertical features.

THE AGE OF KARSTIFICATION

There is general agreement amongst workers as to the likely age of the caves of Mendip. The earliest date suggested for the development of most of the still-accessible caves is the Calabrian (early Pleistocene), and it seems to be generally accepted that the vast majority of cave development has occurred in middle, late and post-Pleistocene times. The major infilled fissure at the Westbury-sub-Mendip limestone quarry shows infilled deposits dating back at least to Cromerian times (Heal, 1970).

Several workers have suggested that Mendip underwent some degree of karstification during Triassic times, and although the evidence for this is inevitably scanty and often somewhat ambiguous, the existence of subterranean drainage networks in Triassic times may be of considerable significance in interpreting the present-day hydrological and speleogenetic patterns of Mendip.

Green and Welch (1965) state that the flanks of the Mendip Hills were clearly defined in Triassic times and were dissected by a series of mature valleys. The Keuper rocks of the area were probably laid down in arid or semi-arid conditions, the climate becoming more humid towards the end of this period. Thus, there seems every possibility that a certain degree of karstification did indeed take place on Mendip during this period. Corbel (1957) stressed the importance of Permo-Triassic denudation on Mendip and suggested that the fissures with Rheatic or later Mesozoic infilling are indicative of arid karstification. Balch (1907, 1937) argued vigorously for some degree of Triassic cave development on the Mendip Hills. He cited the evidence of the Rhaetic fossils in the limestone cavities at Holwell and further suggested that the proto-Wookey Hole cave may predate the Dolomitic Conglomerate rock and that 'There may be, therefore, older outlets concealed below the marl which abuts against the south flank of Mendip, and indeed there are abundant evidences that such outlets exist'.

Balch cited the small cave shelter of Nancy Camel's Hole (602441) in Ham Wood as exhibiting evidence of having been infilled by Triassic deposits. At the far end of this cave, and at roof level, there is indeed a reddish conglomerate deposit, though as yet there is no conclusive evidence at all to suggest either that it is Triassic in age, or that it has not been washed into the cave in comparatively recent times. There are, however, more definite indications of Triassic or pre-Triassic karstification, and of particular interest in this respect is the cave of Chelmscombe Quarry near Cheddar. Warwick (1952, 1955) suggested that this cave is infilled with Triassic material, and Stanton (1965a) points out that in Chelmscombe Quarry the Carboniferous Limestone is cut by a large fissure filled with reddish, angular, Dolomitic Conglomerate and red and yellow marl in sub-horizontal beds. There is also solutional enlargement and similar infilling of some of the bedding planes and joints in the same zone, and on some of these surfaces clear scalloping is visible. The individual scallops vary from 1 to 2.5cm in diameter, and in two exposures appear to be directional, indicating water flow. When the Triassic deposits are removed from the limestone in this area, scalloping is found to be present on the rock. There is a specimen of this fissure wall in the Wells Museum showing the scalloped limestone overlain with a Triassic breccia. Stanton suggested that this is positive evidence that the scalloping was developed before the cave was filled with the Keuper deposits, and is thus of Permo-Triassic age. He stated that the cave was probably developed under phreatic conditions, perhaps as a result of flash flooding in a semi-arid climate.

Perhaps the most convincing evidence of all for the existence of Triassic solutional openings in the limestone was given in the study by Robinson (1957) of the Mesozoic fissure fillings in the Carboniferous Limestone of the Mendip area. She differentiates two groups of vertebrate fauna fills. The first, consisting mainly of mammals and mammal-like reptiles, is of Rhaetic or Lower Liassic age, and is found in fissures of submarine origin. The other group, containing sauropsid reptiles in a marly matrix, is probably of Keuper age. Some fissures are classified as being Neptunian sagged cover dykes which originated as open joints in the Rhaetic or Jurassic sea floor. An example of this is the fissure in Cockhill Quarry, 1.5km north of Gurney Slade. Sub-aerial fissures of Triassic age, for example that in Torhill Quarry 1km east of Wells, are regarded as being non-solutional in origin. Thirdly, she described former underground water courses which were filled with Triassic sediments and are now occasionally exposed by quarrying in the Carboniferous Limestone. Such conduits:

> are usually irregular in cross section, in plane, and in profile. In places they form narrow irregular passages or mere cracks in the limestone. The walls are usually water worn, and are often coated with stalactite. The sediments of the fissure filling are often well bedded, sometimes displaying small-scale current bedding . . . Pieces of stalactite, and recrystallised cave pearls are sometimes present in these fissure openings.

A good example of such a fissure is that in Emborough Quarry, located on either side of the rail track from Radstock to Shepton Mallet. The Triassic deposit is located in the eastern quarry. The lower part of the deposit consists of a homogeneous, well-bedded dark clay, and the upper portion is a conglomerate of large boulders of limestone in a matrix of limestone pebbles, shale flakes and silt. In places the deposit is finely bedded. The large boulders are commonly water-worn on part of their surface and there is evidence that this water action occurred before the deposition of the surrounding matrix. Robinson interpreted these deposits as being cave sediments and suggested that at some point the cave roof and part of the sides collapsed. The homogeneous lower clay represents fine sediments laid down by the cave stream under conditions of slow flow, and the conglomerate represents the collapsed roof and walls of the cave. Fig. 51 illustrates the possible sequence of development of the Emborough Quarry fissure (after Robinson, 1957).

Thus, there is considerable evidence that the Mendips were a true karst area possessing some degree of subterranean drainage in Triassic times; however, the extent of the karstification is still unknown, as are its effects, if any, on present-day hydrology.

CATCHMENT AREAS

The caves of the Mendip Hills will be examined with reference to individual catchments in that, to some extent, cave types tend to be somewhat homogeneous within a catchment area, and to some extent it is possible to describe a 'typical' cave system for a particular area of the Mendip Hills (although in practice there are many exceptions to this rule). The areas that are examined with respect to speleogenesis are : western Mendip, the Rickford–Langford catchment, Cheddar catchment, Wookey Hole catchment, and eastern Mendip. To some extent the caves of each of these catchments show features unique to that particular area. A brief examination will also be made of specific

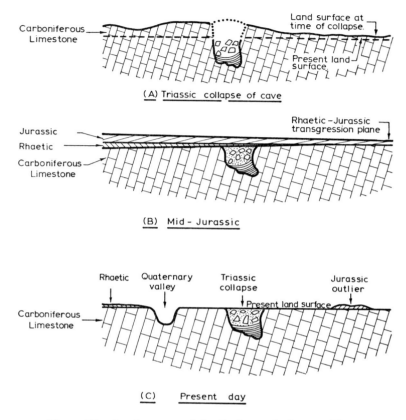

Fig 51 The development of the Emborough Quarry Fissure

cave systems which do not fit into any readily discernible pattern.

Western Mendip

As was discussed in chapter 5, western Mendip—that area west of the A38 road—is characterised in its limestone portions by a total absence of water flowing from other rock formations (except for the River Yeo). The caves of this region are, almost without exception, isolated dry remnants of what were once, presumably, more extensive systems. In most cases it is difficult to identify the former hydrological function of these remnants, as the landscape that existed during their development has now changed greatly. The caves are, with only a few exceptions, very short in length. Examples of such caves include Scragg's Hole (396450), Hutton Cavern (361581), and Denny's Hole (397550). Balch (1937) observed that the Wavering Down portion of this region has virtually no caves in comparison with numerous cavities on the northern edge of the pericline in the Sandford

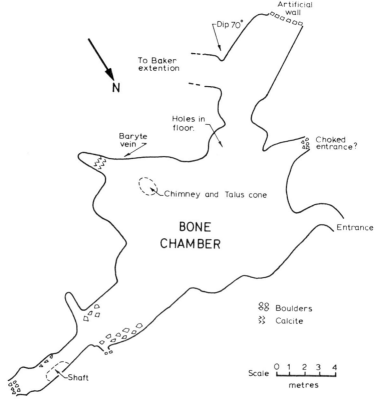

Fig 52 Survey of Banwell Bone Cave

and Banwell areas. He suggested that a possible reason for this is that if the eroded core of the pericline in this area was once filled with Triassic and Liassic rock (before the erosion of the Lox-Yeo Gap), the Banwell Hill flank would have been lower and therefore have received all the run-off waters, and hence be more heavily karstified.

Perhaps the most interesting, and also one of the densest clusters of caves in the area are those on the west end of Banwell Hill in the grounds of 'The Caves' (now a farm). These include Banwell Stalactite Cave (see Plate p 167, *l*), Banwell Ochre Cave and Banwell Bone Cave (382588). Banwell Bone Cave, at an altitude of 76m, was first discovered by miners in about 1800 and had to be dug out to a considerable depth. The cave consists of the large Bone Chamber, some 9m long and 9m wide. At the western end of this chamber is a descent to two smaller chambers with blocked small tubes leading off. To the south-west of Bone Chamber is Baker's Extension, a steeply inclined rift leading to a boulder and clay choke. A shaft at the eastern end of Bone Chamber connects with Banwell Stalactite Cave. There is a chimney in the roof of Bone Chamber at its southern end. A sketch survey of the cave is given in Fig 52. The cave system is developed in steeply dipping limestone (approximately 70°) with an almost due east–west strike. The cave appears to be almost entirely phreatic in origin although the side passages to the main chamber show signs of some vadose development.

Bone Chamber was found to be rich in late Pleistocene bones. Tucker (1966) described traces of a thin stalagmite flooring in two recesses near the roof chimney, and suggested that there is a mark on some of the cave walls where the surface of the deposits originally reached. Further evidence for the removal of fill in this section of the cave is given by the occasional bone which is to be seen calcited to the roof above the bone dig. The cave entrance to the surface appears to have been covered with an angular breccia, as does the bedrock above the chimney;

thus, the cave may have been buried during one of the periods in which Mendip experienced a periglacial climate.

Baker's Extension is developed directly in the bedding, the rift being a very steep bedding plane. Considerable excavation of the secondary infill deposits of this rift has been undertaken. Fig 53 shows a vertical section of the clastic and bone deposits (now destroyed) some 4m vertically from the head of the rift. Fig 54 compares deposits within Baker's Extension entrance to those outside the entrance. The deepest deposit encountered was a greyish-blue clay, inter-bedded at approximately one centimetre intervals by fine seams of yellow ochre. Part of these deposits have become petrified and are extremely hard. This clay ochre sequence dips eastwards at an angle of about 10°. Above this is a deposit rich in iron oxides, some 5m in thickness

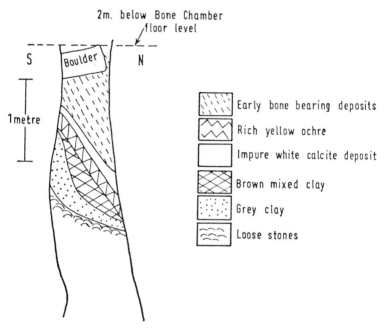

Fig 53 Deposits in Baker's Extension, Banwell Bone Cave
(after Hunt, 1966)

(Hunt, 1966), intermixed with large limestone boulders, grey clay, and dog-tooth calcite spar. Hunt suggests that these deposits

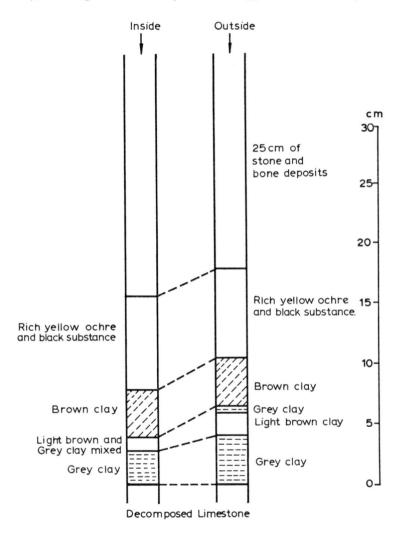

Inside   Outside

cm
30

25 cm of
stone and
bone deposits   25

20

Rich yellow ochre 15
and black substance.

Rich yellow ochre
and black substance

10

Brown clay

Brown clay   Grey clay
                                  Light brown clay   5

Light brown and
Grey clay mixed

Grey clay   Grey clay

0

Decomposed Limestone

Fig 54 Deposits within and without Baker's Extension, Banwell Cave (after Hunt, 1966)

are of pre-Pleistocene age. Above these are water-borne clays
and ochre, and also bone-bearing deposits. Balch (1937) regarded the roof chimney as being an ancient swallet, probably
intermittent in action, and suggested that the bones in the cave
were washed in by this stream and deposited in the sandy,
muddy matrix.

It is not easy to suggest an origin for apparently isolated caves
of this type. In part they appear to be old, possibly random
phreatic solution cavities, slightly modified by later invading
vadose streams, and thus conforming to the Bretz-Davis view of
cave formation. It is of some interest to note that the occurrence
of such isolated chambers is strongly localised in the extreme
eastern and western regions of Mendip, such features being
relatively rare on the central portion of the Hills.

The Rickford–Langford catchment

To some degree, the caves associated with the two risings at
Rickford and Langford may be considered as being transitional
between the dry, abandoned caves of western Mendip and the
active stream caves of central Mendip. The area shows some
features of karstic maturity together with a number of juvenile
drainage phenomena. There are only four active swallet caves
known within the area (East Twin Swallet, West Twin Swallet,
Ellick Farm Sink, and Read's Cavern) and in none of these caves
can the underground route of the stream be penetrated for any
appreciable distance. However, there are a large number of now
dry sinkholes with associated small cave systems; for example,
those caves in the row of depressions near the UBSS hut, including Bath Swallet, Rod's Pot, and Bos Swallet (see Plate p 168, *u*).
In addition, there are isolated remnants of caves, especially in
Burrington Combe itself; for example Aveline's Hole, which may
have functioned for at least part of the time as a resurgence.
Finally, there are what appear to be abandoned high-level stream
sinks in the valley tributary to Burrington Combe; Goatchurch
Cavern and Sidcot Swallet fall into this category. Fig 55 shows

the distribution of the major caves of the Burrington Combe area, together with the surface drainage.

The apparent immaturity of the present-day stream sinks, especially those in the Twin Brook Valleys, together with the presence of large numbers of sinkholes which were probably active in comparatively recent times, imply that within recent times there has been a marked hydrological change in the catchment.

As discussed in chapter 5, virtually all the water sinking within this catchment, drains to both the Rickford and Langford

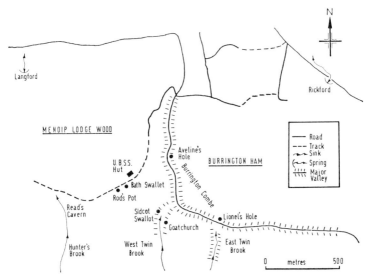

Fig 55 Major caves of the Burrington area

risings. It is of interest to note that water sinking to the west of Burrington Combe must pass beneath this major dry valley to reach Rickford rising. Tratman (1963a) regarded Aveline's Hole as being a former water outlet, now truncated by the down-cutting of the Combe to its present level. This again suggests the existence of a fossil drainage route from the Twin Valley area towards Rickford rising. It may be that one of the pair of risings for this area is in the process of capturing drainage from the other. Rickford appears to be the major and better developed rising of the two, but Langford is at a lower altitude. It is not characteristic of the hydrogeology of the Mendip Hills generally, for two closely connected risings of this magnitude to exist within such close proximity. Donovan (1969a) noted that it was possible that a lower-level rising developed, perhaps near the mouth of Burrington Combe, but was later blocked by the outwash deposits at the mouth of the valley, causing diversion of the drainage to the risings at Rickford and Langford.

The most striking feature of all the caves of the area is their dominantly phreatic character; vadose development is extremely limited and localised even in caves carrying an active stream at present. Donovan regarded the low degree of vadose development as being due to the relatively small catchment areas feeding the sinks, compared with the larger run-off to the major swallets of the southern flank of Black Down (for example Longwood Swallet). Another feature of cavern development in this area, and one relatively uncommon elsewhere in Mendip, is the tendency towards passages forming grid networks; sometimes three-dimensional chambers as in the case of Goatchurch Cavern, and sometimes solely within a bedding unit as in the case of Lionel's Hole. These three-dimensional mazes are characterised by a multiplicity of interconnected tubes, of breakdown chambers, and of many blind phreatic passages. Generally, the cave systems terminate at their lowest point in a series of impenetrably tight rifts. These have been commonly supposed to correspond with a rest level for the local 'water-table'.

The most comprehensive study of the area is that made by Tratman (1963a) wherein he examined the general geomorphology and hydrology of the area, together with the morphology of the major caves. The most extensive cave of the area, and also the best documented, is Goatchurch Cavern in the West Twin Brook Valley (476583). The main entrance to the cave is located just upstream of the present stream sink, and some 13m above the valley floor. A second entrance (the Back Door) is some few metres below and developed in the same limestone bed.

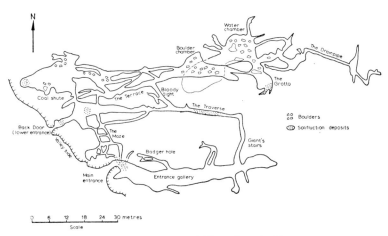

Fig 56 Plan survey of Goatchurch Cavern

Fig 56 shows a plan survey of the cave (after Mendip Caving Group) and Fig 57 is a sectional east–west elevation of the cave (after Balch, 1937). The cave system consists of a series of large, sub-horizontal passages developed almost entirely along the strike, together with a multitude of smaller, more poorly developed tubes (see Plate p 265, *ul*) connecting them, and closely following the dip of the strata. The whole cave is formed within a thin series of beds, and the whole system, as Tratman pointed out, may be considered as an example of the development of a phreatic cave system in steeply dipping limestones as described by Bretz. Much of the evidence for the origin and development of the cave has been lost (especially old stalagmite floors and clastic deposits), as this cave system is a notorious lure for cavers, and hence is extremely well trodden. The Entrance Gallery is almost purely phreatic in form, showing very large scalloping features on the roof and upper parts of the walls—implying a very slow flow of water. The floor deposits, where they are still intact, consist of an upper layer of soft stalagmite, a hard stalagmite layer below, and then a thin layer of cave earth resting on the limestone. Similar deposits occur in the Traverse which runs down from the Back Door entrance through the Dining Room to the bottom of the Giant's Stairway. At this site the deposits are in excess of 2m in depth. Tratman regarded these deposits as being evidence that the phreatic cave was later subjected to vadose stream action, then filled and sealed with stalagmite, then rejuvenated, and lastly, refilled and recovered with stalactite. Tratman regarded certain deposits in the cave (their location is marked in Fig 56) as being of solifluction origin and

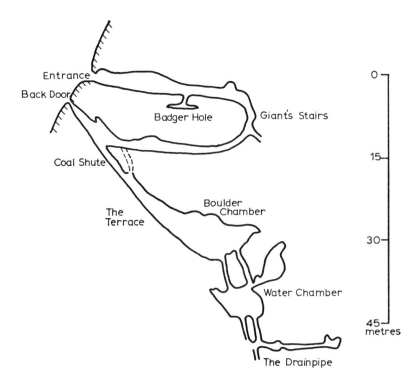

Fig 57 Sectional elevation of Goatchurch Cavern

containing frost-shattered boulders with a late Pleistocene fauna. He suggested the Solutrian amelioration as a possible date. There is some direct evidence for later vadose modification of the Traverse itself. Small, deep, scalloping, associated with rapid water flow, may be found on the slope down from the Back Door entrance on the roof of an undercut, just before the Dining Chamber. The cave terminates in a very small horizontal tube —the Drain Pipe—ending in a small chamber with no negotiable way on.

In the lowest part of the cave beyond the Drain Pipe, there is a small deposit of fluvial gravel which Tratman thought was probably brought in through a now blocked swallet in the valley floor above. Dye tests have proved that the small stream (some-

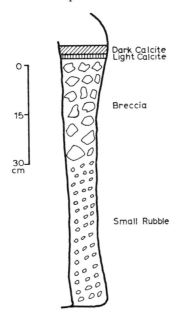

Fig 58 Pleistocene deposits in Goatchurch Cavern

times running beyond the tunnel) is part of the one sinking at Yew Tree Swallet in the main valley. Tratman pointed out that the lower deposits, for example those in the Traverse, could be Entrance Gallery deposits washed into the cave after re-sorting. Fig 58 (after Tucker, 1969) shows a vertical section through the deposits in the floor of the Traverse, a short distance from the bottom of the Giant's Stairway. The upper layer is of thin, dark stalagmite, 1.5cm in thickness, overlaying a softer stalagmite deposit some 0.75cm in thickness. Beneath this is a loosely cemented breccia of Carboniferous Limestone and Old Red Sandstone together with a few pebbles of quartz and some straw stalactites. Below a depth of about 30cm, the deposit is not cemented, and consists of rubble which diminishes in size down-wards. The total depth of the section is some 70cm. Rodent remains (*Microtus*) were found in this deposit, and this tends to confirm Tratman's view that these deposits are indeed of late Pleistocene age.

Rod's Pot, one of the series of now dry sinkholes near the UBSS hut west of Burrington Combe, is much simpler in mor-phology and, apparently, in origin. The cave is developed in limestone beds dipping at an angle of 64–72°. The first part of the cave consists of narrow rifts, which are enlargements of several vertical joints which follow the direction of dip. The second section of the cave from the main chamber onwards is primarily developed in bedding planes, the passages having considerable lateral, but little vertical, extent. The main chamber of the cave consists of two parts. The first part, developed in the dip, has a steep slope whilst the second runs almost horizontally along the strike. The ceiling of the second part contains a pattern of half tubes about 1.5cm in width, the centre of the channel commonly being occupied by a thin calcite vein, suggesting that this was the initial line of weakness along which differential solution by percolating water occurred. The fill in this cave consists almost entirely of sands and pebbles derived from the Old Red Sandstone, and it appears that there has been some degree of removal of this fill by later invading vadose streams.

As was previously mentioned, Aveline's Hole, the noticeable

cave entrance in Burrington Combe below the entrance to West Twin Brook Valley, is thought to be a fossil rising. The cave itself consists of a tunnel descending to a chamber, and then a second chamber separated from the first by a rock bridge. The deposits in the inner chamber originally consisted of a surface layer of stalagmite over a layer of cave earth which contained a late Pleistocene fauna. The outer chamber had a 1m deep deposit of cave earth and beneath it a fine, laminated, silt layer, which Tratman (1963a) regarded as being due to repeated floodings by water welling up from the back of the cave during its final period as an active rising. Again, the general form of the cave is totally phreatic. Two main points suggest that the cave was an ancient rising. The scalloping of the roof just below the niche in the outer chamber indicates an upward and outward direction of flow, whilst the tendency of the main bore passage to sub-divide into numerous smaller rifts and tubes at its furthest extremity is characteristic of many risings; for example Gough's Cave exhibits similar features.

A sequence of development for the Burrington caves has been propounded by Tratman (1963a). He suggested that the initial purely phreatic stages of cave development of the highest-level caves—for example Fox's Hole, Trat's Crack, and Toad's Hole began just prior to the Günz glaciation, when sea level in the Burrington area was at or below 130m OD. During the Mindel-Riss interglacial, with sea level at almost 45m OD, Aveline's Hole became a rising for the high-level caves. During this period the topmost parts of the caves were experiencing vadose modification and paraphreatic conditions had ensued below the water-table. Tratman regarded some of the basal stalagmite in the Entrance Gallery to Goatchurch Cavern as dating from this period. During the succeeding Riss glaciation, the higher caves silted up. The return to interglacial conditions, but with relatively low sea levels, meant that the area reverted to subterranean drainage once more, and that the surface valleys became dry. The Bos Swallet to Bath Swallet series of caves is thought to date from

H

this period, as is Read's Cavern. Aveline's Hole still functioned as a resurgence, though the lower routes to the present-day active rising were developing. During the Würm glaciation, associated with sea levels up to 40m below present-day levels, surface erosion dominated, solifluction deposits entered caves such as Goatchurch, and entrances were eventually blocked by scree deposits. Tratman suggested that during this period, caves such as Bos Swallet and East Twin Swallet were completely blocked. Also during the Würm interstadials, the Rickford and Langford risings became active and Aveline's Hole ceased to function as a resurgence.

During post-glacial times, many of the caves have undergone vadose modification by tiny streams removing some of the old fill. Tratman used the evidence of alleged knick points in Burrington Combe to correspond to phases of downcutting on the surface and hence cavern development. Stanton (1970), discussing the development of Lionel's Hole (see Plate p 265, *ur*) suggested that the cave was formed below a 'water-table' at an altitude of 150m or higher, possibly contemporary with Goatchurch, Read's Cavern and Rod's Pot, and he regarded this base level as being connected with the 168–98m bench on the north-western flank of the hills. It should be noted that there are no absolute dates for most of this chronology for the Burrington area, and that the correlation of cave levels with inferred surface knick points has a somewhat dubious validity.

The Cheddar catchment

The Cheddar catchment is comparatively ill-documented, although considerable research has been undertaken in the area of the rising in Cheddar Gorge itself. Only three feeders to the system, those of GB, Longwood Swallet, and Manor Farm Swallet, are accessible for any distance and have been morphologically examined. Of the other known feeders to Cheddar, some, such as Pine Tree Pot in the extreme north-east of the catchment, are very short and apparently unrelated to present-day hydrology, whilst others, such as Reed's Grotto have yet to yield a negotiable streamway.

To generalise, it may be said that the caves of engulfment within the Cheddar catchment appear to be relatively recent in age and comparatively simple in development, especially in comparison with the caves of the Wookey catchment to the east. However, the caves of resurgence at Cheddar Gorge are complicated and indicate several stages of development. Ford (1963) regarded Cheddar as being the better developed and older resurgence in comparison with Wookey Hole. However, there is some doubt as to whether this is in fact the case. The geomorphology of Longwood Swallet was studied by Atkinson (1967), and GB Cave by Ford (1964a). Both interpretations rely on the concept of passages in the cave being graded to various base levels. In Ford's hypothesis these are specifically external levels on the southern flank of the Mendip Hills which may be correlated with levels of the resurgence caves at Cheddar.

The assumptions made in these speleogenetic studies are that the amount of clastic debris available for the infilling of caves would be at a minimum under interglacial or interstadial conditions, and at a maximum under a fully glacial or periglacial climate with tundra vegetation and much loose debris available. Ford supposed that during fill phases, the flow of water within the caves was much reduced in volume; though as Donovan (1969a) pointed out, reasonably large quantities of water would be required to have deposited the large Old Red Sandstone debris found in many of the caves. Ford explained the stalagmite phases in the fills as being due to active seepage in the absence of any sizable stream; perhaps because of blocking of swallet entrances by permafrost debris which would only allow percolation water to pass. Should this be the case, the clastic fill would correspond to the early stages of a cold climatic interlude, and the stalagmite deposit to the succeeding fully glacial climate.

Two of the major swallet caves will be examined in turn with respect to speleogenesis, and an attempt will be made to correlate their development with respect to time.

GB Cave : GB Cave is located at Charterhouse in an area of gruffy ground some 700m east-south-east of Tyning's Farm, and at an altitude of 253m. Some 1,950m of passages have been explored within the system over a vertical range of 134m. GB Cave is developed in the lowest band of Blackrock Limestone. The present-day sink of the stream at Tyning's Swallet is some 90m east of the accessible cave entrance, which is an older stream sink, and they are separated by a low col. Further to the east, a small stream sinks at Reed's Grotto but, insofar as is known, it does not join the main Tyning's Farm stream within the explored portion of GB Cave.

Basically, the cave consists of a series of inlet passages, of varying dimensions, which link to form the Gorge and Main Passage of the cave system. This then descends rapidly before bifurcating at its lower end. The inlet passages to the system are shown on Fig 59 and include Entrance Passage, Ooze Passage, Mud Passage, Stream Passage, Double Passage, Extension Passage, and Rhumba Alley. Entrance Passage, Ooze Passage, Mud Passage, the Ox-bow (see Plate p 265, *lr*) and Stream Passage are interlinked tubes which all emerge in the Gorge, a short distance apart. The normal route through the cave is via Entrance Passage and Mud Passage. Initially, this is a large, irregularly shaped passage consisting of an upper phreatic bore with a deep vadose trench beneath. Ooze Passage, which is an off-shoot of this, lack the vadose trench. Beyond Ooze Passage, the Mud Passage route to the Gorge is typical of many Mendip vadose streamways, with a steeply descending rift passage heavily scalloped in places and with occasional plunge pools interrupting the steady gradient. In its upper parts, Entrance Passage contains a fill of collapse and stream-laid materials, though much excavation of these deposits occurred during the storm of 10 July 1968.

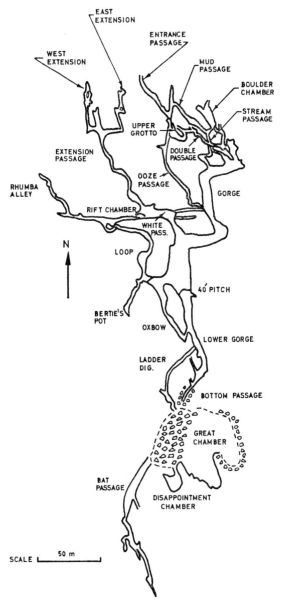

EAST
EXTENSION

ENTRANCE
PASSAGE

WEST
EXTENSION

MUD
PASSAGE

BOULDER
CHAMBER

STREAM
PASSAGE

UPPER
GROTTO

EXTENSION
PASSAGE

DOUBLE
PASSAGE

RHUMBA
ALLEY

OOZE
PASSAGE

GORGE

RIFT CHAMBER

WHITE
PASS.

N

LOOP

40' PITCH

BERTIE'S
POT

OXBOW

LOWER GORGE

LADDER
DIG.

BOTTOM PASSAGE

GREAT
CHAMBER

BAT
PASSAGE

DISAPPOINTMENT
CHAMBER

SCALE   50 m

Fig 59 Plan survey of GB Cave
(after UBSS Survey, 1969)

The Gorge is perhaps the most remarkable single passage in the Mendip caves (see Plate p 266, *ul*). It drops vertically some 95m and reaches a maximum size of some 30m in height and 23m in width in the Main Chamber. The gradient is fairly uniform apart from an oversteepening at the 40 Foot Pot; just beyond the Main Chamber there is a levelling-off of the gradient before the boulder choke at the terminus of the Gorge. There are remnants of roof tubes in Main Passage below the 40 Foot Pot. The Gorge contracts in size, and ends in a series of choked distributaries and a major unstable boulder choke. One of these distributaries, Ladder Dig Passage, leaves the Gorge at roof level, a few metres before the terminal boulder choke. That this was once an important water course is evident from the large half-tube in the roof of the Gorge which makes a right angle turn to it. Ladder Dig Passage extends as a low crawl with a thick stalagmite and clastic fill on the floor, before entering the very base of a very large boulder ruckle. Beyond the boulder ruckle the passage becomes a discrete unit once more (Bat Passage) which then gradually diminishes in size, terminating

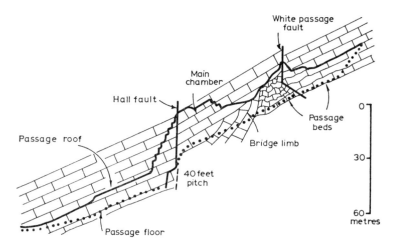

Fig 60 Long-section of the Gorge, GB Cave

in several side passages and narrow, vertical rifts. At the top of the major boulder pile is a very large chamber (Great Chamber) some 40m in width and 66m in length, and a second smaller chamber (Disappointment Chamber). This is thought to be directly above, and probably one and the same with, the boulder choke at the end of the Gorge into which the main cave stream disappears.

The overall trend of the cave is down dip, but the cave does not confine itself to any one particular bedding plane as the strata in this area are much dislocated by faulting. In fact, joints and faults are followed preferentially rather than bedding planes. Fig 60 (after Ford, 1964a) shows a long-section of the Gorge in relation to the structural geology of the area. The contortion of the strata is readily apparent on the walls of the cave, especially in the area of the Gorge immediately below the entrance of Mud Passage, where small anticlines are visible. Again at the 40 Foot Pitch which is developed in a fault, crush breccia and calcite vein fill may be seen. Ford suggests that the two east–west faults, Hall Fault and White Passage Fault, served as important intercepts to the generally north-south flow of water within the cave system, directing flow into the Gorge.

Ford (1964a) evolved a sequence of development for GB

TABLE 9 *The sequence of development of GB Cave* (after Ford, 1964a)

Phase	Process	
1	Phreatic erosion	
2A	Major vadose erosion	First erosion
2B	Diminished vadose erosion	
3A	Rock fall and stream aggradation	First fill
3B	Stalagmite deposition	
4	Major vadose erosion	Second erosion
5A	Rock fall	
5B	Limited stream clearance	
5C	Stream aggradation	Second fill
5D	Limited stream clearance	
5E	Stalagmite deposition	
6	Stream clearance, stalagmite Re-solution	Modern

Cave. Table 9 illustrates the sequence of geomorphological phases in the cave and Fig 61 a-e diagrammatically illustrates this evolution. Ford recognised an initial stage of phreatic erosion followed by an alternating series of stages of vadose erosion and

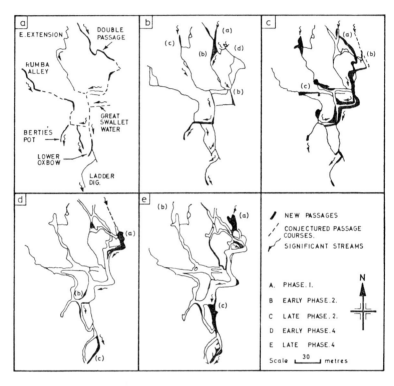

Fig 61 Sequence of development of GB Cave
(after Ford, 1964a)

of deposition. He estimated that the total volume of passages that may be classified as phreatic, comprises less than 5 per cent of the total volume of known passages within the cave. Thus GB Cave is unique on Mendip in the dominance of vadose erosion in its formation. However, the basic plan of the cave system was established during the initial phreatic phase when phreatic streams opened courses through the Entrance series, the Extension, and Rhumba Alley, before being dispersed to the south of the Hall Fault in the lower regions of the cave. Vadose entrenchment occurred when the water-table fell below the elevation of any particular passage, and terminated after the water-table had stabilised at 137m OD with a period of deposition —the commencement of phase 3.

Phase 4 erosion followed a similar sequence. The Extension Passage only shows evidence of a single phase of entrenchment. Basal expansion of the vadose trench, so that one or both walls are undercut is common, and Ford regarded basal under-

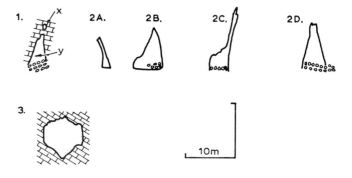

1. Upper Gorge – phreatic passage (x) preserved above vadose passage(y)

2. Basal widening of passages   A. Mud passage.   B. Upper gorge.
                                    C. The Oxbow.   D. Lower gorge.

3. Bridge limb of Gorge – entrenchment below a level of maximum widening

Fig 62 Passage cross-sections, GB Cave
(after Ford, 1964*a*)

cutting as indicating the establishment of an equilibrium profile for that particular passage. Fig 62 shows examples of passage cross-sections in the upper Gorge area which exemplify basal vadose widening. By the end of the second stage of vadose erosion (phase 4) the form of the cave was much as it appears

H*

today. The original main flow of water was via Ladder Dig, and
Ford suggested that this route was abandoned early in phase 4
when the water-table fell some 15m or more to somewhat below
the elevation of the present-day terminal boulder choke.

There are two fill stages apparent in the cave, phase 3—the
first fill, and phase 5—the second fill. The first fill is rarely
visible, though a good exposure occurs in the Bridge Limb of the
Gorge. Fig 63 shows a long-section of the first and second fill

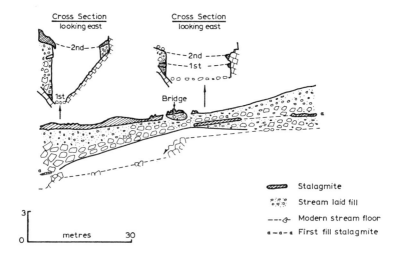

Fig 63 First and second fills, GB Cave
(after Ford, 1964*a*)

deposits of the Gorge in this area. First stream-laid fill is also
found in the Approach Passage to Bertie's Pot and consists of a
sand-cobble mixture 60–100cm in thickness with an overlying
layer of 15–40cm of stalagmite. The sand of the second fill was
laid on top of this. Ladder Dig was filled with a sand–cobble
first fill, and then a stalagmite layer some 15–30cm in thickness.
Later erosion removed much of the stalactite, and a second
stalagmite layer 5–15cm in thickness has been deposited on

the lower floor. This second, uneroded layer is regarded as belonging to phase 5E of the second fill. The second fill is much the greater in volume and has three major components. The basal layer (phase 5A) consists of boulders in a matrix of stream-laid fill. The stream-laid fill is built high above these boulders, indicating that the rock-falls occurred early on in this phase. Above this is a structureless stream-laid fill, generally in the fine sand to large cobble fraction. A large proportion of the material is Old Red Sandstone, and the fill is not indurated. The topmost deposit is of stalactite (phase 5e), and this is of greatly varying thickness. Ford suggested that there was no stream erosion contemporary with the laying down of this layer. Deposits of this second fill are being entrenched and removed in many places and fine examples of it are visible in the Main Chamber, where the fill is some 10m in thickness.

The modern phase (phase 6) is of vadose erosion. All the active streams are now removing this second clastic fill, and eroding stalagmite. Above a level of approximately 200m OD many calcite deposits, which are above stream level, are subject to resolution by drips and seepages. Ford suggested that this implied a fundamental change in the chemical composition of the groundwater now entering the cave, and this probably relates to changes in climate and vegetation cover. Ford regarded the penultimate level in GB Cave (that of Ladder Dig at 150m OD) to be accordant with a fossil series of risings at Cheddar at an altitude of 40–50m OD, and that the present streamway, some 15–21m lower, is accordant with the level of the modern rising at Cheddar.

The dangers of attempting to elucidate the development of a cave by interpretation of fill and erosion stages are again apparent in the case of GB Cave. For example, during the flood of 10 July 1968, considerable erosion and re-deposition of fill material took place. For example, several centimetres of fine sand was deposited in the entrance to Ladder Dig Passage, there was considerable deposition at the end of the Gorge, and the fill in the Entrance Passage was scoured out by as much as 2m. *Longwood Swallet*: Longwood Swallet is located at an altitude of 210m in the deeply incised Longwood Valley, a tributary of Velvet Bottom. The cave extends over a vertical range of 139m with a total passage length of 1,440m. The cave is considerably more complex than GB, with a distinct upper level (Longwood series) with only minor active streams, and an active lower level (August series). In plan the cave is very complex; Fig 64 shows a plan view of the cave system and Fig 65 shows a true length

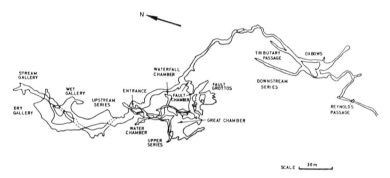

Fig 64 Plan survey of Longwood Swallet

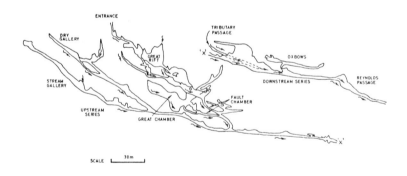

Fig 65 True length section of Longwood Swallet
(from MCG Survey, 1967)

section. There is a sink, normally dry, some 9m down-valley of the entrance, and it is presumed that there are buried sinks upstream of the present entrance. The cave is entered via a series of very narrow, tight rift passages. A short distance from the entrance, the route bifurcates. The upper passage—dominantly a narrow, high rift—leads to the main chamber of Longwood Swallet. The lower route, very ill-developed in its initial stages, is the active stream course. The two routes unite at Fault Chamber, and at the base of this chamber Main Stream Passage is encountered. Downstream, this ends in constricted rifts, and upstream (via large collapsed stream passages) in boulder chokes beneath the valley floor close to the surface.

Atkinson (1967) deduced a chronology for the development of this cave after the fashion of Ford's, for GB. Table 10 shows

TABLE 10 *The sequence of development of Longwood Swallet* (after Atkinson, 1967)

Phase	Process
1A	Phreatic erosion—initiation of Great Fault Chamber
1B	Phreatic erosion—phreas falls from $+$197m to 141m
2A	Major vadose erosion
3A	Aggradation
3B	Deposition of calcite
	(Phreas falls to 120–123m)
4A	Excavation and minor vadose erosion
4B	Major vadose erosion
4C	Collapse
5A	Aggradation
5B	Deposition of stalagmite
	(Phreas falls to 90–93m)
6A	Excavation
6B	Major vadose erosion
6C	Collapse
7A	Aggradation
7B	Deposition of stalagmite
7C	Collapse in upstream Series
	(Phreas falls to 70m—modern level)
8	Modern excavation and minor vadose erosion

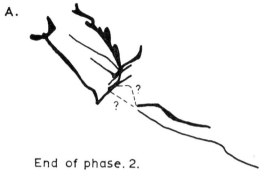

A.

End of phase. 2.

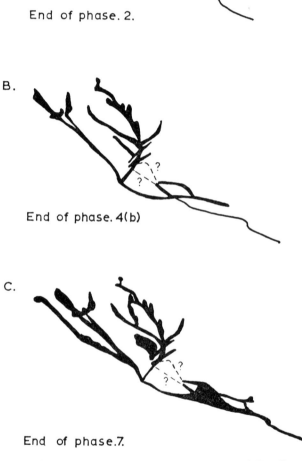

B.

End of phase. 4(b)

C.

End of phase. 7.

Fig 66 Sequence of development of Longwood Swallet
(after Atkinson, 1967)

the sequence of development in Longwood Swallet according to Atkinson, and Fig 66 shows, diagrammatically the stages of development at the end of phase 2, 4B, and 7. As may be seen from the table, Atkinson postulated a development sequence similar to that of GB. The initial stage of phreatic erosion was followed by a fall in the water-table of some 56m to enable major vadose erosion (phase 2a) to begin. This was followed by three stages of aggradation and two further phases of vadose erosion, the latter again corresponding to successive drops in the base level. The modern phase, with a phreas at below 70m, is considered to be one of excavation and minor vadose erosion. Atkinson considered Longwood Swallet to be considerably older than GB Cave, dating from prior to the Penultimate (Mindel-Riss) Interglacial.

Table 11 shows the relative chronologies of Longwood Swallet

TABLE 11 *Relative chronologies of Longwood Swallet and GB Cave* (after Atkinson, 1967)

Longwood	GB	Pleistocene Stages
Phase 1A	–	Unknown
Phase 1B	–	Penultimate Interglacial
Phase 2	–	Penultimate Interglacial
(Phreas at 141m)	–	
Phase 3	–	Penultimate Glaciation
Phase 4	Phases 1 and 2	Last Interglacial
(Phreas at 120–123m)	(Phreas at 135m)	
Phase 5	Phase 3	Early Last Glacial
Phase 6	Phase 4	Chelford Interstadial
(Phreas at 90–93m)	(Phreas at 120m)	
Phase 7	Phase 5	Main Last Glacial
Phase 8	Phase 6	Late and post-Glacial

and GB Cave. It appears that GB originated in the last inter-glacial—there being two rhythms of erosion and deposition in this cave. Longwood demonstrates three full cycles of erosion and deposition, and phases 1 and 2 in GB Cave are correlated with phase 4 in Longwood, both corresponding to a stand level of 120m OD.

Cheddar: Cheddar Gorge contains the greatest concentration of caves of any area on Mendip. The majority of these are small, phreatic tubes in the side of the Gorge itself, and are usually of very limited horizontal and vertical extent. Many of these may, perhaps, represent truncated remnants of former cave systems, though positive identification is extremely difficult. The two cave systems of particular geomorphological significance are those around Gough's Cave—located at the lower end of the Gorge immediately adjacent to the active risings—and Reservoir Hole higher up the Gorge at an altitude of 114m. Ford (1963) recognised three fossil levels of discharge of underground water in the Gough's group of caves. The highest of these, at 100–10m, is at Great Oones Hole; water from this resurgence supposedly discharged into a surface valley running to the north of Lion Rock. The second level, at 61–9m, discharged via Long Hole into a valley floor represented by the top of the spur near Gough's Cave (Donovan, 1969a). The third level, at 40–6m, consisted of Gough's Cave as the major rising. This is the level Ford correlated with the first major vadose phase at GB, the level of Ladder Dig. Water presently resurges at an altitude of some 18m.

These four successive tiers of cave passages appear to be interconnected to a considerable degree, and all consist of predominantly phreatic bore passages terminating in tight rifts or tubes. The lowest level appears to be graded below the level of the present Gorge base, discharging upwards some 9m through boulders to the present outlet; although this may simply represent the water moving upward through fill deposits in the lower part of the Gorge. Ford suggests that the earliest water was drawn down tension joints into relatively open bedding planes at the heads of the caves. Fig 67 shows a long-section through Gough's system of caves, and Fig 68 a plan view of the same complex. Gough's Old Cave is illustrated on the Plate on p 266. There appears to be only one inlet for the water which successively fed this entire series of caves.

As is apparent from the sectional view of the Gough's Cave system, all the passages appear to originate from the Boulder

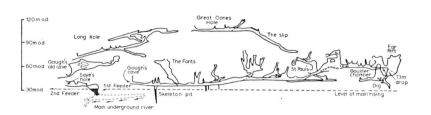

Fig 67 Section, Gough's Caves, Cheddar

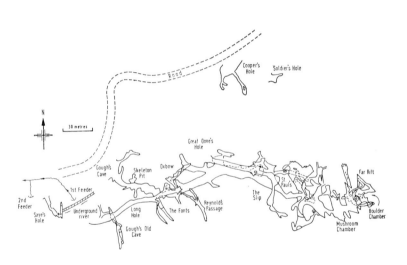

Fig 68 Plan survey, Gough's Caves, Cheddar

Chamber of Gough's Cave. Stanton (1965*b*) undertook an excavation at the base of Boulder Chamber and found a narrow shaft filled with boulders, sand, and clay at one point. Fig 69 shows a plan and section of the deposits encountered in this shaft. It

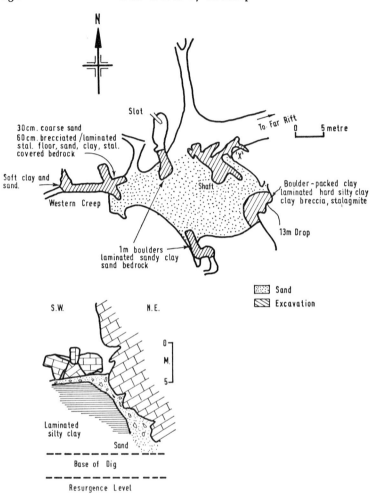

Fig 69 Plan and section, Boulder Chamber deposits, Gough's Cave
(after Stanton, 1965)

would seem that this is the only major inlet below the floor of
Boulder Chamber, and that it was the only important source
of formative water for the Gough's series of caves. From Great

Oones Hole to the deepest point of Boulder Chamber, the drop is 73m vertically—indicating that water was presumably lifted through this height during the formation of Great Oones Hole. It seems probable that the present-day active resurgence passage, which is similar in form to Gough's Cave and the older outlets, will also join this major inlet route somewhere beyond the Boulder Chamber. Thus, the tiers of resurgence levels represented at Cheddar may not continue back in the hill, and there may be just one level of conduit leading back towards the sinks. Table 12 shows the chronological sequence of development at the Cheddar caves (after Ford, 1963).

TABLE 12 *The sequence of development of the Cheddar caves* (after Ford, 1963)

Great Oones-Long Hole		Gough's Bore		Final Sequence	
1	Permo-Triassic				
2A	Bore			1	Great Oones phase
2B	Long Hole				(103m water-table)
3	Stalagmite deposition			1A	Long Hole phase
4	Renewed phreatic		Phreatic	2	
		1	(65–73m water-table)		(65–73m water-table)
		2	Master bore phase (phreatic)	3	Master bore phase (43–50m water-table)
5	Lower stalagmite	3	Laminated clay (phreatic)	4A	Stalagmite
		3A	Clearance	4B	Clearance/coarse sand
		4A	Clay sand	5A	Laminated sands
				6	Second breccia
				7	Local vadose erosion
6	Collapse/earth	4B	Aggradation-Breccia/clay	8A	Cheddarian Breccia } Younger Dryas
7	Recent stalagmite	5A	Stalagmite	8B	Mesolithic Stalagmite } Boreal-Atlantic
		5B	Block Fall, Re-solution	8C	Block fall Re-solution } Iron Age 'A'
8	Modern	6	Flood Clay, Re-solution	9	Earthflow Re-solution } Modern

It seems very certain that the successive levels of caves in the lower Gorge do indeed represent a sequence of levels of discharge of the water at Cheddar, and that these levels presumably correspond to some external influence. However, what is less certain is that these correspond to levels in the swallet caves in the hills behind, and as yet no satisfactory dating has been made either for the age of the inlet caves or for the resurgence caves.

Reservoir Hole, on the left hand side of the Gorge, consists of a descending tube-and-rift complex which intersects a long bore passage, not dissimilar in cross-section and size to the Gough's type of passage. This passage descends evenly to terminate in muddy tubes above the level of the main Gough's Caves. There is ample evidence of intermittent flooding in this zone, though otherwise the cave is dry. In an upstream direction, this passage terminates in boulders beneath Cheddar Gorge and it seems probable that it indeed continues on the far side of the Gorge. Reservoir Hole is a very ancient streamway, the function of which is not entirely clear. It may be that it represents a portion of a main bore passage from one of the Black Down pericline sinks to the main risings at Cheddar. Its dimensions do not suggest that it functioned as the sole conduit for drainage to the Cheddar rising. Should the former be the case, then it is possible that the various swallet caves pursue largely independent courses to the rising, possibly amalgamating only a short distance behind the spring. There is some evidence that swallet streams do remain separate for much of their route in the adjacent Wookey Hole catchment. The Great Aven and Grand Gallery are illustrated on p 282, *ll* and *lr*.

The Wookey Hole catchment

Wookey Hole is probably the most complicated catchment on Mendip, and also possibly the oldest. The caves feeding the resurgence exhibit a wide diversity of type : there are examples of completely abandoned ancient swallets, of swallets which take water only during very heavy rainfall, and of active swallets engulfing major streams. In general, the caves of this catchment are better developed and more complex than those of the nearby Cheddar catchment. In some cases the swallet caves exhibit flights of vertical passage development. Cave genesis within this area is generally supposed to have taken place over a longer period of time than in the Cheddar catchment. Though the rising at Wookey Hole is more ancient than that at Cheddar there are no obvious high-level exits apparent in the immediate vicinity of the cave as there are at Cheddar, though this may be due to the burial of such exits.

As was remarked in chapter 5, Wookey Hole is linked, albeit tenuously, with the smaller rising at Rodney Stoke : however, only the former rising will be considered. The major explored caves known to feed to Wookey Hole rising are those of Swildon's Hole, St Cuthbert's Swallet, and Eastwater Cavern. These three caves are morphologically disparate, hydrologically dissimilar, and in all probability, of different ages. Only two caves, Swildon's Hole and St Cuthbert's Swallet will be examined in detail, together with the resurgence cave at Wookey Hole. A brief description of Eastwater Cavern is also given.

Swildon's Hole : Swildon's Hole is undoubtedly genetically the most complex cave on Mendip, and in many ways the most interesting. Its great popularity, together with the relative ease of access to all but the remotest parts of the system, have meant that perhaps more work has been carried out in this cave, both for academic analysis and to further the extension of the cave, than in any other cave in the British Isles. However, the origin and the full developmental history of the cave are still not completely clear and will probably require further exploration, especially in the fossil streamway series. The examination of the development of this cave is largely based upon the work of Ford (1960, 1962, 1963, 1965*b* & *c*, 1968) together with a more recent study of the Shatter Passages extensions by Atkinson (1966).

The total length of explored passages within this system in 1971 was 7.3 km, extending over a vertical range of 174m. The cave is located on the western flank of the North Hill pericline at the lower end of a shallow blind valley, at an altitude of 252m in a small closed depression at the Shale–Blackrock Limestone contact. The valley floor above this point is knicked back for some 500m in adjustment, suggesting that this has been the major sink for the cave for a considerable period of time. Part of the cave—the abandoned South-east Inlet and Shatter Passage series—lies under the continuation of this valley towards Priddy, though the main active streamway adopts a more westerly course under the right hand flank of the valley before making a sharp turn southwards to flow under Priddy Green at a depth of some 150m. The present terminus of the active streamway (Sump 12) is located close to the Queen Victoria Inn in Priddy Village, and in its course to Wookey Hole the streamway is likely to pass close to the large depressions of Whitepit and Sandpit Hole, immediately to the south of Priddy Village. Fig 70 shows a simplified plan survey of the cave system; the major sections of the cave referred to in the text are named and the present-day active streamway is shown as a solid black line. The layout of the cave may best be described by dividing it into several morphological zones. The main streamway of the cave is over 1.3km in length and is divided into a series of passages separated by sumps of which there are thirteen in all. By convention, the sections of open streamway are described with Roman numerals, for example Swildon's iv, and the sumps using Arabic numbers, for example Sump 4.

The first portion of the cave to Sump 1 is steeply-graded with a large passage size and a predominantly vadose form. Although in longitudinal section the profile is reasonably smooth, in detail it is very irregular, the passages alternating between steep flights of potholes and short zones of gentle gradient. Except in reaches close to Sump 1 there is comparatively little stream-laid fill. Transportation of clastic material from the surface and from within the cave is rapid through this zone. Beyond Sump 1 the gradient of the cave is drastically lowered, and apart from occasional oversteepened sections, as in Swildon's ii, Swildon's iv, and Swildon's xii, the stream meanders over a fill ranging from gravel to fine silt, in smooth phreatic passage.

There are also a series of now abandoned inlets, two such in-

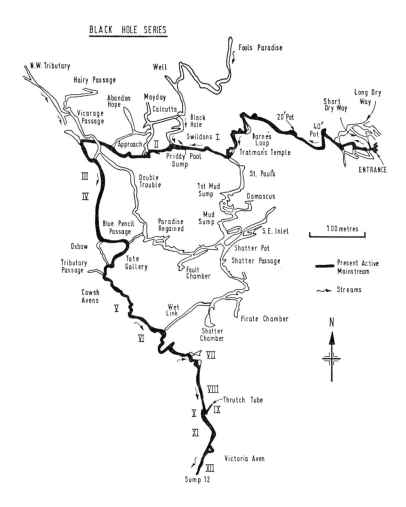

Fig 70 Key survey of Swildon's Hole

lets joining the active streamway in the Water Chamber. These are the Short Dry Way and Long Dry Way (Pretty Way) respectively, and both are of limited horizontal extent. The major fossil inlet to the cave is the Black Hole series, which originates from a now buried sink to the north-west of the present stream sink and joins the present streamway via a series of small passages in lower Swildon's I and Swildon's II. In its upper parts, the Black Hole Inlet has a rift-like form, similar to the Swildon's I streamway, though in its lower part the gradient is flatter and there are many phreatic features apparent. A third inlet series, long abandoned, is the South-east Inlet comprising the Swynne-Puke series and Sidcot Passage (Pyke, 1962); these discharge into the Fossil Master Cave at Shatter Pot.

The third major section of the cave is the Fossil Master Cave, consisting of a complex of largely phreatic passages which are now entirely abandoned. The two major arms of this system are the Vicarage Passage–Double Trouble series–Paradise Regained, and the St Paul's–Paradise Regained arm. They become confluent at Shatter Pot, forming a large phreatic bore passage (Shatter Passage). Close to the limit of present exploration, this passage splits into two, or perhaps three, distributaries; Crystal Passage, Shatter Chamber Passage, and Pirate Chamber Passage. Shatter Chamber is very close to the large caverns in Swildon's VII of the active streamway. Two other major, and probably recent, inlets to the cave are known, both almost totally vertical in nature, descending via a series of large avens. These are the Priddy Green Sink, located on Priddy Green adjacent to Manor Farm, and the Victoria Aven Inlet, immediately above Sump 12 and possibly connected to now infilled depressions in front of the Victoria Inn. There are several known examples of relatively modern passages, normally small and predominantly vadose, which connect the Fossil Master Cave to the present-day active streamway; examples of these include Blue Pencil Passage— connecting Paradise Regained with Swildon's IV, and the Wet Link connecting lower Shatter Passage with Swildon's VI. The entire cave can be explored by non-divers with the exception of the length of streamway beyond Sump 9.

Under normal hydrological conditions the main streamway has the largest discharge of any water in the cave. The principal tributary is the Black Hole stream, but this is an underfit to the size of its passage. The Black Hole stream is very consistent in its discharge, suggesting a diffuse percolation origin, and under conditions of semi-drought, it may have a larger flow than the main stream at the point at which they join (just prior to Sump 1). There are no other major streams in the system, though main stream flow is much augmented by minor tributaries and by heavy drips from the roof. There are also small vadose streams found in many parts of the Fossil Cave, commonly crossing the old phreatic streamway at right angles and disappearing into tiny holes.

The majority of Swildon's Hole is developed in the basal 8om of the Blackrock Limestone, though part of the cave penetrates into the underlying shales. Chert filling is not common in the bedding planes exposed in the cave, but in the drier parts of the upper cave there is a tufaceous filling in some of the bedding planes, and in others a wash-out of strongly oxidised shale. Swildon's Hole is partly developed in the Priddy Fault, and several passages cross this fault; for example the Swildon's iv streamway and Fault Chamber. Bedding planes are important controls in the development of the cave, and the controlling planes seem to occur in groups, with considerable thicknesses of strata between and in which there is very little development. The upper part of the cave is very largely controlled by bedding, almost following the dip, but as the thalweg lessens in gradient, the cave begins to truncate out from the contact into higher strata. A characteristic of many of the phreatic parts of the cave is that passages often jump from one controlling group of bedding planes to the one above by means of a single, steep up-step of up to 12m, followed by a gradual descent along the new bedding plane. This gives rise to the characteristic up-and-down stepping passages of this cave. Bedding planes exert a significant control over more than half of the total length of known passage. In addition, the Priddy Fault and associated jointing has apparently caused a high density of cave passages in the region of the fault, and Ford considered this to be because many vein fills are easily penetrated, though a fill of crystalline calcite is not in itself more easily soluble than Limestone.

Figure 71 shows a passage cross-section and an extended

CROSS SECTION   **LONG SECTION**

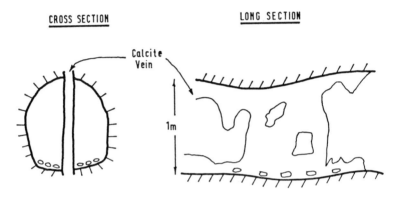

Fig 71 Calcite vein fill, St Paul's series, Swildon's Hole
(after Ford, 1963)

section in the St Paul's series where the calcite vein fills have proven more resistant, both to vadose and phreatic erosion, than the surrounding massive limestone. Away from the Priddy Fault, joints show little calcite filling; they are large and extend over the full height and lengths of the passage they guide. Ford was unable to detect any important pattern in joint systems over the cave as a whole.

The development of the Swildon's Hole cave system may be considered in three stages, and the following account is based upon Ford's analysis (1965*b*), together with relevant additions and other possibilities. Ford suggested that the three successive stages of development of the cave were responses to successively lower water-tables, the level staying constant over a fairly long period to enable cavern development to proceed, and then falling rapidly to the next level. Although the idea of strict water-table control in the sense implied by Ford (ie controlled by the rising) is perhaps open to some doubt, it seems indisputable that there were indeed two, and possibly three rest level controls on the development of Swildon's Hole. The known extent of the cave

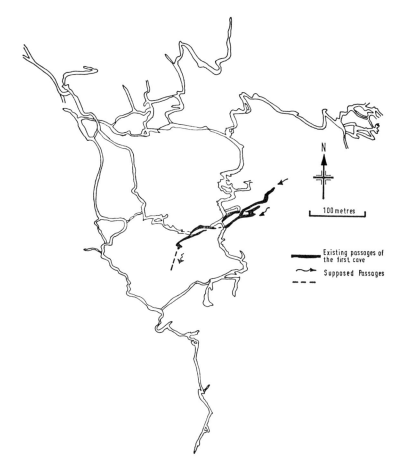

Fig 72 The First Cave, Swildon's Hole

of the first stage is shown as a solid black line in Fig 72. The stream that fed this series was considerably smaller than the present-day stream, and sank about 150m down the valley from the present sink. Borings made in the Swildon's Valley show approximately 60cm of soil underlain in the lowest point of the valley by stream-borne gravels and sands. Just downstream and on the left hand side of the valley from the present sink, these fluvial deposits abruptly cease, suggesting that this was the location of the original sink.

Only a very short segment of the first cave is known; this consists of the South-east Tributary Passage, Sidcot Passage, Candy's Calamity, and Fault Chamber. The main stream passage appears to have been Sidcot Passage with South-east Inlet as a tributary. Sidcot Passage is now completely filled with a coarse gravel of large sandstone pebbles; these appear to be stream fill, left in an abandoned sump which acted as a sediment filter. The fact that such large cobbles exist at such a depth in the cave, suggests that the way to the surface beyond this filter is likely to be relatively open and unobstructed. These passages cross Shatter Chamber and climb straight up to Fault Chamber, probably leaving it via the choked chimney at the western end. Fault Chamber now acts as a minor inlet, containing splash pots of the Cowsh Aven type. The route of the first cave downstream of this point, is completely unknown. All the known passages of the cave are phreatic, and Ford regards them as having been developed in response to a water-table at 168–83m OD. Later in the development of the first cave, an alternative route to Fault Chamber, via the Greasy Chimney, was opened up and Greasy Chimney shows scalloping in the appropriate direction. Contemporary with the development of the first cave streamway, but totally independent of it in destination, were a series of tiny anastomosing phreatic tubes which descend bedding planes in the fault zone. Ford named these tubes 'chippolatas'. Several of these are apparent on the north side of one main passage through Paradise Regained from Fault Chamber to Blue Pencil Passage.

There is also a fine example near the end of Damascus in the St Paul's series.

The first cave was abandoned in response to the establishment of a new base level at 146m OD at Shatter Pot. Several draw-down passages were developed at the lower end of South-east Tributary, and the sequence of capture of drainage to the lower level is shown in Fig 73. The change over from phreatic to

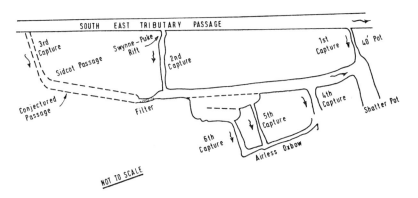

Fig 73 Capture sequence of South-east Inlets, Swildon's Hole (after Ford, 1963)

vadose conditions in the South-east Inlet, which accompanied this drop in base level, is shown in the lower of the two shafts which drop from Keith's Chamber to the Airless Ox-bow. This has rough walls and potholes characteristic of vadose passages.

The extent of the second cave is shown in Fig 74, where the active passages are outlined in black. The stream which had previously sunk at the entrance to the South-east Inlet series now abandoned this sink and was engulfed further up the valley at the shale junction. It developed the Long Dry Way to the Water Chamber, and beyond this point probably went due west to rejoin the present active streamway just downstream of the 20 Foot Pot. However, the existence of this passage is largely

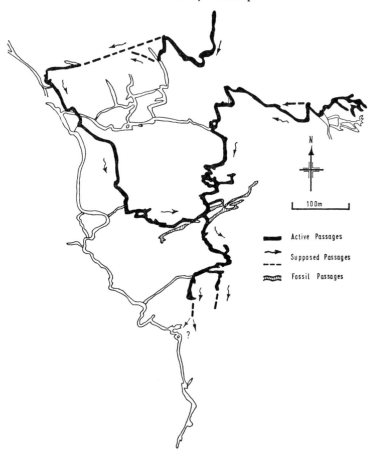

Fig 74 The Second Cave, Swildon's Hole

conjectural and it may be that it followed the line of the present streamway. This second cave inlet passage was contiguous with the present-day streamway until Barnes' Loop. The Loop, now heavily calcited, marks the original course of the stream. In this section of the active streamway, the original phreatic bore passage is apparent in the roof over much of its length. The second cave streamway diverged from the present active stream course at Tratman's Temple where it drained towards Shatter Pot, developing the St Paul's series en route. In this zone, the passage utilised segments of the earlier west-trending chippolata passages both uphill and downhill and hence demonstrates a meandering course in the St Paul's series. Beyond the Mud Sump, this main streamway rejoined the first cave at the mouth of the Airless Ox-bow to continue down Shatter Pot.

The other major inlet to the second cave was via the Black Hole series. Ford suggested that a stream, now defunct, draining from north of Nine Barrows Lane was responsible for the development of this series, though work by the writer has failed to demonstrate the existence of an ancient sink corresponding to the Nine Barrows Valley in this area. Furthermore, it has not been possible to trace water seeping underground near Priddy Pool into the Black Hole series. It may be that the Black Hole series was excavated by the main Swildon's stream and is, therefore, not fully contemporaneous with the St Paul's system. The Black Hole route leads via Fool's Paradise to the northern end of Vicarage Passage via unknown passages, through the Double Trouble series and Paradise Regained to reach the first cave at Fault Chamber junction. The position of the link passage from the Black Hole series to Vicarage Passage is not obvious, as there are no well-defined passages, choked or otherwise, leading off from Fool's Paradise in the area immediately upstream of the Well—this being the likeliest place for the link. Vicarage Passage again demonstrates the use of chippolata tubes to reach a great joint (Glistening Gallery in the Double Trouble series). This was climbed eastwards to a second great joint, Doomed Grotto. There is evidence of several ancient sumps in the down-dipping segments of the Vicarage Passage–Double Trouble area. The development of the second cave inlet from Black Hole meant that flow in the section of passage between Shatter Pot and Fault Chamber junction, which had originally been opened by the first cave stream flowing west, was now reversed with the flow being to the east. Evidence of this may be seen in several places in this section of passage where scallops indicating opposite directions of flow may be seen on the same rock surface. During this period, Fault Chamber was a back water, as is evidenced by deep pocketing at its entrance.

Beyond the initial ponded section of Shatter Pot, where the passages are constricted and muddy, the main bore of the second streamway passage is encountered in Shatter Passage. Just beyond this point, at the Crystal Pool, the passage sharply diminishes in its dimensions and it seems probable that the original route of the water beyond this point was to the left of the present passage via an unknown route to the Pirate Chamber area. Later this route was abandoned in favour of the presently open route via the aven into Pirate Chamber. The entrance passage to Pirate Chamber is heavily scalloped and of small dimensions, indicating that flow was probably very rapid during this period and that this passage functioned for only a relatively short time. Pirate Chamber is developed in the strike, and shows solutional pocketing. The limit of exploration at this point is a boulder choke over a layer of thick mud and shattered stalagmite, beneath which there is an older collapse visible. It is possible that the Pirate Chamber route was abandoned as the main streamway when this initial collapse occurred, and that Pirate Chamber itself represents the backing up of water behind this obstacle. When this occurred, the lowest water route was developed to Shatter Chamber. Atkinson (1966) suggested that the Wet Link connecting this area of Shatter Passage with Swildon's vi streamway developed as an early capture passage, diverting water from the second cave to the third cave. The course followed by the second fossil cave, beyond the collapse in Shatter Chamber and Pirate Chamber, is of considerable significance in evaluating the sequence of development for Swildon's Hole. Shatter Passage seems almost certain to connect with the high, boulder-strewn chambers of Swildon's vii, thereby marking the amalgamation of one branch of phase 2 drainage with the modern streamway beyond Swildon's vii. Should there be a connection between

(*above left*) The Drainpipe, a phreatic passage in Goatchurch Cavern (*above right*) The First Chamber in Lionel's Hole, showing roof breakdown along a well developed bedding plane (*below left*) Manor Farm Swallet after a major collapse during the floods of July 1968 (*below right*) The Ox-bow passage in GB Cave

Page 266
(*above left*) The Gorge in GB Cave (*above right*) The stream in Gough's Old
Cave (*below left*) The Great Aven, Reservoir Hole (*below right*) Grand Gallery,
Reservoir Hole

Pirate Chamber beyond the boulder choke, and Shatter Chamber or Swildon's vii, this would imply that the main active streamway beyond this point was also the old Master Cave of phase 2 and thus development of the vii, vi and v streamways would have to be explained in terms of a series of progressive upstream captures of the Shatter Pot drainage by the embryonic third phase streamway. However, there is indirect evidence to suggest that the Shatter Passage streamway may continue, as a discrete unit, beyond Swildon's vii. There are small passages joining the streamway downstream of Sump 7, very similar in form to Blue Pencil Passage consisting of a small phreatic slot and a deep vadose trench, and trending steeply upwards from the present streamway (for example the Thrutch Tube in Swildon's ix). It may be that these passages are drawdown features from the fossil cave or chance connections between the two streamways, and thus may indicate the presence of the fossil cave close to the modern streamway in the Sump 9 area. However, the lower portions of the streamway from Swildon's viii onwards are characterised by the presence of phreatic bore passages looping up to 8m above and below the present graded stream channel. These passages have a bore comparable to that of many of the cave passages of the phase 2 streamway, and hence may represent the now isolated remnants of the Shatter Passage drainage route. If indeed the connection between the two streamways occurs within this zone, then the interpretation of the three levels of passage development within Swildon's Hole as being a response to external changes in base level on the flank of the Mendip Hills, must be viewed with some suspicion.

After an unknown length of time, probably extending over several thousands of years, a further drop in the rest level—to an altitude of approximately 125m—occurred in Swildon's ii, and this caused the abandonment of the second cave and the development of the third, or present-day, active system. Fig 75 shows the extent of the third cave. Two major drawdowns occurred in the cave in Swildon's ii, iii, and iv and also in Swildon's i. The

I

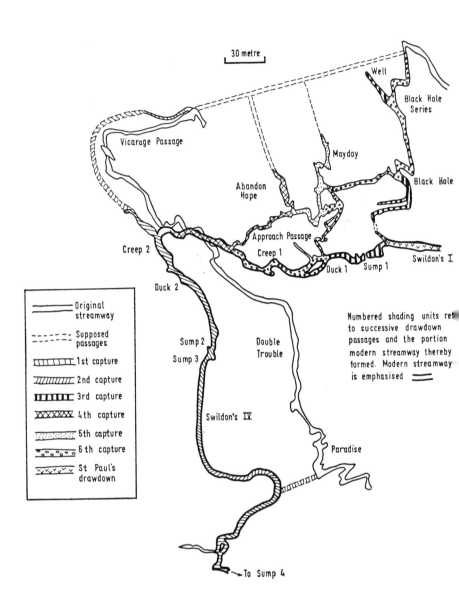

Fig 75 Formation of Swildon's ɪɪ–ɪᴠ by successive captures

Inside the figure:

30 metre

Well

Black Hole
Series

Vicarage Passage

Mayday

Abandon
Hope

Black Hole

Approach Passage

Creep 2

Creep 1

Swildon's I

Duck 1   Sump 1

Duck 2

Numbered shading units ref
to successive drawdown
passages and the portion
modern streamway thereby
formed. Modern streamway
is emphasised

Sump 2
Sump 3

Double
Trouble

Swildon's IV

Paradise

To Sump 4

Legend:

— Original
  streamway

----- Supposed
      passages

[hatched] 1st capture

[diagonal] 2nd capture

[vertical] 3rd capture

[XXXX] 4th capture

[dotted] 5th capture

[circles] 6th capture

[V marks] St Paul's
          drawdown

development of the II, III, and IV sections of streamway was accompanied by a remarkable series of successive headward captures of Black Hole–Vicarage Passage inlet water, beginning downstream in Swildon's IV and extending as far as the Priddy Pool passage in Swildon's I. Thus this section of streamway evolved from downstream to upstream in a short succession of sections.

The first diversion of the second cave water occurred when water from Fool's Paradise was diverted via Wright's Dig (just south of the entrance to Blue Pencil Passage in Paradise Regained) to what is now the junction of Tributary Passage and the main stream in Swildon's IV. The water then continued down to develop the present streamway. The original passage is still visible in the roof of Swildon's IV from the Tate Gallery downstream.

According to Ford, a second, later diversion of Black Hole water occurred at the southern end of Vicarage Passage. This corresponds to the short passage leading to the Muddy Sump from the Big Bend in Swildon's II streamway. This passage is almost certainly connected with the North-west Stream Passage (entered from Vicarage Passage) being at the same horizontal level and having very similar passage types. If this is the case, then the way in which North-west Stream Passage functioned as a drawdown for Black Hole water is not obvious, as North-west Stream Passage is largely horizontal and terminates in descending, tight, muddy tubes, normally water filled. A second branch to this passage (Heaven and Hell Passage) is slightly higher, but again is dissimilar in form to the remainder of the drawdown passages of the phase 2 to phase 3 change over. It may be that Ford is correct and that Heaven and Hell Passage is connected to Vicarage Passage—perhaps in the area of Hairy Passage—though the two are separated by a considerable horizontal distance. Alternatively, it may be that North-west Tributary is a more recent addition to the cave system, perhaps developing during the early/middle stages of the third cave and having since been abandoned.

This diversion would have opened the downstream ends of Swildon's ɪɪ and Swildon's ɪɪɪ, and the Arch and high-level Ox-bow sections of Swildon's ɪv. The third drawdown in this series opened the direct link between Vicarage Passage and Swildon's ɪɪ, thus adding the section between the Big Bend and Creep Two to the Swildon's ɪɪ streamway.

The fourth capture, from further upstream in the Black Hole series, first discharged into the Swildon's ɪɪ streamway via Abandon Hope and Approach Passage, and later via the more direct route Abandon Hope–Kenney's Dig–Swildon's ɪɪ streamway, just downstream of Duck One.

The fifth capture caused the creation of the north end of the Mayday series and the short stretch of passage between Calcutta and the ɪɪ Foot Overhang. Originally this water climbed ɪɪm upwards to join the pre-existing Abandon Hope route, but later adopted a route through the lower Mayday series and Kenney's Dig, to the Swildon's ɪɪ streamway. The passages in this capture are largely vadose.

The sixth and final diversion of Black Hole–Vicarage Passage water occurred via the Black Hole and the Well Chamber which both feed to the Priddy Pool Passage immediately upstream of the first sump. By this stage all the passages except for the Black Hole–Priddy Passage route were completely abandoned, and the present-day main stream passage was open from Sump ɪ downstream, having thus developed by the successive addition of passage increments upstream. Ford pointed out that the junction of any two segments is usually marked by some sort of obstacle, for example, Sump ɪ, Duck One, Creep Two, Duck Two. Fig 76 illustrates diagrammatically the sequence of captures of Black Hole water by the modern streamway.

For much of the time period discussed above, the main stream of the cave continued on its route of Swildon's ɪ–St Paul's series–Shatter Passage. However, contemporary with the fifth capture of Black Hole water, its route was diverted, an old chipolata route being re-excavated to funnel water from the first Mud

Sump into Swildon's II streamway, downstream of the first Duck.
The passages between Swildon's II and the first Mud Sump are
totally unknown, as is the exact point of egress into the stream-

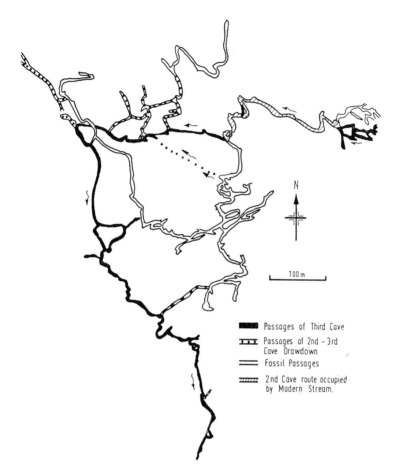

Fig 76 The Third Cave, Swildon's Hole

way. Once this diversion had been accomplished, water would
only flow down Shatter Pot under flood conditions. The rare
deposits of coarse clastic fill to be seen in the passages of the

second cave—for example those in the low-level Ox-bow in the St Paul's series—date from this period. The final capture of the second to third cave transition occurred when the St Paul's series was abandoned in favour of the modern streamway route from Tratman's Temple to the first sump.

An interesting feature of the developmental phase associated with the drawdown to the modern streamway, was the development of ponding, over a considerable period of time, in Shatter Passage and west of Fault Chamber. The location of the Shatter Passage pond is now marked by deep, still-water sediment deposits. The pond extended as far as the second Mud Sump, which may be regarded as a vestige of this underground lake. At one time the pond surface corresponded to the level of the passage immediately upstream of the second Mud Sump, and was responsible for cutting the markedly flat roof of the passage in this area. The second pond stretched from just west of Fault Chamber to Wright's Dig, and one rest level of the water is marked by the extensive corrosion notch some 20m north of Wright's Dig. These ponds were later drained by numerous channels, now largely covered in sediment or calcited over.

Since the second capture, the only new passages to evolve have been links between the second and third caves, usually created by small vadose trickles, trenching the second cave for a short distance before continuing their independent, steeply graded route to the streamway. Blue Pencil Passage is a good example of such a vadose trench cut in the base of a pre-existing, wide, paraphreatic slot. Fine examples of this modern vadose interception trenching are also apparent in the central portion of Vicarage Passage.

Another minor feature of modern stream action is described by Ford (1965c). This occurs in the heavily potholed section of Swildon's 1. (The Double Pots just upstream of Barne's Loop are a fine example.) The large potholes, each over 1m in depth, were drilled by a large stream, presumably in the early and middle stages of the development of the third cave. Upstream and downstream of the potholes, the streamway of the cave is commonly wide. A slot-like trench which now contains all the stream flow has been drilled through the contiguous walls of these potholes. A long-section and cross-section of the Double Pots are shown in Fig 77. Ford proposed the following sequence for the

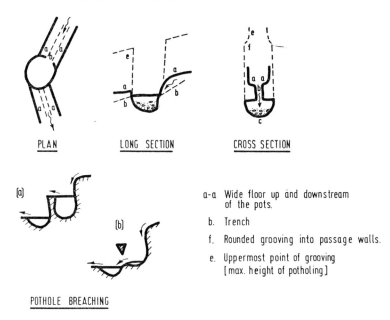

PLAN   LONG SECTION   CROSS SECTION

POTHOLE BREACHING

a-a Wide floor up and downstream of the pots.

b. Trench

f. Rounded grooving into passage walls.

e. Uppermost point of grooving [max. height of potholing]

Fig 77 Pothole trenching, Swildon's Hole
(after Ford, 1965a)

development of this feature. In the first phase a large stream drills the hanging potholes. In the second phase, stream flow is reduced and a secondary trench is cut through the potholes, usually to a level lower than their bases. This reduction could be caused by changes in the surface catchment area or hydrological parameters within the catchment. In the third phase, discharge increases but the depth of the secondary trench is sufficient to absorb the greater flow, so there is no rejuvenation of the original potholes. The incised trench is widened and new potholes develop

superimposed upon the original features. The first potholes are
preserved in places as remnants high on the passage walls. In
the final phase, flow is again reduced and a second narrow
trench is cut in the secondary potholes. Thus a palimpsest of
vadose erosional forms is preserved in several places in the
Swildon's I streamway. In the Black Hole series only the remnants of the first and second trenches are apparent (best seen at
the bottom of the Black Hole itself.) The absence of the third
trench is probably because water ceased to flow in the Black
Hole series prior to the time of the third trenching.

A further feature of the present-day cave is the considerable
degree of re-solution of calcite deposits that is taking place. No
convincing reason has yet been put forward to explain what
must be a change in the aggressivity of the water percolating
into the cave system, though presumably it reflects some change
in the vegetation or soil composition of the catchment. This
phenomenon of re-solution is also apparent in many other major
Mendip caves, for example Stoke Lane Slocker.

Several morphological features of the cave system are worthy
of note. Ford (1968) remarked on the occurrence of isolated
vadose trenches in Swildon's Hole streamway. These trenches
consist of a stream trench cut through the upward limb of an old
phreatic loop (see Plate p 299, *ul*) and connected both upstream
and downstream by wholly phreatic passages. Ford suggested
that these features are confined to the highest crests in any given
sequence of phreatic loops. Fig 78 (after Ford, 1968) shows
perhaps the best example of this feature, in a portion of Swildon's
II streamway. This length of passage consists of sections of vadose
trenching very similar to Swildon's I, alternating with low pebble-
filled sections of typically phreatic bore passages. High in the
roof of the vadose trenches (up to 18m deep) the original
phreatic loop crest is well preserved. These vadose sections
correspond to the downcutting of the phreatic loop, and the low
pebbly crawls between them to the now infilled downlimb of the
phreatic bore. Thus the stream is approximating to a state of

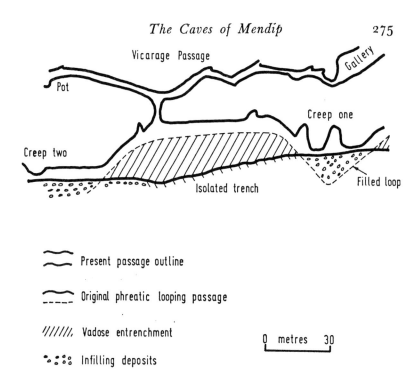

Fig 78 Vadose trenching in Swildon's II

grade by aggradation and degradation of the original up- and down-dipping bore tube. This type of passage, developed under phreatic conditions where bedding planes have tended to force the water downwards and joints upwards, is well demonstrated in the Paradise Regained series of passages. Fig 79 shows a longitudinal section of part of Paradise Regained and Vicarage Passage, demonstrating these loops. The same figure also shows a long-section of Swildon's streamway between Sump 7 and Sump 12. This is perhaps the most perfect development of up- and down-dipping passages. The long and deep Sumps 9 and 12, are developed in major downward limbs of the phreatic bore. The Ducks in Swildon's viii and Swildon's xi are the base of smaller

I*

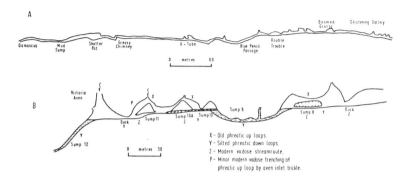

Fig 79 Loop passages and cutoffs—Paradise, XII, Swildon's Hole

down loops. The upward loops between, are clearly demonstrated in the roof of Swildon's VIII and IX and in the bypasses to Sumps 10a and 11. In this case, later development has proceeded in a different fashion to that in Swildon's II, the present-day stream being drilled a constricted passage beneath the phreatic loop and having separated by some horizontal distance from it. Sumps 10a and 11 are examples of this development. In this case the phreatic up loop will be preserved as a remnant and will not be entrenched by the main stream as in Swildon's II.

The series of development in upper Swildon's Hole is summarised in Table 13, and that for the entire cave in Table 14. Fig 80 summarises the model for the overall development of Swildon's Hole in relation to its rising, as postulated by Ford. The model refers to only two of the three major stages of development. Passages left blank correspond to the phreatic conduits of the first 'water-table', those in black correspond to phreatic passages of the second 'water-table', and diagonally hatched passages to vadose conduits. The development of the cave system, via a series of sub-water-table loops descending some distance below the piezometric surface before returning to it, is shown. The letter B shows blind chimneys driven upwards by solution

TABLE 13 *The sequence for the major inlets and upper streamway, Swildon's Hole* (after Ford, 1963)

Upper Swildon's Dry Passages	Upper Swildon's Stream Passage	Swildon's I	Black Hole Inlet	Swildon's II
1 Early phreatic loop		1a Phreatic	1 Phreatic	1 Phreatic
2 Phreatic	1 Phreatic	1b Phreatic wt drops 50m	2 Phreatic wt drops 30m	2 Phreatic
3 Stream capture Some Vadose Trenches		2a First vadose trench	3a First vadose trench	
		2b Cutting out of first trench	3b Cutting out of first trench	
4a Collapse and aggradation	2 Major vadose entrenchment	3a Aggradation		3 Paraphreatic/vadose
4b Stalagmite		3b Stalagmite		4a First vadose trench
		4a Second vadose trench	4a Second vadose trench	4b Cutting out
5 Final vadose trench		4b Cutting out of second trench	4b Cutting out of second trench	5 Second vadose trench
	3 Final vadose trench	5a Third vadose trench	C A P T U R E D	
		5b Cutting out of third trench		
6a Collapse and aggradation	4a Collapse and aggradation	6a Stream aggradation	6a Light Stream aggradation	6a Clay aggradation
6b Limited re-excavation	4b Limited re-excavation	6b Limited re-excavation		6b Cobble aggradation
6c Stalagmite	4c Stalagmite	6c Stalagmite	6b Stalagmite	6c Stalagmite
7 Weak re-excavation and Re-solution	5 Re-excavation and Re-solution	7 Re-excavation and Re-solution	7 Block fall, weak clearance and Re-solution	7 Re-excavation and Re-solution

The Caves of Mendip

and closing at the water-table. Subsequent passages short-circuiting upward or downward loops are also shown on the figure, as is the vadose trench descending from the surface sink to the 'water-table'.

TABLE 14 *Final sequence of Swildon's Hole* (after Ford, 1963)

Phase	Conditions	Comments
1A	Phreatic	Chipolata phase
2A	Phreatic	SE Inlet, 168–183m water-table
2B	Phreatic	SE capture passages
3	Phreatic	Shatter Passage phase 140–6m water-table
4A	Vadose-phreatic	Wright's Dig capture, first vadose trench
4B	Vadose	Cutting out
5A	Stream aggradation	First fill
5B	Stalagmite phase	
6A	Paraphreatic	127m water-table
6B	Vadose	Second trench, 109m water-table
6C	Vadose	Cutting out
7A	Vadose	Third trench water-table below 100m
7B	Vadose	Cutting out
8A	Stream aggradation	Recent fill and stalagmite
8B	Limited re-excavation	
8C	Stalagmite	
9	Vadose	Modern erosion, re-excavation

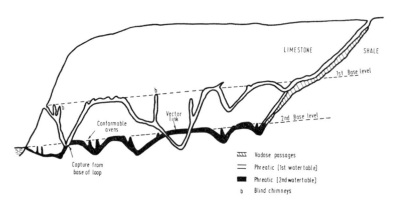

Fig 80 Overall model of Swildon's Hole development (after Ford, 1963)

Ford's model was largely based on the assumption that Swildon's Hole drained to the rising at Cheddar, and he attempted to correlate the 30m vertical spacing of the major stream conduits in Swildon's Hole with a similar vertical spacing of the resurgence caves at Cheddar. The present-day Swildon's stream drains to Wookey Hole. It was tested under conditions of abnormally high stage, and thus there is no reason to suppose that even under these conditions water resurges at Rodney Stoke (which is known to be linked to Wookey Hole), and certainly no evidence to suggest that any water leaks to Cheddar. The rising at Wookey Hole demonstrates only two levels of exit for the water (a correlation with the features of St Cuthbert's Swallet is possible on this basis). However, it is difficult to explain the succession of passage development in Swildon's Hole as being controlled by events at the rising if the rising for Swildon's Hole during the early stages of its development was indeed at Wookey. In addition, the fact that all the levels of water-exit at Cheddar are known to unite within a few hundred metres of the active spring, and the possibility that the second and third streamways in Swildon's Hole coalesce, tend to cast doubts upon the assumption that swallet caves can respond with such delicacy to changes at their resurgence.

St Cuthbert's Swallet : St Cuthbert's Swallet (543505) is a second major feeder to Wookey Hole, and is also the second most extensive cave known on Mendip. Total passage length explored to date is estimated at 7km, extending over a vertical range of some 150m. The system has several entrances, only one of which is presently accessible to man, located where the St Cuthbert's tributary valley Fault intersects the old main surface drainage route to Cheddar. The sinks are developed close to the Shale-Blackrock Limestone boundary.

A detailed study of the cave was undertaken by Ford (1963) and the following account is in large part based upon this work together with his two later and more simplified descriptions of the system (Ford, 1964 *a* & *b*). In addition, the Bristol

Exploration Club (BEC) commenced publishing a series of monographs in 1968, detailing the exploration, genesis, and development of the cave system as a whole. Due to the complexity of the cave, no accurate comprehensive survey is presently available, and the sketch survey (Fig 81) accompanying this account (adapted from Johnson, 1967) is purely diagrammatic.

St Cuthbert's Swallet is very different in form to Swildon's Hole, and basically consists of a three-dimensional maze of criss-crossing passages and large chambers. The active streamways intersect this network at intervals, but there is no true stream passage of the Swildon's Hole type until the Gour Hall area, beyond which point the cave ceases its predominantly vertical development and assumes a horizontal trend. The large chambers and rabbit-runs of the middle series of the cave are characterised by much collapse, extensive fill deposits, and considerable calcite deposition. The system is considered by Ford to be older than Swildon's Hole.

Ford divided the cave into four morphological sub-divisions. First, the series of partly collapsed chambers between the Long and Coral Chambers and the September series. These are developed in the bedding (the dip is approximately 40°), and are developed close to the base of the Blackrock Limestone. Secondly, the Gour Rift which follows a major fault line. The south-eastern portion of this rift is occupied by the main streamway, though Cerberus Hall, Lake Chamber, and Mud Hall are also developed in this line of weakness. Thirdly, the Warren area, linking the central chambers with the Gour Rift, and consisting of small, relatively poorly developed passages. Main Stream Passage, the Railway Tunnel, and Everest Passage fall into this category. Fourthly, Ford recognised a series of recent inlet passages feeding either to the central chambers or directly to the rift area, but being much younger than either. The major inlets are Pulpit, Arete, Maypole, and the High Chamber series. These streams have united before the Gour Hall area to form the main stream. This streamway then leaves the Gour Rift at the Duck,

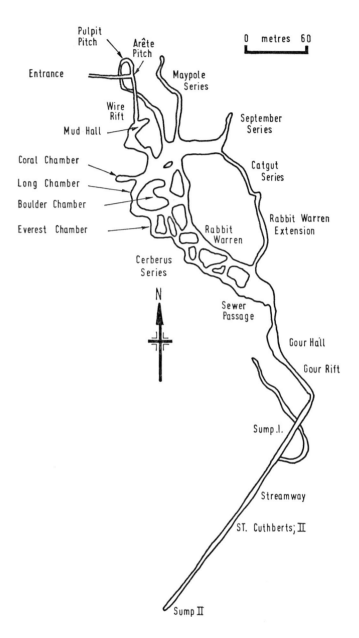

Fig 81 Sketch survey of St Cuthbert's Swallet

and has been explored for a further 400m, in a lofty rift passage, to a sump (Sump 2). This portion of the streamway is generally evenly graded, though one oversteepened section occurs about half-way between Sumps 1 and 2.

The development sequence of the cave follows the familiar pattern for Mendip caves of an initial stage followed by phreatic erosion followed by vadose action and infilling, and further vadose re-excavation. A simplified sequence for the development

TABLE 15 *The sequence of development in St Cuthbert's Swallet* (after Ford, 1964)

Phreatic	Phase 1	Phreatic erosion—Bore Passages
	Phase 2	Phreatic erosion—expansion and disintegration of Bore Passages

Cave drained of phreatic water

	Phase 3A	Stream deposition—coarse deposits then finer sediments
	Phase 3B	Stalagmite
	Phase 4A	Stream deposition
	Phase 4B	Stalagmite
Main Fill	Phase 5A	Stream deposition
	Phase 5B	Stalagmite
	Phase 6	Stream deposition
	Phase 7	Stream deposition
	Phase 8A	Vadose erosion—Mudhalls Pothole
	Phase 8B	Stalagmite
	Phase 9A	Vadose erosion—High Chamber
	Phase 9B	Stalagmite
Re-excavation	Phase 10	Stream deposition—sand phase
	Phase 11A	Vadose erosion—Maypole/Pulpit
	Phase 11B	Stream deposition
	Phase 11C	Recent stalagmite
	Phase 12	Vadose erosion (modern)

of the cave is given in Table 15. Ford suggested that approximately two thirds of the volume of the explored cave is due to phreatic erosion.

In the first phase the major inlet was via the Rocky Boulder series and Upper Traverse Chamber. During this period the water-table was at or above 200m OD. The water then drained into Gour Rift via the bore passages of the Warren series. These bore tubes are almost circular in cross-section and almost straight. There are four main bores, arranged in a vertical sequence, the highest being the oldest and the lowest (from the head of Everest passage to the Dining Room) being the youngest. Velocities of flow during this stage were low, the water seeping slowly from the reservoir area of the central chambers to the Gour Rift, through a network of pipes. Thus passage development was exceedingly slow.

Ford referred to the second stage as being one of phreatic disintegration. During this period the initial mesh of bore passages was dismembered, the central chambers were much enlarged, a direct connection between these chambers and the rift was established (through Long Chamber and Curtain Chamber), and a new inlet series was formed via the September series. At the end of this phase the water-table dropped to about 117m OD (the reason for this large drop in base level is discussed in the section dealing with Wookey Hole).

As the base level dropped so vadose stream courses were opened in the upper cave, for example the Arete and Wire Rift Passages. These streams undermined the central chamber complex, causing considerable collapse. The further history of the cave consists of alternating phases of erosion and fill by vadose water. The main fill noted by Ford consisted of several phases and sub-phases, and during this time almost the entire cave below 200m OD was filled with sediment.

The first fill, consisting of an unsorted mixture of sand, silt, and cobbles can be seen in the west wall of Everest Passage just below Plantation Junction. Two later phases of coarse fill may be seen in the north wall of the Railway Tunnel. The vadose streams thus blocked the direct route to the rift, and were diverted through the original phreatic loop into Lake and Mud Hall Chambers.

The modern phase is one of re-excavation of the fill deposits.

Initially, water from the Arete route and from Upper Traverse Chamber cleared much of the fill in the central complex and reopened the channels via Everest Passage and the Fingers to Main Stream Passage. The large gours in Gour Hall are deposits calcited on to a wall of fill, which is still evident up-stream of Beehive Junction. In the upper parts of the cave the fill was less extensive, and hence vadose trenching of new passages predominated in this zone. The initial vadose erosion was followed by a further stage of calcite deposition, with remnants preserved on the north side of the Dining Room. When stream activity recommenced, much of the cave was filled with sand and silt from the surface (for example, the sand deposits in the Upper Traverse). The main stream route was via the Pulpit during this period, though it became reduced in size towards the end of the stage and cut slot trenches through its potholes similar to those in the Swildon's Hole streamway.

Eastwater Cavern: The third major explored cave system known to drain to Wookey Hole is that of Eastwater Cavern, lying approximately midway between St Cuthbert's Swallet and Swildon's Hole and again, largely developed close to the Shale-Limestone boundary. However, in form and hydrology it is unlike the other two major inlet caves, and in many ways more closely resembles the small, abandoned swallet caves of the area, for example Sludge Pit or Cuckoo Cleeves Cave. No geomorphological study has been made of this cave and data on it is generally lacking, though a survey and brief description of the cave has been published (Wells, 1955).

The upper part of the cave is largely developed in a series of bedding planes (see Plate p 299, *ur*) and consists of narrow, inclined passages commonly exhibiting minor vadose trenching. These passages then drop to a level of approximately 130m OD via a series of vertical pitches, for example Primrose Pot, Dolphin Pot, and the Twin Verticals. Below the drops, vadose trenching is intense for a short distance but the passages all terminate as small, choked rifts at a depth of some 128m below the entrance. The cave contains some elements of the three-dimensional maze seen in the St Cuthbert's Swallet, there being many isolated chambers, often collapsed, and linked by muddy, phreatic tubes.

The most recent phase of development of the cave appears to be a relatively modest degree of vadose trenching by a series of small streams. Only the passage below the junction of the Dolphin Pot and Twin Vertical routes has been extensively modified by this action, however. Commonly, these vadose trenches are blocked by fill deposits and can only be followed for short distances.

Eastwater Cavern thus appears to be almost a fossil cave system, which perhaps developed in the same manner as the adjacent swallets of Sludge Pit and Nine Barrows—in response to one base level only. Unlike Swildon's Hole and St Cuthbert's Swallet, the fall in base level did not cause renewed passage genesis and modification, but rather a virtual abandonment of the system, perhaps in favour of the development of new swallet caves further up the valley.

The Wookey Hole Caves : Wookey Hole (532480) is the outlet for the swallet caves described above and for much of the re-maining subterranean drainage of the southern flanks of North Hill and Pen Hill. It is also the most extensively explored of the active resurgence caves, some 607m of horizontal passage extending over a vertical range of 130m, being known. Unlike the Cheddar resurgences, which discharge from one side of the Cheddar Gorge, the Wookey Hole resurgence is located at the head of a short gorge which is, in all probability, the result of headward regression of the rising and subsequent cavern collapse (see Plate p 99, *l*). However, the cave is almost certainly con-nected genetically with the well developed old gorge at Ebbor (a short distance to the west). The rising lies at the base of a deposit of Dolomitic Conglomerate which probably infills a Permo-Triassic valley. The caves are developed close to the eastern wall of this old valley, and the cave itself is partly developed in Dolomitic Conglomerate and partly in Carboniferous Limestone. There is no noticeable dry valley system above the present point of resurgence of the water. Ebbor Gorge itself is cut in Carboniferous Limestone and is completely dry. A plan survey of the explored cave system, together with the surface topography is given in Fig 82.

The streamway of the cave consists of a series of shallow loops (sumps) to the Fourth chamber, followed by a major dip looping from the Fourth to the Twentieth chambers (see Plate p 299, *ll*). The intervening chambers, with the exception of the Ninth, are simply rifts with small air surfaces. Beyond the Twentieth chamber, the main streamway again descends steeply to a depth of over 25m before an open passage is reached in the Twenty-Second chamber. However, the streamway rises from another deep loop beyond this point. Outwards from the Ninth chamber, the cave is developed on several divergent levels, of which one is the Show Cave.

It seems likely that the entrance complex developed as a purely local phenomenon in response to the proximity of the outlet and that between the Ninth and Twentieth chambers only one main outlet channel exists. There is a high-level passage leading off from the air surface in the Ninth chamber which is connected with the small caves on the eastern side of the Wookey Hole Gorge.

From the Twentieth chamber, a major high-level route leads off, climbing steadily at an angle of 45° for some 600m to a boulder choke (Reynolds, 1970). At this point the cave enters the Dolomitic Conglomerate and the passage bifurcates. Both routes lead back into the limestone and one is presumed to be very close to the surface. Downstream of the Twelfth chamber the cave is developed in conglomerate, and upstream of that point, in the limestone; though there appears to be little noticeable difference in the passage morphology developed in the two lithologies. The Twenty-Second chamber consists of a series of rifts and chambers above the stream (Lloyd, 1971). Such features seem to be developed at the crest of each of the streamway loops.

The origin of Wookey Hole cave is complex, and several

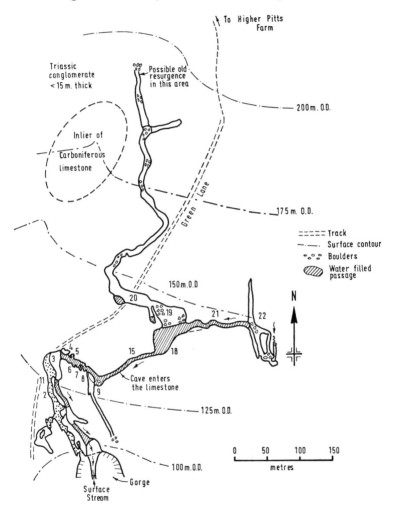

Fig 82 Survey of Wookey Hole and surface topography
(adapted from Hanwell, 1970)

slightly divergent theories have been advanced to explain it. Balch (1929) emphasised the close relationship between Ebbor Gorge and the resurgence. He suggested that the Permo-Triassic valley of Wookey Hole considerably pre-dated Ebbor Gorge as a drainage channel, and that Ebbor Gorge only became active following the re-emergence of the area from the Jurassic marine transgression. During this period a Jurassic dam blocked the original Wookey Hole outlet. Finally the dam was breached and the old system of caves behind the dam was reactivated. Balch described five successive levels of outlet for the waters at Wookey, and regarded them as marking stages in the removal of the Jurassic dam. Hyaena Den is considered to be an outlet corresponding to the intermediate discharge levels. Ford (1963) undertook a detailed study of the morphology of the cave system and the sequence of development he postulated is shown in simplified form in Table 16.

TABLE 16 *The sequence of development at Wookey Hole* (after Ford, 1963)

Phase 1A	Phreatic penetration—water-table at 85–88m OD
Phase 1B	Phreatic—Badger Hole phase. Water-table at 79–82m OD
Phase 1C	Phreatic—water-table at modern level
Phase 2	Mousterian—local Solutrean occupation of Badger Hole and Hyaena Den
Phase 3A	Breccia and clay-cobble fill at Wookey Hole
Phase 3B	Recent stalagmite phase
Phase 4	Blockfall and re-solution beginning in Romano-British or earlier

Ford's theory was expanded by Hanwell (1970), in the light of the discovery of the Twentieth chamber and the passages beyond. To clarify the explanation of this postulated development sequence, a block diagram of the area between Priddy and Wookey is shown in Fig 83 (after Hanwell, 1970). This shows the surface features between the sinks at Swildon's, Eastwater, and St Cuthbert's, and the outlet for the water. In addition, the approximate geological structures are shown. The tongue of

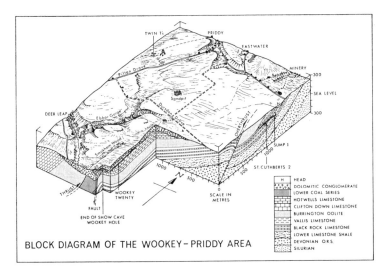

BLOCK DIAGRAM OF THE WOOKEY – PRIDDY AREA

Fig 83 Block diagram of the Wookey–Priddy area

Dolomitic Conglomerate in the Wookey area is apparent, extending up the flank of Mendip to an altitude of 247m. The Ebbor Thrust is also shown. Fig 84 (after Hanwell, 1970) shows a possible explanation for the dry passages beyond the Twentieth chamber and for the present-day active stream course. Ford suggested that a natural barrier in the Ebbor area prolonged phreatic development in the caves beyond it and in St Cuthbert's Swallet, until the dam was breached. Initial breaching occurred at approximately 215m OD, this exit no longer being apparent on the surface. At a later stage a second breaching of the dam occurred at a lower level, and downward leakage to this level took place well behind the dam. The up- and down-dipping loops of the explored section of the Wookey Hole streamway correspond to the phreatic up- and down-dipping passages of Ford's model for Mendip cave development, and the ascending reach of the Twentieth chamber to the main line of leakage.

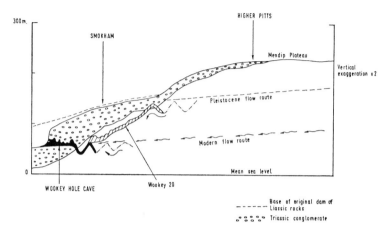

Fig 84 Long-section from Priddy to Wookey

The dam that impounded the waters in this area may, as Balch suggested, have been of Lower Lias clays, though it seems more likely that it consisted of the grits of the Carboniferous Lower Coal Series, as in the Stoke Lane area of eastern Mendip. It may be that the Twentieth chamber represents the higher-level outlet to Wookey Hole Cave and its subsequent capture by the present exit route. This early resurgence is now no longer visible on the surface but may be in the Kid's Hole area of Ebbor Gorge. There may also be a high-level upstream continuation of Wookey Hole towards the swallets of the Priddy area. There is some evidence of inward scalloping in the Twentieth chamber, and this suggests that the passage may have functioned as a swallet immediately prior to its abandonment.

The Stoke Lane area

The area on the northern flank of the Beacon Hill pericline, draining to the risings at Ashwick Grove and St Dunstan's Well differs markedly, with respect to cave form and development, from any other area on Mendip. These catchments lie just to the west of that area of Mendip in which the Liassic cover is still preserved. As removal of this cover has proceeded from west to east, it may be assumed that the karst in this area has had less time to develop than in other areas of Mendip. In addition, the Quartzitic Sandstone Group lying stratigraphically above the Carboniferous Limestone is still partially preserved in the area, especially on the southern side of the River Mells Valley, and the presence of this impermeable layer would have effectively inhibited the development of throughflow systems in the limestone until comparatively recent times. Thus, it might be expected that the caves in this area would be essentially immature, and to a certain extent this is the case. For example, almost all the swallet caves of the area are small and constricted and can only be followed for relatively short distances underground. However, the abundance of major abandoned stream passages and large, sometimes isolated, chambers apparently largely independent of present-day subterranean drainage, implies that it would be an oversimplification to regard this as a juvenile karst area.

The major control on current cave development within the area is undoubtedly the Mells River Valley to the north of the limestone outcrop—changes in the rate of downcutting of this stream seem to correlate with phases of cavern development within the area. For example, the last major phase of incision of this river appears to have been responsible for the disappearance underground of the streams flowing in the numerous north–south valleys crossing the limestone outcrop. Most of these valleys are now dry beyond the limestone-shale contact, and show great oversteepening at the point at which they are tributary to the Mells Valley. It is noticeable that the number of swallet streams in this area is greater than for any other region of comparable size on Mendip, sinking streams occurring at regular intervals of approximately 700km along the limestone-shale contact.

Very little work has been undertaken into the origin of the cave systems of this area, and much of the literature that is available is largely descriptive rather than analytical; for example, Welch (1932*b*) and Drew (1964). Three distinct types of cavern development are apparent in the area. First, are old, isolated chambers sometimes showing some degree of lineation. These seem to occur most commonly under the interfluves between the dry valleys, though it is possible that similar chambers have been destroyed during the downcutting of the valleys. The high-level chambers in Stoke Lane Slocker and Balch Cave are examples of this type. Secondly, there is a network of old, abandoned streamways, often of considerable dimensions, and apparently largely phreatic in origin. These old stream courses appear to converge on the present-day rising at St Dunstan's Well, though they are graded to a level somewhat above the present resurgence. It seems that, to some degree these passageways are linked with the old chambers. Hillier's Cave and Shatter Cave are examples of such abandoned streamways. Thirdly, there is a series of apparently very recently developed swallets, usually very simple in form and very immature. Commonly, they descend rapidly, following the dip in their initial courses, and rarely can be followed for more than 100 m or so. On occasions these streamways intersect the higher-level older passages developed in the area (for example, in Fairy Cave and in Stoke Lane Slocker). Examples of such systems include Withybrook Slocker and Larkshall Slocker. The only extensively explored cave networks in this area are those in the Fairy Cave Quarry and the Stoke Lane Slocker Systems—both feeders to St Dunstan's Well—and only these systems will be examined.

Stoke Lane Slocker (GR669474) has the largest sinking stream on the Mendip Hills. The sink is located midway along the Stoke Lane Valley, some 500m north-east of the church and at an altitude of 171m OD. It is of note that this sink is a considerable distance beyond the shale-limestone contact. The explored length of the system is some 2,000m and the total drop 18m,

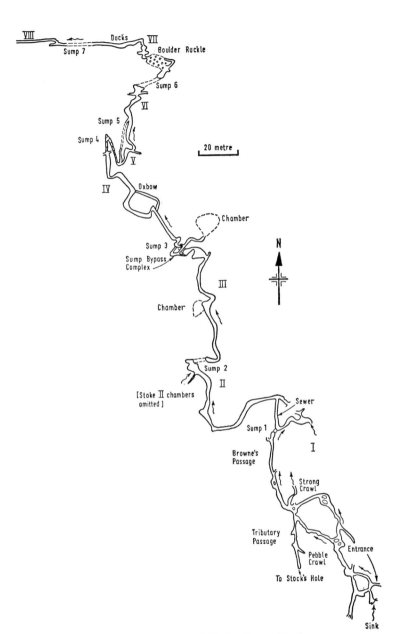

VIII   Ducks   VII
Sump 7   Boulder Ruckle

Sump 6

VI

Sump 5

Sump 4

20 metre

V

IV   Oxbow

Chamber

Sump 3

Sump Bypass
Complex

N

III

Chamber

Sump 2

II

[Stoke II chambers
omitted]

Sewer

Sump 1

I

Browne's
Passage

Strong
Crawl

Tributary
Passage

Pebble
Crawl

Entrance

To Stock's Hole

Sink

Fig 85 Key survey of Stoke Lane Slocker
(from Wessex CC and CDG Surveys)

with the stream emerging at St Dunstan's Well some 22.7m lower than the sink. On the eastern side of the valley, and almost directly opposite Stoke Lane Slocker entrance, is Browne's Hole. This cave consists of an entrance network of phreatic bore passages which lead up to a narrow up- and down-dipping phreatic tube, almost circular in cross-section, which runs almost due east towards the East End Valley, and presumably at one time took active drainage from this area. The cave is now dry, except under most extreme conditions of flood when it has been known to function as a resurgence. That it was once a resurgence for a considerable period of time is indicated by the typical widening of the entrance passage (compare with Aveline's Hole) which suggests outflow of water at considerable velocity. On the opposite side of the valley, and just down the valley from the Stoke stream sink, is an infilled arch which may well be a continuation of Browne's Hole, and it thus seems likely that Browne's Hole and Stoke Lane Slocker are part of an ancient east–west trending system that was intersected by the down-cutting of the Stoke Lane Valley.

There is evidence to suggest that the stream sink is a relatively recent feature. The valley below the sink is only some 1m higher than the stream course immediately above the swallet, and the former stream channel is clearly apparent below the sink—old meander bluffs still being visible. All these features tend to indicate that the cave system is not the work of the present Stoke Lane stream. There is no evidence of old, abandoned stream sinks further down the valley. However, there is evidence for the existence of more than one old entrance a few metres above the present sink, though whether or not these were created by the present Stoke Lane stream is debatable. A complete survey of the known cave streamway is shown in Fig 85. The discovery of another heavily collapsed and calcited entrance to Stoke Lane Slocker (Stock's Hole), some 30m up the western side of the valley above the entrance, and apparently linking with the Tributary Passage in Stoke Lane Slocker, gives further weight to the theory that the present stream has played little or no part in the excavation of its present-day route.

The accessible portions of Stoke Lane are divided into sections, Stoke Lane I to VIII, each section being separated from the next

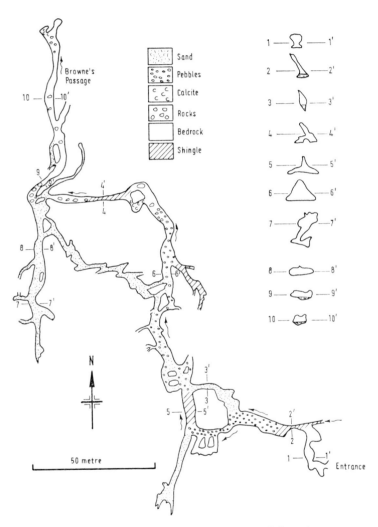

Fig 86 Stoke Lane I, cross-sections and deposits

by a sump. As these divisions also tend to form morphological units, the features of the cave will be discussed using these sub-divisions. Fig 86 shows the passages of Stoke Lane 1, together with floor deposits and passage cross-sections. Stoke Lane 1 is basically a grid of passages at right angles to one another, run-ning almost due north–south and east–west. Occasional small chambers up to 3m high, occur at the nodes of the grid, but the average passage height for the series as a whole is approximately 1m. There are also limited, partially mud-filled passages at heights of up to 3m above the main level. Many of the smaller tunnels are blind. Throughout this series the large amounts of cobble-sized flood debris on the passage floor indicates the frequency with which the stream changes its course; even during the past twenty years in which the cave has been accessible, the Stoke Lane stream is known to have changed its course several times in this entrance series. The great majority of the passages in the grid network are of dominantly phreatic origin, with only comparatively minor and apparently recent vadose modi-fication.

Passages developed in the bedding are commonly due to the washing out of more important shale bands, and correspond to the east–west passages of the grid. North–south passages de-veloped in joints tend to be vertical rifts or slightly ovoid in character. In certain parts of the series there are passages apparently almost totally unmodified by vadose action. Browne's Passage near Sump 1 is an example, and presumably this route has been adopted only recently by the main stream. Browne's Passage exhibits the classic features of phreatic origin : ovoid passage form, joint-determined cavities, spongework and fret-work. Immediately prior to Sump 1 the network seems to become concentrated in two passages, only one of which—Browne's Passage—is accessible.

Floor deposits vary within this series. Fine sand and silt, the product of deposition under low flow rate conditions, occur in parts of Browne's Passage, in Tributary Passage at Rabbit Warren,

Ox-bow Passage, and Fingertip Link. In some cases, flow-stone has built up over these deposits, suggesting that the stream that laid them down was not the present-day Stoke Lane water. Rounded pebbles occur in the entrance series and in Pebble and Stony Crawls. Large numbers of Old Red Sandstone cobbles are present and these deposits may be used to determine past courses of the modern stream. Calcite deposits occur widely

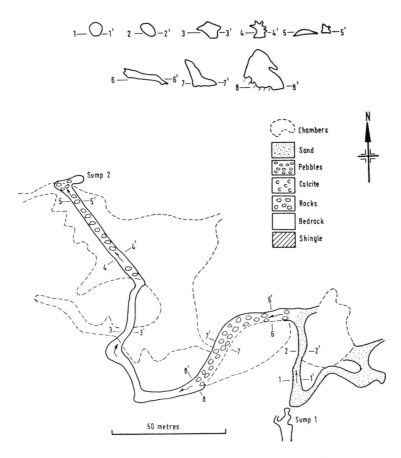

Fig 87 Stoke Lane II, cross-sections and deposits

throughout the cave (generally above the streamway) but in Browne's Passage and its approaches, obvious signs of re-solution are apparent.

Fig 87 shows Stoke Lane II, together with floor deposits and passage cross-sections. In Stoke Lane II the grid net of passages is almost entirely lacking. The stream passage trends towards the north-west in a series of meanders, indicating that the influence of dip and strike is less marked than in the entrance series. For the greater part of its length, the stream passage follows joint control, producing a passage that is a larger version of the joint-controlled passages in Stoke Lane I, except that there is a greater degree of vadose modification. The section of passage between the Changing Room and the south-western extension of Bone Chamber is developed along the strike and may be controlled by the presence of the chambers in the roof above. Floor deposits are generally absent, as the stream commonly occupies the full width of the passage. However, there are numerous boulder-strewn sections of streamway, again associated with the presence of large chambers overhead.

Stoke Lane Slocker III and IV are shown in Fig 88, again with passage cross-sections and floor deposits. In this portion of the streamway the passage is almost exclusively joint-controlled, and there is a noticeable degree of passage control by the joint system running at 330°. The passage in Stoke Lane III is very similar to that in II except that floor deposits, varying from cobble to sand size, occur more frequently as the channel gradient lessens. Sump 3 is a low, wide, gravel-floored feature, and appears to act as a trap for the larger calibre stream load, as downstream of this point, floor deposits are rarely more than sand sized. A network of small phreatic bore passages, some 1–2m in height, exists above Sump 3 and connects with a large chamber some 30m high, developed in the dip. This chamber is unlike the other cavities in the cave system. The continuation of the streamway towards Sump 4 becomes progressively lower and wider in cross-section; sometimes the guiding joint is visible

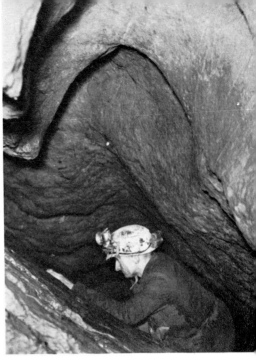

Page 299

(*above left*) The Wet Way in Swildon's Hole, showing a vadose trench cut into an initially phreatic passage (*above right*) A bedding plane rift with associated phreatic features in Eastwater Cavern (*below left*) The Twentieth Chamber in Wookey Hole (*below right*) The ladder pitch in Lamb Leer

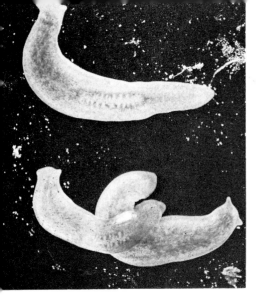

Page 300

(*above left*) *Crenobia alpina* (Dana), a flatworm found as a troglophile in several Mendip caves. The length of each individual is about 10mm (*above right*) *Polymicrodon polydesmoides* (Leach). Probably the most common millipede in British caves and common in many Mendip caves. Usually considered to be a troglophile, the natural length of the adult is 17–21mm. Collembola are primitive wingless insects known as springtails. They are among the most common inhabitants of Mendip caves. The variation in shape is astonishing and two differing species of Collembola are illustrated in the plates (*below left*) and (*below right*). The latter shows the appendage at the hind end of the body that acts as a spring. Life sizes vary from 1 to 5mm

as a niche in the roof. However, as the floor is covered in stream-borne deposits in this stretch, it is not possible to ascertain the true passage shape. Some degree of vadose undercutting of the walls is apparent even at Sump 4.

Beyond Sump 4 the cave continues in a northerly direction through Stoke Lanes v and vi via a series of muddy breakdown chambers and passages. Beyond Sump 6 the cave makes an abrupt right angle turn to the west, and from there to the explored limits (Stoke Lane viii), continues in a series of constricted, low, bedding-controlled passages with frequent water-filled sections. There is also considerable collapse in this zone. Often the passage assumes a double form, being developed in two adjacent shale bands. Fig 89 shows the passage cross-section close to Sump 7 where such development is apparent.

The overall course of the Stoke Lane stream is curious in that it flows in a largely north-east direction until it reaches almost the limit of the limestone outcrop, before adopting a due westerly course towards St Dunstan's Well. The unknown portion of its course to the resurgence must, therefore, be almost entirely developed along the strike of the strata.

Above, and connected with the streamway of Stoke Lanes ii, iii, v and vi is a series of large chambers, over 20m in height in places, and at an absolute elevation of 189–94m od—the land surface above being 197–230m od. These chambers appear to be the products of random solution along lines of weakness under relatively static water conditions. They have all been modified by later collapse due to their inherently unstable structure and proximity to the surface. Fig 90 shows a cross-section of a typical chamber in Stoke Lane ii. The majority of the chambers also show extensive calcite deposition. No signs of re-solution are apparent within the chambers, and no sign of vadose action is apparent. Therefore, it may be presumed that they formed as solution chambers well before the present-day streamway below. However, their regular occurrence along the course of the Stoke Lane stream may imply that they did at

K

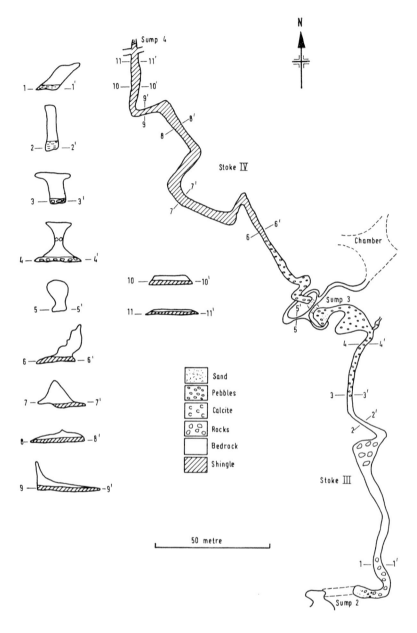

Fig 88 Stoke Lane III and IV cross-sections and deposits

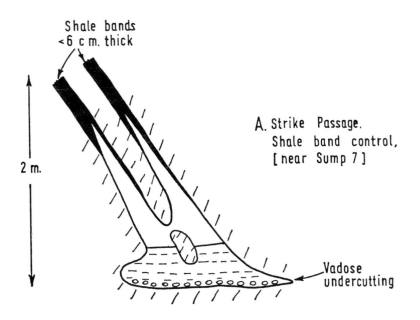

Shale bands
<6 c m. thick

2 m.

A. Strike Passage.
Shale band control,
[near Sump 7]

Vadose
undercutting

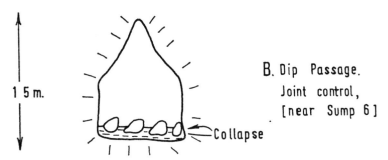

1 5 m.

B. Dip Passage.
Joint control,
[near Sump 6]

Collapse

Fig 89 Stoke Lane VII, passage development in shale bands

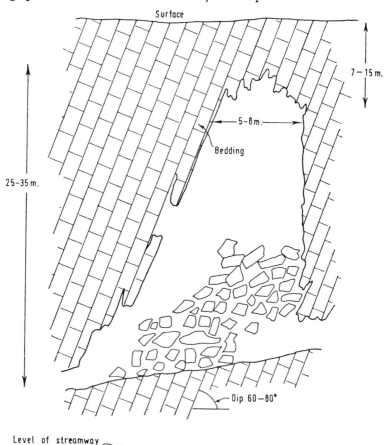

Fig 90 Cross-section of Stoke Chamber with geology

one time form a continuous, if ill-developed, water conduit.

Fairy Lane comprises the most westerly of the dry valleys associated with the St Dunstan's Well rising. It is completely dry throughout its length, and the stream sinking at Midway Slocker may be supposed to be the water that originally excavated the valley. A large number of caves have been discovered by quarrying in the Fairy Cave Quarry at the north-eastern extremity of this valley. None of the caves had a natural opening to the surface, and many of those discovered have since been destroyed by further quarrying operations. The rising of St Dunstan's Well lies north-north-east of the quarry.

Despite the large number of caves discovered, there appear to be only two old stream caves in the area, the Balch Cave–Shatter Cave route, and Hillier's Hole, these becoming confluent under the quarry floor. The north-eastern extremity of Hillier's Hole consists of an up- and down-dipping ancient streamway trending towards the present-day rising at St Dunstan's Well, but some metres above it. Balch Cave is more complex, consisting of an upper series of high-level passages similar to those in Stoke Lane Slocker, an intermediate ancient phreatic streamway similar to that in Hillier's Hole, and a lower, constricted active stream course—possibly the water from Withybrook and Midway Slockers. This streamway is probably a much later feature which has intersected the old cave. Shatter Cave is the southerly extension of the Balch Cave high-level abandoned stream course,

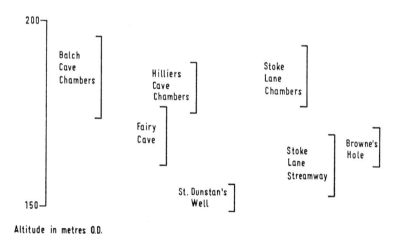

Fig 91 Altitudinal ranges of East Mendip caves

and trends towards a now infilled sink in the Withybrook Valley. The course of the cave is partly influenced by the St Dunstan's Fault, but over much of its course the cave is strike orientated. Whitaker (1969), remarked on the scalloping apparent in the Underpass, Tor Chamber, and Erratic Rift and on the presence of two distinct stage levels etched into the sides of the rift.

It may thus be seen that the origin and development of caves in this region are extremely complex, and possibly unique on the Mendip Hills. There is a distinct correlation of cave levels in the area with respect to altitude, especially with regard to the high-level chambers and the intermediate-level abandoned stream courses. The altitudinal range of these features is shown in Fig 91. It seems apparent that cave development in this area has been very closely related to the evolution of the topography. A possible sequence of development might be as follows.

Initially, the northerly outlets to the limestone massif were blocked by grit banked up to the north, with only a limited leakage of water into the proto-Mells River Valley. The present-day dry valley system running south to north, would have existed as a system of shallow trenches during this period. Development of the highest-level chambers, with some orientation and slow flow towards the Mells Valley, may have occurred during this stage. With the further downcutting of the Mells and of the south–north valley systems, a proto-series of phreatic streamways may have developed with an exit in the vicinity of the present-day St Dunstan's Well, but at a somewhat higher level. That St Dunstan's Well was the only available resurgence during this period is suggested by the strike-dominated courses of these proto-systems—for example, Hillier's Cave, Shatter Cave, and the Browne's Hole–Stoke Lane System. The passage remnants above the third sump in Stoke Lane Slocker may be a part of this route.

A third stage corresponded to the rapid downcutting of the Mells River and consequent incision of the tributary valleys. The Stoke Lane Slocker–Browne's Hole system was bisected during this period; Browne's Hole functioned as a resurgence, and eventually the present-day Stoke Lane stream sank in the western side of the valley floor. During this period also, the new swallet sinks were established at or close to the southern limit of the tributary valleys. Thus these valleys were left dry, and they now hang above the Mells Valley. St Dunstan's Well became fully active at its present level, and present-day stream sinks followed older lines etched out by the phreatic water. In the case of Stoke Lane Slocker, the cave from Sump 6 onwards appears to be an entirely modern feature cut by the present stream, and it may be that the ancient high-level route pursues an independent course along the strike.

Other Caves

The characteristic features of some of the major Mendip caves have been discussed, and the considerable differences in their morphology and hydrology noted. There are also many smaller cave systems on the Mendip Hills which are difficult to explain simply as being smaller versions of the larger systems. For example, there are numerous caves developed in surface depressions of varying depths. The locations of many of these depressions suggest that they, and the cave beneath them, have developed from concentrated inflow of water, probably in the soil from the immediately surrounding region, rather than simply being the abandoned sink of a surface stream course. Examples of such caves include Hunter's Hole, Alfie's Hole, Ubley Hill Pot, and perhaps Whitsun Hole, although the last mentioned may well have been a true stream sink. All these caves, characteristically, show considerable development in their upper portions, but tighten up rapidly with depth. They contain no large stream, but normally a small, usually tight and in- accessible streamway. Commonly, they contain a heavy mud fill, derived from the surrounding area.

There are also totally isolated caves, all of which tend to be located close to the flanks of the hills. Lamb Leer is the classic example of an isolated cave, consisting of large chambers developed by local solution on the fault belt (see Plate p 299, *lr*) and later modified by an invading stream. There are also a number of truly ancient swallet caves, in which the original development was probably similar to that of the major swallet caves of Mendip, but in which this development was terminated early on and was not followed by phases of downcutting and passage extension. Such caves are especially common on central Mendip, and descend steeply to a depth of 60–80m before the gradient of the streamway becomes gentler, and the passage commonly narrows and becomes inaccessible. This suggests gradation to a base level at approximately this height, followed by the loss of the cave stream, perhaps due to stream capture or a change in the local hydrological regime, effectively terminating further development of the system. All these caves show considerable initial phreatic development followed by deep subsequent vadose trenching, and in many cases at least one fill stage, together with limited re-excavation by modern small invading streams. Nine Barrow's Swallet, Sludge Pit, and Cuckoo Cleeves are examples of this type of cave. A typical cave of this type, Sludge Pit, will be examined in more detail.

Sludge Pit (537513) is located at an altitude of 268m OD, some 400m north-east of Eastwater Farm, in a very shallow depression at the shale–limestone boundary. The cave extends over a vertical range of 58m and has a total passage length of approximately 610m. There is a large concentration of poorly developed swallet caves within a very small area around Sludge Pit—Nine Barrow's Swallet, Eastwater Cavern, and North Hill Swallet. This is seemingly an excessive density of cave sinks for such a limited area, and they may represent different sinks for the same stream, and as such may link together at depth. There is no large, fully integrated cave within the area. The initial exploration of Sludge Pit is described by North (1968), and a sketch plan survey of the cave is shown in Fig 92 (after Warburton, 1967). Fig 93 shows typical passage cross-sections within the cave. The entrance to the cave in the depression consists of a descending narrow tube leading to the head of a 6m vertical drop. This pitch is developed at the shale-limestone contact, and at its

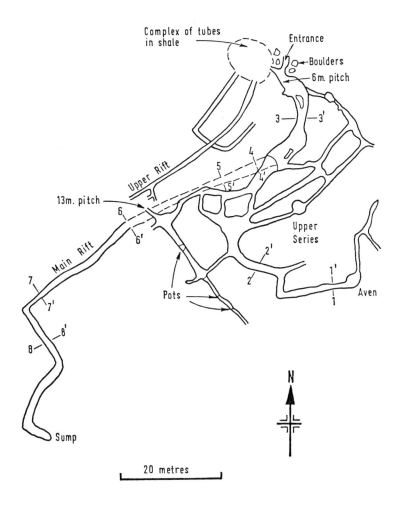

[Section nos. refer to figure 93]
Fig 92 Survey of Sludge Pit

K*

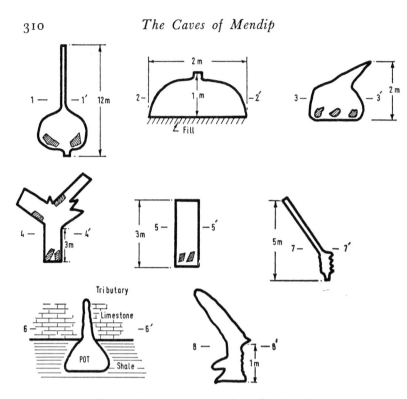

Fig 93 Passage cross-sections, Sludge Pit

foot numerous small passages lead off upstream into the shale. These passages may be followed for a short distance as they subdivide and become smaller. Downstream, the main passage consists of a lofty rift, up to 30m in height, alternately following dip and strike and descending steeply along the dip before terminating in a static sump. The form of this passage varies between an inclined rift when the passage is guided by the bedding, and a narrow vertical rift belling out in its lower 3–6m as a result of collapse and stream undercutting, when joint guided. Stream Passage is partly developed in shale and partly in limestone.

A short distance downstream from the pitch, and at the point at which the Stream Passage shows a sharp steepening of gradient, a high-level network of well developed phreatic passages, oval in cross-section, leads off at roof level. This network is largely horizontal (see section) and shows considerable infilling by clastic deposits. In addition there are a large number of intersecting, deep, canyon-like rift passages with only minor phreatic development in their roof, and again these appear to exploit major structural lines of weakness within the limestone. It is possible that Sludge Pit initially developed from the concentration of water in various small channels in the limestone-shales, and that these coalesced to form the well developed sub-horizontal phreatic network of tubes. At this stage there would be no surface sink for the cave. Later, the present sink at the shale-limestone contact, developed and followed a predominantly down-dipping course, in part modifying the earlier phreatic network, and in part cutting a new route. The deep vadose trenching may be associated with this phase. Finally, the supply of water to the cave ceased and it became a fossil swallet system. The existence of such caves—developed by flow in the Lower Limestone Shale and having no relation to surface drainage—seems possible in view of the probable movement of water through the Lower Limestone Shale previously described on eastern Mendip.

On the extreme eastern limits of the Mendips, where the Jurassic oolites overlie the Carboniferous Limestone, two caves are known which are developed in the Oolitic Limestone. One of these, Cloford Quarry Cave (717444) is developed at the Carboniferous-Jurassic unconformity surface (the oolite is only some 2–3m in thickness here). The passages in the oolite seem to converge on a central sink in the Carboniferous Limestone (Drew & Smith, 1972). No other instances of such unconformity-guided caves are known within the area.

CONCLUSION

In summary, it is difficult to make valid generalisations about the origin and development of the caves of Mendip, as a wide variation in the degree of complexity and the mode of origin is apparent. Most workers agree that the majority of the major caves date from mid-Pleistocene times onwards, and that all show alternations of vadose and phreatic development, infilling with clastic deposits, and subsequent re-excavation. To a degree, it may be said that a certain sequence of development is associated with a certain catchment area, but this is only true in the broadest sense.

7

The Biology of the Mendip Caves

Mary Hazelton

The biology of the Somerset caves will be discussed with particular reference to the caves of the Mendip Hills. This is a region of outstanding interest to all biospeleologists for here, in an isolated area, there exists a fauna of very ancient origin. The caves have been subjected to a variety of forms of contamination, brought in from the surface since the beginning of the century when caving first developed as a sporting activity. In a few individual cases the contamination of the underground habitat is very much earlier. Thus within the caves in addition to the long-evolved, true-relict cave fauna, there are species that are in the process of adapting to the cave conditions, as well as elements directly brought into the cave environment by contamination and which are of an ephemeral nature and unlikely to survive.

Relict cave faunas have been the subject of much discussion. Jeannel (1943) likened them to 'living fossils'; Birstein defined relicts 'as those animals . . . for which the evolution has stopped or at least slowed, and which have conserved the appearance of their distant ancestors'. Vandel (1965) believes that the true cave animals, the troglobites, generally represent a fauna at the end of the evolution of phyletic lines. It is normally accepted that the true-relict cave faunas took refuge in the hypogean zones to escape from changing environmental conditions that made life on the surface impossible for them. These changes were frequently brought about by climatic variations of which the Pleistocene glaciations represent the most extreme example, although other causes, such as changes in sea level, could have played a major part.

When studying the fauna found in caves at the present time, different groups of animals are found in different parts of the caves. For example, very few of the species regularly found in the entrance (threshold) zone of the cave will be found in the dark (hypogean) zone where there is no measurable light. A third zone, the deep threshold, with its own distinctive fauna, can be distinguished between the threshold and hypogean zones. The recognition and inter-relationships of the species associated with each of these three zones is of prime importance to the biospeleologist, and any serious worker must have a sound knowledge of the cave from which he is collecting. Additionally, distinctions should be made between troglobites, troglophiles and trogloxenes. Troglobites spend their entire life underground and are not able to survive under surface conditions. Troglophiles, which form the greater part of the Mendip cave fauna, may in some cases pass their whole life-cycle underground, but they are capable of life on the surface. A trogloxene is, literally, an underground 'guest', which has accidentally found its way into a cave. Such individuals will only have a limited survival time unless, by chance, they find their way out of the cave again.

In this account, the species that have been determined from Mendip caves are presented by phylum and class, and the caves in which each species has been found are listed. Fuller information, including details of the collector and the date of collection, can be found in the Biological Records of the Cave Research Group of Great Britain. These are listed in the bibliography under Hazelton (1965–71).

PHYLUM PLATYHELMINTHES

CLASS TURBELLARIA (flatworms)
Rhabdocoela
  Typhloplanidae   *Typhloplanid*
  Tricladida   Aveline's Hole
  Dendrocoelidae   *Dendrocoelum lacteum* (Mueller
                                       O.F.)
                                    Stoke Lane Slocker
  Planariidae   *Crenobia alpina* (Dana)
                                    Eastwater Cavern, Lamb Leer Cavern,
                                       Swildon's Hole
                                    (?) *Phagocata vitta* (Dugès)
                                    Fairy Cave, Rickford Farm Cave
                                    Polycelis felina (Dalyell)
                                    St Cuthbert's Swallet

Comparatively few Turbellaria have been collected from the caves of Somerset. The very fragile nature of these animals makes collecting difficult without damaging the specimen. It is a very interesting group in which troglobite species have been recorded, but not in this country. The single example of a Typhloplanid—from the Aveline's Hole—must, for lack of further evidence, be dismissed as accidental. *Phagocata vitta*, on the other hand, is recognised by all the Continental workers to be a troglophile living, in particular, in springs and subterranean waters. No doubt it is from here that this species, and probably *Crenobia alpina* (see Plate p 300, *ul*) as well, find their way into the caves, where they are to be found in the soft mud at the bottom of pools, or slow-moving streams. *C. alpina* has been collected under much wetter cave conditions that *P. vitta*. Planarians have been observed (by E. A. Glennie) devouring Collembola living on the surface pools. I think in this country that *C. alpina* is a troglophile, although there does seem to be divided opinion about this on the Continent. Both of these species, in caves, are depigmented and have eyes. *Polycelis felina* can only be considered as an accidental visitor to caves; it can be found above ground in great numbers in shallow pools, ditches, streams, ground springs, and other marshy places.

PHYLUM MOLLUSCA

CLASS GASTROPODA
Mesogastropoda
  Littorinidae   *Littorina littorea* (L.)
                                     Gough's Cave

Basommatophora
  Lymnaeidae   *Lymnaea peregra* (Müller)
                                  Stoke Lane Slocker
Stylommatophora
  Endodontidae   *Discus rotundatus* (Müller)
                                 Sidcot Swallet, St Cuthbert's Swallet, Swildon's Hole
  Arionidae   *Arion ater* (L.)
                                 Stoke Lane Slocker
  Clausiliidae   *Clausilia bidentata* (Ström)
                               Loxton Cave
  Helicidae   *Helicella caperata* (Montagu)
                             Goatchurch Cavern
                           Cepaea hortensis (Müller)
                           Loxton Cave
                           Helix pomatia (L.)
                         Lamb Leer Cavern
  Zonitidae   *Retinella nitidula* (Draparnaud)
                       Stoke Lane Slocker
                       Oxychilus alliarius (J. S. Miller)
                   Goatchurch Cavern
                     Oxychilus helveticus (Blum)
                 Goatchurch Cavern, St Cuthbert's Swallet

Oxychilus cellarius (Müller)
Dundry Stone Mine, Loxton Cave,
Sidcot Swallet, Swildon's Hole
Oxychilus draparnaldi (Beck)
Goatchurch Cavern, Mouse Hole
Vitrea crystallina (Müller)
Goatchurch Cavern, Sidcot Swallet

Limacidae *Agriolimax agrestis* (L.)
Stoke Lane Slocker
Limax maximus L.
Lamb Leer Cavern

CLASS BIVALVIA
Heterodonta
Sphaeriidae *Pisidium nitidum* Jenyns
Pen Park Hole

All the Molluscs collected from caves belong to recent times, and most of them are trogloxenes, to be found where conditions are damp and vegetable debris has been brought into the caves. The following are, however, a few which Leruth considered as troglophile (Leruth, 1939): *Discus rotundatus*, common to the threshold or deep threshold area of caves all over Europe including this country, and *Oxychilus cellarius* (Müller) in many caves of this country and also on the Continent, sometimes quite a long way into caves, but not often recorded from the large caves. The same applies to *O. draparnaldi*, and *Vitrea crystallina* which is perhaps the best example in this country of a troglophile Mollusc. It is to be found in the dark zone, tucked away in damp crevices. The occurrence of *Lymnaea peregra* is quite accidental and it must have been washed into the cave from a local ditch. The strange discovery of *Littorina littorea* in Gough's Cave is open to speculation; one would like to think it was a relict from the days when the sea lapped round the edges of the Mendip Hills. Two dead shells were found, one buried in cave earth, and the other in a sand-filled crawl, neither places used by the normal visitors. Perhaps Mr Gough himself was fond of these winkles for his meal underground when he first explored this cave in 1898.

PHYLUM ANNELIDA (worms)

CLASS OLIGOCHAETA

Enchytraeina
    Enchytraeidae   *Enchytraeus* sp.
                         Pen Park Hole, Swildon's Hole
                         Enchytraeus albidus Henle
                         Reservoir Hole

Tubificina
    Tubificidae   *Tubifex tubifex* (O. F. Müller)
                         Eastwater Cavern, GB Cavern,
                           Swildon's Hole
                         Tubifex ignotus (Stolc)
                         Swildon's Hole

Lumbricina
    Lumbricidae   *Eiseniella* sp.
                         GB Cavern
                         Eiseniella tetraedra (Savigny)
                         Holwell Cave, Goatchurch Cavern
                             Allolobophora chlorotica
                               (Savigny)
                         Axbridge Ochre Cavern, Stoke Lane
                         Slocker
                             Allolobophora longa Ude
                         Goatchurch Cavern, Sidcot Swallet
                             Allolobophora caliginosa
                               (Savigny)
                         Goatchurch Cavern
                             Lumbricus rubellus Hoffmeister
                         GB Cavern, Lamb Leer Cavern
                             Denbrobaena rubida (Savigny)
                         Dundry Stone Mine

Dendrobaena rubida (Savigny)
f. *tenuis* (Eisen)
Eastwater Cavern, Goatchurch
Cavern, Great Oones Hole
Dendrobaena rubida (Savigny)
f. *subrubicunda* (Eisen)
Goatchurch Cavern
Eiseniella tetraedra (Savigny)
f. *typica*
Mich:
Sidcot Swallet, Swildon's Hole

CLASS HIRUDINEA (leeches)
Gnathobdellida
Erpobdellidae

Erpobdella octoculata (L.)
Stoke Lane Slocker
Trocheta subviridis Dutrochet
Longwood Swallet

The *Enchytraeus* and *Tubifex* worms so far recorded from Somerset caves are all trogloxenes, although more information with regard to distribution might show that *Enchytraeus albidus* is troglophile in habit. Of the Lumbricids, Leruth (1939) considers quite a few of these to be troglophile, especially where there are great numbers of them in the cave. Amongst those he mentions are *Eiseniella tetraedra* and *Dendrobaena rubida*. However, in this country there is at the moment no such evidence, and they should be considered trogloxenes.

The two examples of Erpobdellidae are probably chance visitors, although both of the species recorded have been found in caves on the Continent.

PHYLUM ARTHROPODA

CLASS DIPLOPODA sub-class CHILOGNATHA (millipedes)
Glomerida
Glomeridae

Glomeris marginata (Villers)
Goatchurch Cavern, Sidcot Swallet

Chordeumida
    Craspedosomidae

Polymicrodon polydesmoides (Leach)
Dundry Stone Mine, Elm Cave, Fairy Cave, GB Cavern, Goatchurch Cavern, Great Oones Hole, Holwell Cave, Quaking House Cave, Sandford Levvy, Sidcot Swallet, Stoke Lane Slocker, Swildon's Hole, Wookey Hole Cave

    Brachychaeteumidae

Brachychaeteuma bradeae (Bröl. et Brade–Birks)
Dundry Stone Mine, Goatchurch Cavern
Brachychaeteuma sp.
Goatchurch Cavern, Holwell Cave

Polydesmida
    Polydesmidae

Brachydesmus superus Latzel
Aveline's Hole, Blake's Farm Cave, Elm Cave, Goatchurch Cavern, Great Oones Hole, Sidcot Swallet, Swildon's Hole, Wookey Hole Cave
Polydesmus angustus Latzel
Quaking House Cave
Polydesmus coriaceus Porat
Loxton Cave, Swildon's Hole
Polydesmus gallicus Latzel
Swildon's Hole
Polydesmus gallicus Latzel? v. *tolsana* Brölemann
Holwell Cave
Polydesmus sp.
Goatchurch Cavern

?? Polydesmidae ??*Polydesmus* sp.
Fossilised in breccia
Goatchurch Cavern

Julida
Blaniulidae *Archiboreoiulus* sp.
Goatchurch Cavern
Blaniulus guttulatus (Bosc)
Goatchurch Cavern, Great Oones Hole, Holwell Cave, Sidcot Swallet, Swildon's Hole
Boreoiulus tenuis (Bigler)
Great Oones Hole
Boreoiulus ? *tenuis* (Bigler)
Goatchurch Cavern
Proteroiulus fuscus (Am Stein)
Browne's Hole, Stoke Hill (Freestone Mine)
Isobates varicornis (C. L. Koch)
Goatchurch Cavern, Gough's Cave
Iulidae *Tachypodoiulus niger* (Leach)
Dundry Stone Mine, Quaking House Cave
Iulus (*Micropodoiulus*) *scandinavius* Latzel
Great Oones Hole
Cylindroiulus latestriatus (Curtis)
Stoke Hill (Freestone Mine)
Cylindroiulus luridis (C. L. Koch)
Great Oones Hole

CLASS CHILOPODA (centipedes)
Geophilomorpha
Geophilidae *Necrophlaeophagus longicornis* (Leach)
Elm Cave

Lithobiomorpha
Lithobiidae   *Lithobius pilicornis* Newport
                                       Gough's Cave
                                           Lithobius forficatus (L.)
                                       Sandford Levvy
                                           Lithobius variegatus (Leach)
                                       Great Oones Hole
                                           Lithobius tricuspis Meinert
                                       Lamb Leer Cavern
                                           Lithobius duboscqui Brölemann
                                       Goatchurch Cavern
CLASS SYMPHYLA
Scutigerellidae   *Scutigerella causeyae* Michel-
                                       bacher
                                       Fairy Cave

There are numerous colonies of Diplopods in many of the smaller Mendip caves, where there is always a considerable amount of detritus such as rotting wood and, in the earlier days of caving, candlewax droppings; and in a few cases bat guano. All these encourage the growth of various moulds, so that taken all round, in these situations there is a plentiful supply of food to encourage the formation of colonies of these animals. The species most frequently recorded are *Polymicrodon polydesmoides* (see Plate on p 300), *Brachydesmus superus* and *Blaniulus guttulatus*. The last two mentioned are widely recorded from caves on the Continent. Vandel (1965) considers that these three species are recent troglophiles. They certainly appear to be well established as such in this country. *Boreoiulus tenuis*, a very depigmented species, has been recorded only from one cave, and perhaps a second, in Somerset. Leruth considers it to be a troglophile also. The rest of the species must be considered to be trogloxenes.

Dr F. A. Turk considers that all the *Lithobius* spp. in the Chilopoda should be considered as trogloxenes with the exception of *Lithobius duboscqui* which may be found in the hypogean zone, and should be classed amongst the troglophiles.

PHYLUM ARTHROPODA

CLASS INSECTA sub-class APTERYGOTA
  Collembola (springtails)
    Hypogastruridae   *Hypogastrura purpurescens* (Lubbock)
                             Biddlecombe Rift Cave, Eastwater Cavern, Swildon's Hole
                             Hypogastrura bengtssoni (Agren)
                             Mouse Hole
                               Schaefferia willemi (Bonet) syn. *Schaefferia octoculata* Womersley)
                             Lamb Leer Cavern, Stoke Lane Slocker
                               Schaefferia emucronata group
                             Biddlecombe Rift Cave, Blake's Farm Cave, Bristol Waterworks Heading, Foxes Hole, Goatchurch Cavern, Lamb Leer Cavern, Sandford Levvy, Swildon's Hole, White Spot Cave
                               Schaefferia sp.
                             Browne's Hole
    Neanuridae   *Neanura muscorum* (Templeton)
                             Cuckoo Cleeves, Shatter Cave
                               Neanura sp.
                             Sandford Levvy
                               Anurida granaria (Nicolet)
                             Cuckoo Cleeve, Denny's Hole, Dundry Stone Mine, Fairy Cave, Goatchurch Cavern, Loxton Cave, Reservoir Hole, Rickford Farm Cave, Sandford Levvy, Sidcot Swallet, Stoke Lane Slocker,

Swildon's Hole, Wookey Hole Cave
Anurida sp.
Swildon's Hole

Onychiuridae   *Onychiurus ambulans* group
Elm Cave, Goatchurch Cavern, GB
Cavern, Loxton Cave
Onychiurus fimetarius (L.)
Reservoir Hole, Swildon's Hole
Onychiurus fimetarius group
Banwell Bone Cave, Banwell Stalac-
tite Cave, Biddlecombe Rift Cave,
Browne's Hole, Eastwater Cavern,
Fairy Cave, GB Cavern, Goat-
church Cavern, Gough's Cave,
Great Oones Hole, Holwell Cave,
Lamb Leer Cavern, Nancy Camel's
Hole, Quaking House Cave, St
Cuthbert's Swallet, St Dunstan's
Well, Sandford Levvy, Stoke Lane
Slocker, Swildon's Hole
Onychiurus schoetti (Lie Petter-
sen)
GB Cavern, Pen Park Hole, St Cuth-
bert's Swallet
Onychiurus dunarius Gisin
Read's Cavern
Onychiurus cf. *dunarius* Gisin
Swildon's Hole
Onychiurus spp.
Axbridge Ochre Cave, Great Oones
Hole, Swildon's Hole

Isotomidae   *Folsomia candida* Willem
Balch Cave, Hillier's Cave, Pen Park
Hole, Pine Tree Pot, St Cuthbert's
Swallet, Stoke Lane Slocker, Wind-

sor Hill Cave, W/L Cave

Folsomia fimetaria (L.)

GB Cavern

Folsomia cf. *diplophthalma* (Axelson)

GB Cavern

Folsomia quadrioculata (Tullb.)

St Cuthbert's Swallet

Folsomia sp.

Longwood Swallet, Loxton Cave, Shatter Cave, Stoke Hill (Freestone Mine)

Isotoma notabilis Schäffer

Blackmoor Swallet, GB Cavern, Goatchurch Cavern, St Cuthbert's Swallet, Sandford Levvy, Swildon's Hole

Isotoma sp.

Lamb Leer Cavern, St Cuthbert's Swallet

Entomobryidae

Lepidocyrtus cavernarum Moniez—see *Pseudosinella immaculata*

Lepidocyrtus curvicollis Bourlet

Goatchurch Cavern, Holwell Cave, Sidcot Swallet, Wookey Hole Cave

Pseudosinella boneti Bagnall

Great Oones Hole

Pseudosinella immaculata group

Great Oones Hole, Swildon's Hole

Pseudosinella sp. cf. *tarraconensis* Bonet

Read's Cavern

Pseudosinella sp.

Dundry Stone Mine, Goatchurch

Cavern, Nancy Camel's Hole, Wookey Hole Cave

Heteromurus nitidus (Templeton)

Browne's Hole, Fairy Cave, GB Cavern, Goatchurch Cavern, Gough's Cave, Lamb Leer Cavern, Rod's Pot, Sandford Levvy, Sidcot Swallet, Stoke Hill (Freestone Mine), Swildon's Hole

Heteromurus sp.

Dundry Stone Mine

Tomoceridae
Tomocerus minor (Lubbock)

Bristol Waterworks Heading, East-water Cavern, Elm Cave, Goat-church Cavern, Gough's Cave, Mouse Hole, Nancy Camel's Hole, Rod's Pot, Sandford Levvy, Sidcot Swallet, Swildon's Hole, Windsor Hill Cave

Tomocerus longicornis (Müller)

Browne's Hole, Sandford Levvy, Sidcot Swallet

Tomocerus sp.

Elm Cave

Neelidae
Megalothorax sp.

St Cuthbert's Swallet

Undetermined Neelidae

Goatchurch Cavern, Gough's Cave

Sminthuridae
Arrhopalites caecus (Tullb)

Lamb Leer Cavern, Shatter Cave

Arrhopalites pygmaeus (Wankel)

Sandford Levvy

Arrhopalites pygmaeus group

Lamb Leer Cavern

Readers will have noticed that the smaller and shallower caves of Mendip have far more records concerning the Collembola, or springtail (see Plates p 300, *ll* and *lr*) than the larger and deeper caves. This may be caused by the greater ease with which collectors can gain access to these small caves with the result that more Collembola are collected. Or, and this seems more likely, it is the direct result of caving activities, that is to say numerous parties exploring these so-called 'easy' caves with the inevitable pollution, ie an increase of organic detritus, which in turn, grows bacteria and moulds which attract many species of Collembola. In the larger, and especially the deep caves there is far less contamination from without the cave, so that one may with some confidence presume that Collembola colonising the dark zones of larger caves are more likely to belong to the hypogean fauna of the cave, and may develop an increased tendency towards troglobitism. There is much work to be done on the ecology of this order, and there are many questions awaiting an answer not the least of which is, how these colonies of tiny, very vulnerable animals, managed to become established in the cave environment at all, surrounded as they are by predators such as Acari, Coleoptera, Insect larvae and many other foes. A comparative list of the numbers of a given species recorded in Somerset from the smaller and shallower caves and from larger deeper ones, may be of interest.

In favour of the larger caves :

Schaefferia emucronata	5 to 4
Onychiurus schoetti	Totally in favour
Onychiurus dunarius	Totally in favour
Hypogastrura purpurescens	2 to 1
Anurida granaria	2 to 1
Isotoma notabilis	1 to 1

In favour of the small cave system :

Onychiurus fimetarius	2 to 1
Pseudosinella immaculata	2 to 1

Folsomia candida   5 to 3
Heteromurus nitidus   19 to 3
Tomocerus minor   10 to 1

Onychiurus schoetti and *dunarius* have not been found outside caves and mines in any part of the country to date, and we may tentatively suggest that they are indeed troglobites.

PHYLUM ARTHROPODA

CLASS INSECTA sub-class PTERYGOTA

Plecoptera
  Nemouridae
    Nemoura cambrica Stephens larva
    GB Cavern, St Cuthbert's Swallet
    Nemoura sp. larva
    Goatchurch Cavern
  Perlidae
    Dinocras cephalotes (Curtis)
    Swildon's Hole

Hemiptera
  Veliidae
    Velia caprai Tamanini
    St Cuthbert's Swallet
    Velia sp.
    Aveline's Hole
  Nepidae
    Nepa cinerea (L.)
    Swildon's Hole

Trichoptera
  Phryganeidae
    Phryganea grandis (L.)
    Lamb Leer Cavern
  Limnephilidae
    Limnephilid larva
    GB Cavern
    Stenophylax permistus McLachlan
    Larva
    Lamb Leer Cavern, Sandford Levvy

Potamophylax latipennis (Curtis)
larva
GB Cavern
Stenophylax sp. larva
Longwood Swallet
Stenophylax sp. or *Mesophylax* sp.
Wing casts in limestone
Cooks Wood Cave
Halesus sp.
Fairy Cave

Polycentropidae *Plectrocnemia conspersa* (Curtis)
larva
Bristol Waterworks Heading, Longwood Swallet, Swildon's Hole
Plectrocnemia geniculata McLachlan
larva
GB Cavern, Swildon's Hole
Plectrocnemia sp. larva
Swildon's Hole
Polycentropus flavomaculatus (Pictet)
Swildon's Hole
Polycentropid larva
GB Cavern

Philopotamidae *Philopotamus montanus* (Donovan) larva
Swildon's Hole
Wormaldia occipitalis (Pictet) larva
Swildon's Hole
Wormaldia sp. larva
Longwood Swallet
Trichopteran larva unidentified

Eastwater Cavern, GB Cavern

Lepidoptera (Butterflies and Moths)

Plusiidae	*Scoliopteryx libatrix* (L.)
	Sandford Levvy
Geometridae	*Triphosa dubitata* (L.)
	Biddlecombe Rift Cave, Browne's Hole, Lamb Leer Cavern, Sandford Levvy
Plutellidae	*Acrolepia granitella* (Treitschke)
	Great Oones Hole
Caradrinidae	*Hadena* sp. larva
	Goatchurch Cavern

These four orders, Plecoptera, Hemiptera, Trichoptera and Lepidoptera, do not, in this country, contain any species that can be called a troglobite. The larval forms of many species of Trichoptera have been found in the Mendip caves, as may be seen from the list given above. The adult fly cannot live underground, so that most of the Caddis larvae found in the cave streams never complete their full life-cycle. If the imago emerges near the cave entrance the adult fly may survive; many being nocturnal fliers would have a chance to get out of the cave. However, many emerge a long way underground and have no hope of survival. This state of affairs has probably been going on for countless ages, as is well illustrated by the discovery by Mr J. H. Tucker of Trichoptera wing casts in the limestone of Cooks Wood (see Plate p 365, *u*). The hibernating moths *Scoliopteryx libatrix* and *Triphosa dubitata* are to be found in far more of the Mendip caves than are listed above, and are familiar to most cavers, but it was not until Mr Tucker made his most interesting study of these moths that it was discovered that they not only spend a large part of their lives in the caves, but after a foray will return to their own particular niche (Tucker, 1964).

PHYLUM ARTHROPODA

CLASS INSECTA sub-class PTERYGOTA
Coleoptera
  Carabidae   *Trechoblemus micros* (Herbst)
                             Blake's Farm Cave, Hillier's Cave,
                             Pen Park Hole, Stoke Lane Slocker,
                             W/L Cave
                                Trechoblemus micros (Herbst),
                                    larva
                             Pen Park Hole
                                Bradycellus harpalinus (Serville)
                             Swildon's Hole
                                   Abax parallelopipedus (Piller &
                                       Mitterpacher)
                             Lamb Leer Cavern
  Haliplidae   *Haliplus lineatocollis* (Marsham)
                             Swildon's Hole
  Dytiscidae   *Hydroporus disretus* Fairmaire
                             Swildon's Hole
                                   Ilybius fuliginosusu (F.)
                             Swildon's Hole
                                   Agabus guttatus (Paykull)
                             Eastwater Cavern
                                   Agabus conspersus (Marsham)
                             GB Cavern, Swildon's Hole
                                   Agabus sp. ? *bipustulatus* (L.)
                             Swildon's Hole
  Hydrophilidae   *Hydraena gracilis* Germar
                             Swildon's Hole
                                   Helophorus flavipes (F.)
                             Swildon's Hole
                                   Helophorus aquaticus (L.)
                             Swildon's Hole

     Helophorus brevipalpis Bedel
Stoke Lane Slocker
     Megasternum obscurum
     (Marsham)
Swildon's Hole
     Anacaena globulus (Paykull)
Blake's Farm Cave

Silphidae   *Choleva glauca* Britten
Goatchurch Cavern
     Catops fuliginosus Erichson
Loxton Cave
     Catops sp.
Dundry Stone Mine

Staphylinidae   *Lesteva pubescens* Mannerheim
Eastwater Cavern, Goatchurch Cavern, Swildon's Hole
     Ancyrophorus aureus Fauvel
Balch Cave, Blake's Farm Cave, Eastwater Cavern, GB Cavern, Hillier's Cave, Loxton Cave, St Cuthbert's Swallet, Stoke Lane Slocker
     Stenus juno F.
Swildon's Hole
     Xantholinus vel. gen. aff.
Sandford Levvy
     Philonthus fuscipennis
     (Mannerheim)
Gough's Cave
     ? *Philonthus* sp. larva
St Dunstan's Well
     Dianous coerulescens (Gyllenhal)
Stoke Lane Slocker
     Quedius mesomelinus
     (Marsham)

Foxes Hole, Goatchurch Cavern, GB Cavern, Gough's Cave, Loxton Cave, Sandford Levvy, Sidcot Swallet, Swildon's Hole

    Quedius mesomelinus (Marsham) larva

Goatchurch Cavern, GB Cave, Sidcot Swallet

    Quedius nigrocaeruleus Fauvel

Holwell Cave

    Atheta (Glossola) gregaria (Erichson)

Rod's Pot

    Ischnopoda umbratica (Erichson)

Rod's Pot

    Staphylinid larva

Eastwater Cavern

Cantharidae   *Cantharis* sp. larva

Goatchurch Cavern

Dermestidae   *Anthrenus* sp. larva

Swildon's Hole

Dryopidae   *Elmis maugei* Bedel. larva

Stoke Lane Slocker

Helodidae   *Helodes minuta* (L.)

Swildon's Hole

    Helodes minuta (L.) ab. *laeta* Pantz

Swildon's Hole

Cryptophagidae   *Cryptophagus distinguendus* Sturm

Goatchurch Cavern

    Cryptophagus setulosus Sturm

Goatchurch Cavern, Sidcot Swallet

Leptinidae   *Leptinus testaceus* (Mueller
                                        P. W. J.)
                          Elm Cave, Goatchurch Cavern, Great
                                Oones Hole, Mouse Hole

The Mendip caves have their fair share of beetles. As will be seen by a glance at the list, there are representatives of both aquatic and land-living forms. Many of the water beetles are typical of species found in streams and pools, and have been brought into the caves by flood water. *Agabus guttatus*, however, does seem to find the cave habitat compatible, and has been recorded from many caves in Britain. Balfour-Browne found that this species frequents 'narrow trickling streams, springs and wells' (Balfour-Browne, 1950). In this country and in Europe, it appears to be a mountain species. That is to say it prefers a low temperature. Of the two Carabid species recorded in Mendip, *Trechoblemus micros* is interesting; indeed this is the most interesting of all the beetles recorded from this area. The adult has been found in five different caves and the larval form in one cave; it is without doubt a troglophile (Leruth, 1939; Jeannel, 1926). A noteworthy collection of this species was that carried out by E. A. Glennie and O. C. Lloyd in Pen Park Hole, where both adult and larval stages were found in the great natural cavern in the heart of the then newly reopened mine (Hazelton 1957–8). Other troglophile beetles recorded in Mendip caves are *Lesteva pubescens, Ancyrophorus aureus, Quedius mesomelinus*, all of which are recorded in European caves. *Q. mesomelinus* is frequently found in caves where there is bat guano, but it does not seem to be restricted to these caves in any way, as there are many records of its occurrence where there are no bats. *Leptinus testaceus* is frequently to be found underground, sometimes in considerable numbers (Leruth, 1939). It is a blind species and also frequents the nests of small rodents, birds and bees. It has been recorded from four of the smaller caves in Mendip and may well be an accidental visitor.

PHYLUM ARTHROPODA

CLASS INSECTA sub-class PTERYGOTA

Diptera (True, two-winged, flies)

Tipulidae   Tipulid larva
GB Cavern, Stoke Lane Slocker
Limonia nubeculosa Meigen
Goatchurch Cavern, Quaking House
Cave, Sandford Levvy

Trichoceridae   *Trichocera maculipennis* Meigen
Eastwater Cavern, Lamb Leer Cavern

Psychodidae   *Psychoda* sp.
Stoke Lane Slocker

Culicidae   *Culex pipiens* L.
Balch Cave, Banwell Ochre Cave,
Biddlecombe Rift Cave, Coral
Cave, Elm Cave, Fairy Cave, Goat-
church Cavern, Gough's Cave,
Lamb Leer Cavern, Mouse Hole,
W/L Cave
Dixa sp.
St Cuthbert's Swallet

Chironomidae   *Tanypodinae* sp.
Blake's Farm Cave
Anatopynia sp.
Stoke Lane Slocker

Simuliidae   *Simulium* (*Eusimulium*) sp.
? *latipes* (Meigen) larva
St Cuthbert's Swallet
Simulium (*Esimulium*) *costatum*
Friederichs
Swildon's Hole
Simulium (*Eusimulium*) *costatum*
larva
Swildon's Hole

Simulium (*Eusimulium*) sp.

St Cuthbert's Swallet
    Simulid larvae
Swildon's Hole

Mycetophilidae   *Speolepta leptogaster* (Winnertz)

Goatchurch Cavern, Gough's Cave,
    Lamb Leer Cavern, Quaking House
    Cave
        Speolepta leptogaster (Winnertz)
            larva
Elm Cave, Quaking House Cave, St
    Cuthbert's Swallet
        Exechia subulata Winnertz
St Cuthbert's Swallet
        Exechia sp.
Swildon's Hole
        Exechiopsis sp.
Swildon's Hole
        Rhymosia fenestralis (Meigen)
Mouse Hole
        Rhymosia dziedzickii
            Edwards, F. W.
Sidcot Swallet
        Rhymosia fasciata (Meigen)
Goatchurch Cavern
        Mycetophilid sp. larva
Goatchurch Cavern, Hillier's Cave

Sciaridae   *Sciara* sp.

GB Cavern, Eastwater Cavern
        Bradysia sp.
Goatchurch Cavern, Gough's Cave,
    Holwell Cave, Lamb Leer Cavern,
    Pen Park Hole, St Cuthbert's
    Swallet, Stoke Hill (Freestone
    Mine)

Phoridae
Triphleba unicalcarata (Becker)
Goatchurch Cavern, Sidcot Swallet
Triphleba antricola (Schmitz)
Dundry Stone Mine, Goatchurch Cavern, Sandford Levvy
Triphleba sp (nec. *antricola* (Schmitz) *distinguenda* (Strobl))
Gough's Cave
Phoridae Gen. et sp. indet.
Aveline's Hole

Heleomyzidae
Heleomyza serrata (L.)
(= *Leria serrata* (L.))
Cuckoo Cleeves, Gough's Cave, Great Oones Hole, Hillier's Cave, Lamb Leer Cavern, Long Hole, Quaking House Cave, Sandford Levvy, Sidcot Swallet
Heteromyza rotundicornis (Zetterstedt)
Swildon's Hole
Tephrochlamys rufiventris (Meigen)
Denny's Hole, Goatchurch Cavern
Eccoptomera microps (Meigen)
Long Hole
Scoliocentra villosa (Meigen)
Goatchurch Cavern, Quaking House Cave, Sandford Levvy
Scoliocentra caesia (Meigen)
Goatchurch Cavern, Great Oones Hole, Long Hole

Sphaeroceridae
Sphaerocera sp.
Gough's Cave
Crumomyia nigra (Meigen)
Chelmscombe Quarry Cave, Foxes

Hole, Goatchurch Cavern, Hillier's
Cave, Mouse Hole, Quaking House
Cave, Sidcot Swallet
  Paracollinella caenosa (Rondani)
Sidcot Swallet
  Limosina racovitzai Bezzi v.
  microps Duda in Czizek
Elm Cave, Great Oones Hole, Swil-
don's Hole
  Limosina ? *racovitzai* Villeneuve
Fairy Cave
  Limosina cf *humida* (Halliday)
Mouse Hole
  Limosina sp.
W/L Cave
  Limosina bequaerti Villeneuve
Lamb Leer Cavern, Sidcot Swallet
  Limosina silvatica (Meigen)
Elm Cave, Goatchurch Cavern, Long
Hole, Sidcot Swallet
  Limosina clunipes (Meigen)
Blake's Farm Cave
  Limosina sp.
Great Oones Hole

Calliphoridae   *Calliphora erythrocephala*
              (Meigen)
Lamb Leer Cavern
  Melinda gentilis Robineau-
  Desvoidy
Dundry Stone Mine, Goatchurch
Cavern
  Melinda sp.
W/L Cave

Most caves have a population of various kinds of flies, the

majority of which are to be found in the threshold zone and in the moist parts of the small caves which in this context must count as threshold zones. It is of interest to note that of the over five thousand accepted species of Diptera in this country, only a comparatively few species are recorded from caves—under fifty in the caves of Mendip—and of these, only a fraction can be found to be spending their life-cycle under cave conditions. The rest find their way into the caves by accident, such as the flooding in of the *Simulium* larvae into Swildon's Hole where they can be found clinging to the underside of stones in the water chamber. Others arrive from their breeding area in the rich detritus of the open threshold. Some find their way into other litter, such as bat guano, where eggs are laid; others follow the fungus trail; and more follow the caver and the occasional litter he brings with him. The *Trichocera*, of which one species is recorded from the Mendip caves, are popularly known as the 'winter gnats', and are to be found in cool shady places. Both the adult of the larva of *Trichocera maculipennis* have been recorded from caves, but never in great depth. Leruth (1939) considers it as a troglophile-guanophile, and in this country, where these conditions prevail, it may well be as Leruth says; but in the many caves where it is found without the presence of bats, one must say that it is only an accidental visitor.

A true troglophile that most cavers must recognise, and its larva too, is the well recorded Mycetophilid species *Speolepta leptogaster*. There are few caves where the headlamp does not pick up the silver thread of these larvae, hanging from a rock on the wall, or gleaming on some damp detritus. The dainty adult fly makes short flights from point to point. Some species of adult flies, however, are loathe to fly, and may be seen running across detritus or over stalagmites. One such fly is the *Triphleba antricola*, the male of which has no wings. It has been recorded from three caves in Mendip, and is as near to a troglobite fly as will be found in this country; although *Limosina racovitzai*, also recorded from three or four Mendip caves, is nearly in the same category. The Heleomyzids and the Sphaero-cerids all lay their eggs in decomposing animal and vegetable matter and rotting wood with fungus. Caves with such detritus will be likely to have representatives of these two families. There are some species such as *Scoliocentra villosa* and *S. caesia* which are to be found in badger holes and rabbit burrows, as well as in the detritus of small caves, and these may well be named threshold troglophiles.

PHYLUM ARTHROPODA

CLASS INSECTA sub-class PTERYGOTA

Siphonaptera
Ceratophyllidae — *Dasypsyllus gallinulae* (Dale)
This must have been brought into the cave by a visitor—most likely on a caver's boot.
Loxton Cave

Hymenoptera
Ichneumonidae — *Exephanes ischioxanthus* (Gravenhorst)
Hillier's Cave
Proctotrupidae — *Exallonyx longicornis* (Nees)
Banwell Bone Cave
These are both probably accidentals, although there are records of Proto-trupidae species in the entrance zones of caves in Britain and Europe.

CLASS CRUSTACEA

Cladocera
Daphniidae — *Daphnia* sp.
Mangotsfield Well (Bristol)

Cyclopoida
Cyclopidae — *Cyclops agilis* C. L. Koch

Bristol Water Works Heading, Swildon's Hole
  Cyclops languidus Sars
Eastwater Cavern
  Cyclops viridis (Jurine)
Pen Park Hole, Swildon's Hole
  Cyclops bicuspidatus (Claus)
Pen Park Hole, Swildon's Hole
  Paracyclops fimbriatus (Fischer)
Swildon's Hole
  Cyclops sp.
Mangotsfield Well (Bristol)

It is interesting to note that nearly all the collections of Cyclops in Mendip were made in the larger caves. Of the five species collected, *Paracyclops fimbriatus* and *Cyclops viridis* are accepted troglophiles (Jeannel, 1926, Leruth, 1939, and Vandel, 1965, *et al*). *Acanthocyclops bicuspidatus* is an extremely cosmopolitan species, but I consider that it may well be classed as a local troglophile; for example, in Pen Park Hole where it was found in great numbers in the lake, although this cave and mine had been closed and 'lost' for a long time, and there is no surface water in the area above these workings. *P. fimbriatus* and *C. viridis* may be pre-glacial and have survived the rigours of the last Ice Age.

PHYLUM ARTHROPODA

CLASS CRUSTACEA
Isopoda
  Asellidae
    Asellus (Proasellus) cavaticus Schiödte
    Cuckoo Cleeves, GB Cavern, Gough's Cave, Longwood Swallet, St Cuthbert's Swallet, Swildon's Hole
    Asellus (Proasellus) meridianus Racovitza

L*

Swildon's Hole
Asellus sp.
Great Oones Hole, Stoke Lane Slocker

Oniscidae   *Oniscus asellus* L

Elm Cave, Lamb Leer Cavern, Mouse Hole

Trichoniscidae   *Androniscus dentiger* Verhoeff

Biddlecombe Rift Cave, Blake's Farm Cave, Dundry Stone Mine, Elm Cave, Fairy Cave, Gough's Cave, Gough's Old Cave, Great Oones Hole, Loxton Cave, Mouse Hole, Quaking House Cave, Rickford Farm Cave, Sidcot Swallet

Trichoniscus pygmaeus Sars

Elm Cave

Isopoda not identified

Goatchurch Cavern

Androniscus dentiger has been recorded from a number of the smaller caves in Mendip. This little salmon-pink Isopod must be familiar to numerous cavers. It is a troglophile, being recorded from caves all over Britain, and parts of Europe as well. The rest may be considered to be threshold fauna or accidentals with one great exception—*Asellus* (*Proasellus*) *cavaticus*. This crustacean is a troglobite whose origins lie way back in pre-glacial times (Leruth, 1939). It is not possible, as yet, to be more precise, as there is still a great deal not known about the true origin of this Crustacean. It has, without doubt, survived in the crevices of the permeable rocks and in the water-table since before the last glacial period. In many of the larger caves of Mendip, specimens of *Asellus* (*Proasellus*) *cavaticus* have been collected. The majority have proved to be sub-adult, and amongst the adults so far, no males or ovigerous females have been identified. It is interesting to note that even amongst the adults all the specimens have been very small (3–5mm), comparable in size to the juvenile forms of *Asellus* (*P.*) *cavaticus* to be found in the caves of South Wales. In Mendip, these little Crustaceans may be found in small pools, and have probably either been washed out of their normal crevices by flood water, or have come out from these areas to browse on the micro-flora. Sometimes they are to be seen out of water on the wet rocks, where they have either been chivied by some predator, or have found a useful patch of bacteria or micro-flora to feed on. The surprising thing is that these fragile creatures are able to survive amongst the ravishing hordes of omnivorous fauna to be found in these caves, in particular the *Niphargus*, which has frequently been observed carrying off Asellids to some secluded spot where an uninterrupted feast may be enjoyed. One comes to the conclusion that there must be vast populations of *Asellus cavaticus* hidden away in the water-table, and sheltering there in the crevices of the limestone. A happening which supports this idea was reported to me a few years ago by the South Wales Caving Club, when in the sump of Ogof Ffynnon Ddu, following a period of flooding which had subsided, hundreds of *Asellus cavaticus* were observed in the sump water and on the wet walls of the sump area.

PHYLUM ARTHROPODA

CLASS CRUSTACEA
  Amphipoda
    Gammaridae   *Gammarus pulex* (L.)
                        Longwood Swallet, St Cuthbert's Swallet, Stoke Lane Slocker, Swildon's Hole
                        Niphargus aquilex Schiödte
                        Holwell Cave, Mangotsfield Well (Bristol), Rickford Farm Cave,
                        Niphargus kochianus kochianus Bate
                        Holwell Cave, Pen Park Hole, St

Cuthbert's Swallet
Niphargus fontanus Bate
Eastwater Cavern, GB Cavern,
Gough's Cave, Lamb Leer Cavern,
Pen Park Hole, Rod's Pot, St Cuth-
bert's Swallet, Ston Easton Well,
Swildon's Hole, Wookey Hole
House Well
Crangonyx subterraneus Bate
Gough's Cave

The Amphipods found in the Mendip caves in all cases bar one, are in every way as interesting as the Isopods. The one exception is *Gammarus pulex* (see Plate p 365) which is flooded into the caves from pools, streams and ditches, in all stages of its development. It loses pigmentation underground, where it appears to thrive, but it has never been proved that it can breed to the third or fourth generation successfully in the cave environment. On being brought out into the light of day it soon recovers its natural colour, and one must consider this species to be a sturdy trogloxene. On the Continent there are a few caverni-colous Gammarids, in particular *Gammarus pulex subterraneus*, referred to by Vandel (1965, p 135). On the other hand, the following four Amphipods, *Niphargus aquilex*, *Niphargus fon-tanus*, *Niphargus kochianus* and *Crangonyx subterraneus* are all troglobites, and derived from very ancient fauna. These four species of cave-dwelling animals, are not of the same antiquity. They are all species that were originally marine and which, for a variety of reasons, invaded the caves via estuarine and river gravels, and the crevices of the permeable rocks and phreatic water ways. The time scale of this slow transfer and its many causes are the subject for most interersting discussion. It seems likely from its distribution, that *Niphargus aquilex* is, relatively, the most recent arrival. E. A. Glennie is of the opinion that the invasion of the caves by the other two *Niphargus* species, *fontanus* and *kochianus*, was at a much earlier date—perhaps during early Tertiary times. The male of *Niphargus kochianus* has very rarely been collected and identified, so that the discovery of a male, female and juvenile of this species, in St Cuthbert's Swallet during 1966, was an important contribution towards our knowledge of this species. *Crangonyx subterraneus* has a very wide distribution (Eurasia, South Africa, South America, Vandel, 1965), and it is found in many sites in the southern halves of England and Wales. In 1966 a male and juvenile were found by Mr N. L. Thomas of the Bristol Exploration Club, who also discovered the male of *Niphargus kochianus,* mentioned above.

PHYLUM ARTHROPODA

CLASS ARACHNIDA

Opilionida

Phalangidae   *Phalangium opilio* L.
                       Great Oones Hole

Liobunidae   *Liobunum blackwalli* Meade
                       Goatchurch Cavern, Great Oones Hole

Nemastomidae   *Nemastoma chrysomelas* (Hermann)
                       Goatchurch Cavern, Gough's Cave, Great Oones Hole

Araneae (spiders)

Nesticidae   *Nesticus cellulanus* (Clerck)
                       Browne's Hole, Loxton Cave

Argiopidae   *Meta merianae* (Scopoli)
                       Banwell Bone Cave, Browne's Hole, Drunkard's Hole, Dundry Stone Mine, Goatchurch Cavern, Holwell Cave, Stoke Lane Slocker
                       Meta menardi (Latreille)
                       Browne's Hole (probable), Lamb Leer

Linyphiidae

Cavern, Sandford Levvy

Lophocarenum nemorale (Blackwall)
Goatchurch Cavern
  Lessertia dentichelis (Simon)
Rickford Farm Cave
  Erigone dentipalpis (Wider)
Sidcot Swallet
  Porrhomma convexum (Westring)
Blake's Farm Cave, Sidcot Swallet, Stoke Lane Slocker, Swildon's Hole
  Porrhomma egeria Simon
Elm Cave (juvenile), Goatchurch Cavern
  Porrhomma sp.
Blake's Farm Cave, GB Cavern
  Centromerus prudens (O. P. Cambridge)
Goatchurch Cavern
  Lepthyphantes zimmermanni Bertkau
Drunkard's Hole, Goatchurch Cavern
  Lepthyphantes ericaeus (Blackwall)
Sidcot Swallet
  Lepthyphantes pallidus (O. P. Cambridge)
Gough's Cave

The Opilionids so far recorded from the caves of Somerset, are really only accidentals whose normal habitat is amongst the matted grasses and loose soil on the hillsides. They appear to be quite at home under cave conditions, but there is no evidence that any of the species that have been found in these caves ever complete their full life-cycle in the hypogean zone. There are true cave Opilionids in a few of the European caves, and in other parts of the world.

Amongst the spiders found in the Somerset caves, there are no troglobitic species; unless one likes to class *Meta menardi* and *Meta merianae* as threshold troglobites, for this is the most likely place to find them living and breeding. *M. menardi*'s thimble-like egg sacs (see Plate p 366, *l*) may often be found hanging in the sheltered crevices of the entrance zones of many caves, where incidentally, the adults have a plentiful supply of daily food amongst the numerous flies that are usually to be found in these situations. There is, however, an abundance of species of troglo-phile spiders in the Mendip caves; in fact most of the spiders recorded are, in varying degrees, troglophiles, in particular the *Porrhomma* spp. and *Lessertia dentichelis*. These species are as near troglobites as will be found in these caves. Most cavers will have seen, in the crevices deep down in many caves, the beauti-fully made, tiny hammocks of web woven by the *Porrhomma* spiders. There seems no doubt that some of the *Porrhomma* species breed under cave conditions.

PHYLUM ARTHROPODA

CLASS ARACHNIDA

Acari (mites)

Veigaiaidae	*Veigaia transisalae* (Oud.)
	Sandford Levvy
Urodinychidae	*Urodinychus* sp.
	Wookey Hole
Parasitidae	*Parasitus coleoptratorum* (L.)
	Gough's Cave
	Eugamasus magnus (Kramer)
	GB Cavern, Goatchurch Cavern, Great Oones Hole, Holwell Cave, Sidcot Swallet, Swildon's Hole
	Eugamasus magnus (Kramer)

var. *monticola* Berlese
Goatchurch Cavern
    Eugamasus anglocavernarum
    Turk
GB Cavern
    Eugamasus loricatus (Wankel)
Elm Cave, Hillier's Cave, Sidcot Swal-
let
    Eugamasus cornutus (G. et R.
    Can.)
Loxton Cave
    Eugamasus tragardhi (Trag.)
    Oud
Rod's Pot
    Pergamasus crassipes (L.)
Goatchurch Cavern
    Pergamasus alpestris Berlese
GB Cavern, Swildon's Hole

Laelaptidae	*Zercoseius* sp.
	Swildon's Hole
Macrochelidae	*Geholaspis minimus* (Hull)
	Goatchurch Cavern
Ixodidae	*Ixodes vespertiliones* Koch
	Goatchurch Cavern, Great Oones Hole, Holwell Cave, Quaking House Cave, Sidcot Swallet
Pachygnathidae	*Pachygnathus oblongus* (Halbert)
	Blackwood Swallet
Nanorchestidae	*Speleorchestes ventricosus* Hirst
	St Cuthbert's Swallet
Rhagidiidae	*Rhagidia spelaea* (Wankel)
	Fairy Cave, GB Cavern, Gough's Cave
	Rhagidia gigas (Can.)
	Fairy Cave

	Rhagidia intermedia Willmann
	St Cuthbert's Swallet
	Rhagidia saxonica Willmann
	Browne's Hole
Tydeidae	*Tydeus* sp.
	Swildon's Hole
Anystidae	*Anystis baccarum* (L.)
	Goatchurch Cavern
Tetranychidae	*Tetranychopsis horridus* (Can. et Fanz.)
	Swildon's Hole
Bdellidae	*Bdellodes longirostris* (Herm.)
	Aveline's Hole
Acaridae	*Tyrophagus castellanii* (Hirst)
	Holwell Cave
	Acarus siro L.
	Swildon's Hole
Oppidae	*Oppia clavipectinata* (Mich.)
	Wookey Hole
Tyroglyphidae	*Acotyledon rhizoglyphoides* (Zach.)
	Wookey Hole
Glycyphagidae	*Blomia freemani* Hughes
	Swildon's Hole
Hermanniidae	*Hermannia* sp.
	Nancy Camel's Hole
Notaspididae	*Notaspis coleoptratus* (L.)
	Sandford Levvy

The Acari recorded from the Somerset caves must only scratch the surface of this order, which one would expect to be represented in far greater numbers and variety of species, especially in the smaller caves in the Mendip Hills. The majority of these animals are very small, so that, when collecting species of this size in the darkness of the hypogean area, collectors are aided by any sudden movement by the animal, or by the gathering to-gether of species in a small community (perhaps on the surface of the water of a small pool) so that a dozen or so tiny, white specks become much more visible objects. Unfortunately, this does not normally occur with the Acari. With regard to the ecology, and perhaps the history of cave fauna, this is a very important order. Dr F. A. Turk, who has studied the cave Acari for many years, is of the opinion that some species, such as *Rhagidia spelaea, R. tragardhi* and *R. gigas*, may be re-garded as troglobites in Britain, and that they are relict fauna from pre-glacial times (Turk, 1967). Dr Turk also suggests in his review, that the 'British hypogean populations are gradually evolving away from the Continental ones and that they may have been isolated for some considerable time'.

The *Eugamasus magnus* group in Britain also contains troglo-philes and, in *Eugamasus loricatus*, a species that is probably troglobitic, for the only place outside caves where it has been found was in the nests of moles. Three other species which Dr F. A. Turk considers to be troglophile are *Veigaia transisalae*, which is probably derived from the soil-living populations, but protonymphs and deutonymphs have been recorded in hypo-gean zones. *Pachygnathus oblongus* was described by Halbert (1920) from two specimens in an inter-tidal area, but he thought that they were not really denizens of this area. Dr Turk remarks that the occurrence of this species in a cave suggests that it may be a member of the true crevice fauna (Turk, 1967). *Ixodes vespertiliones* is associated with bats, and the rest were probably accidentals which have been blown or swept into the caves, or carried in with the mud on cavers' boots.

The occurrence of bat roosts in a cave has a fundamental affect on the invertebrate fauna of the cave. This has been recognised for some time, especially amongst the European biospeleologists, who found that the piles of bat droppings (guano) beneath the bat roosts held a special fauna, which they named guanophile. This fauna, found in and on the guano, which is comprised of mostly fly and beetle larvae and adults, Collembola, mites and millipedes, is mostly trogloxene—attracted into the cave by the rich source of food contained in the guano itself and in the bacteria and moulds growing on it. The cave-dwelling fauna is, of course, also attracted to the guano, but in their case it is an extra bonus to their meagre existence and they will not, like the trogloxenes, die off when this source of food disappears. In the caves of Mendip it is rare to find a large bat roost, and therefore it is not possible to study a guanophile population in this area. Most of the bats found are Lesser Horse-shoe bats, which roost in small groups of two or three at a time, in isolated niches in the deep thresholds of many Mendip caves.

CONCLUSION

It has not been possible in this review to discuss in detail all the fauna that has been recorded from the caves of Mendip. It is sufficient, however, to show that a great deal has been accomplished, and the cavers of Mendip can be justly proud of their biospeleologists. The initial exploratory work and first de-tailed collections by E. A. Glennie in the 1930s have been extended by many later recruits, and the stage has been set for serious biospeleological research into the many problems revealed. The work has been that of amateurs—often inspired amateurs—who have had the wholehearted support of professional biologists, who since 1938 have examined and named, as far as is possible, every specimen recorded in the Biological Records of the Cave Research Group of Great Britain.

8

The Cave Archaeology and Palaeontology of Mendip[1]

E. K. Tratman

All deposits in caves record part of the history of the cave. In general this chapter deals with deposits on the floors of caves, especially those near the cave mouths, where evidence of human activity is more frequent. Cave deposits are historical documents but have often been treated with scant respect. This holds true for Mendip, where miners, railway companies, quarrymen and cave diggers have been responsible for the destruction of the records. For past damage it is reasonable to accept the plea of ignorance, for it must be remembered that, till quite recently, even archaeologists digging in caves used picks and shovels, and only kept rudimentary records. Nowadays such a plea is unacceptable, though it is frequently difficult and sometimes downright impossible to strike the right balance between necessary commercial projects and preservation. Nor must it be overlooked that archaeological excavation, by its very nature, destroys the evidence so that, if possible, portions of the deposits should be left undisturbed for a future generation to investigate. Any excavation must be accompanied by adequate records made at that time, and subsequently published.

In the Mendips there are so few sites left, and so few more

[1] Manuscript January 1972.

that are likely to be discovered, that a policy of conservation must be applied.

The very title of this chapter limits its contents to the study of deposits in caves. These do not give a continuous record of the activities of man and beasts on the Mendips. Nor do they give a continuous record of the faunal changes. There are substantial gaps in the record that can only be filled from sites other than caves, but such sites are outside the scope of this chapter.

This chapter deals solely with the Mendips and sites on them. It does not deal with sites on adjacent areas, such as the Carboniferous Limestone of the Clevedon Ridge or the Walton Bone Cave, the Durdham Downs Bone Fissure, Bristol (567752)[1], nor with the Alveston Bone Fissure north of Bristol (614503).

Cave deposits are formed in a variety of ways, such as by solution leaving the insoluble residue, by weathering, transport by water, and so forth. They can frequently provide evidence of climatic change. Re-sorting, mixing, and redistribution can occur. It is salutary to recall 'The Great Storm and Flood' of 1968 on Mendip, when, in a matter of hours, deposits which had taken thousands of years to accumulate were displaced and redistributed on a massive scale. Stream action may also occur much more gradually. For example, in Swildon's Hole, animal bones and Roman pottery can be found in a number of places down the streamway. Their origin is almost certainly the major Roman site known to exist close to the present-day swallet. Eventually, some of this material will be washed through to Wookey Hole.

Wide fissures, opening directly to the surface, may have served in the past as natural pitfalls, or even dens for animals, and thus their remains will accumulate at the base. Such sites are usually only found by mining or quarrying activities. They are difficult

---

1 All the National Grid references in this chapter are prefaced by 'ST'.

to deal with and to interpret. The majority of deposits with which the archaeologist has to deal are those at or near the cave mouth. Here, the main components are the weathering products from the cliff above the cave, from the roof and walls of the cave itself, and material washed or carried in from outside.

ARCHAEOLOGICAL EXCAVATION

This is not the place for a treatise on archaeological methods, but something must be said about these. Excavations of cave deposits are difficult to conduct properly. In general, methods suitable for surface sites must be modified for use in caves. Some special points are noted here.

Recent material will often fall down and become mixed with older material. This is particularly likely to happen against the cave walls. Admixture of deposits may be indicated by the occurrence of pieces of stalagmite floor not in their original positions. Layers in caves are often very thin, difficult to trace, and rarely horizontal. The general rule must be to excavate in natural layers, and not in arbitrary ones. Evidence of disturbance must be looked for and carefully recorded. Measurements must provide for three-dimensional location of finds on plans and sections. This can be readily accomplished by the use of a grid system, the size of the grid squares being adapted to the site. The grid need not be tied to the National Grid, but preferably should be. In any case, the National Grid Reference method of recording should be applied. Height position can be obtained by levelling in from a fixed position. An arbitrary height can be allocated to this position, and the height chosen should allow for ample depth to be reached without having to resort to negative heights. For example, an arbitrary height of 10m will allow a depth of 10m to be reached below datum, without running into negative figures. Depth measurements should not be recorded as a depth from the surface of the deposits. Sections must be drawn at more than one place, and plans at each successive natural level. The prime datum level should be marked with a chisel in the rock. Subsidiary levels can also be so marked, or indicated by some other method. Care must be taken to avoid cumulative errors in setting up subsidiary levels. The prime level should be tied to the altitudes on the Ordnance Survey map.

Each item found must be recorded in the field log book at that time. Here is recorded the location information for each specimen : the layer number and the nature of the layer material, how it was lying (eg horizontally or vertically), and its relationship to other items close by. A summary of these is put on a label and wrapped with the specimen. The label remains with the specimen until it has been catalogued and marked with a catalogue number. The field log is copied daily into the permanent log, in which additional data can be recorded as may be considered necessary. When a specimen has been given a catalogue number, all the appropriate data is entered in the catalogue with a cross-reference to the page in the log, and an entry in the log of the catalogue number.

The excavator must be prepared to wash and preserve, if necessary, the finds made. The preservation and even washing may, on rare occasions, have to be done for him by experts at a museum. If a preservative is used it must not be one that precludes a later attempt to use the material for a C^{14} dating technique.

A series of soil samples should be taken at recorded levels, down one or more section faces. These can be kept for analysis later. One set can be used for granulometry and the other for pollen analysis. Though pollen is apt to be destroyed in alkaline deposits, such as those in caves, some may survive, and can be recovered if large enough samples are used. It is a matter of a kilogramme rather than a gramme. Further soil samples should be washed through sieves of varying mesh to recover remains of small animals, such as rodents, that may have been missed during sorting on the site. Shells of Mollusca and remains of beetles may also be found by this method.

In setting down the records, actual observations of facts should be kept separate from interpretations of the facts. It is a good thing to write down interpretations at the time, even though they may be upset by later evidence. Finally, a report must be prepared and published. Failure to publish is a great archaeological crime.

THE SITES

Limits of space prevent anything like a full description of sites being given. Minor sites are given very brief mention or none at all.

The arrangement adopted is to deal with sites numbered in their order of time, taking the earliest first. At a number of sites, archaeological horizons of differing date occur, and so some sites may appear in several sub-divisions.

A number of sites have yielded material datable to the Pleistocene, and the nomenclature recommended by West (1968, pp 219 and 230) is followed. The dates are given in many cases. For the earliest sites these follow the summary given by Warwick (1971), with supplementary ones where necessary. Where radiocarbon dates are given they are taken, generally, from the Council of British Archaeology, British Archaeological Abstracts Supplement 1971. In this publication, full references are given. The dates are based on the 'Libby' half-life of carbon-14, taken as 5,568 ± 30 years. They have not been corrected for the Suess effect. All dates are given BC. To convert these to BP (Before Present) add 1,950 years to the BC date.

Where faunal remains are listed, the internationally accepted name is given (eg in Kurtén, 1968). To save repetition a correlation table is given in appendix 1 where the common English name appears opposite the Latin one.

For the earlier sites, the cultural phases exhibited fall into the Palaeolithic, which in this aspect is coincident with part of the Pleistocene.

PLEISTOCENE–PALAEOLITHIC SITES

1 Westbury-sub-Mendip Quarry (506504)[1]

The earliest mammalian cave fauna established for Mendip has been recovered from a large bone fissure in the north face of this quarry (see Plate p 399). The site first came to notice in August 1969. The fissure was then 10m wide at the top, tapering downwards to bedrock at a depth of 15m. The filling has been proved to extend from west to east for at least 20m. There is shattered limestone above, and the main deposit is divisible into two parts. An upper part is stratified to a depth of 7m and contains considerable quantities of bones and teeth. Below this, down to bedrock, is a mass of yellow sands, gravel and clay, which contains a limited amount of very well mineralised bone fragments, and has yielded one tooth of a *cervid*.

The fauna of the main mass includes *Crocuta crocuta, Felis leo spelaea, Ursus arctos* and *Ursus spelaeus* (both very common), *Homotherium sp.* and *Dicerorhinus etruscus*. These last two animals have never before been recorded for Mendip (Heal, 1970), and are species found in the Cromer Forest Bed of the Middle Pleistocene and are datable as 325000 BP. This very ancient material may have been derived from some unknown secondary or intermediary source.

A single flint implement came from near the top of the main bone deposit, and another from close to the base. The former has some resemblance to the Mousterian–La Micoque stage, and the latter has some resemblance to the still earlier Levallois flake type. Most of the material has been quarried away. A considerable quantity of stratified material was recovered, and is now in the geology department of the University of Bristol.

2 Banwell Bone Cave (38225881)

This cave presents a major problem for dating. It was discovered in 1824, and was originally dug by William Beard. He

[1] A fuller account appears in *Proc Univ Bristol Spel Soc* 1974, **13** (3).

found in the main chamber vast quantities of animal bones, mainly of *Bos sp.* He left many bones carefully stacked up and these can still be seen. Much of Beard's collection of bones is at the County Museum, Taunton.

There is a roof opening, and it was probably through this that most of the animals fell, for limb bones have been found in their normal anatomical arrangement. The main animals represented, besides *Bos sp.*, were *Mammuthus primigenius, Coelodonta antiquitatis, Felis leo, Ursus arctos* and *U. spelaeus, Gulo gulo, Alopex lagopus* and *Rangifer tarandus. Equus* is absent, though Balch includes it in his list. Sutcliffe (1955) made a study of the antlers of *Rangifer tarandus* and suggested that the cave was on a migration route between summer and winter grazing. On the whole, the fauna best fits to the Gippingian glaciation.

On the other hand, there are a number of flint implements in the Weston-super-Mare Museum (Davies, 1926, p 208) which are marked as coming from this cave. The implements are of late Upper Palaeolithic facies and do not fit to the presumptive Gippingian date. They would accord with a late Weichselian date. There are now two entrances to the cave, the natural roof opening and the man-made entrance. There is evidence from inside the cave, of other entrances now not visible on the surface, and the contrived entrance lies through one of them. Perhaps the implements were found when this, and adjacent cuttings were made. If so there may well be a late Upper Palaeolithic occupation site awaiting discovery.

There were considerable undisturbed deposits left in the cave by Beard. Most, if not all, of these have been disturbed by digging to establish the connection between the Bone Chamber and the Stalactite Cave below, and the final use of explosives added to the disturbance in a major way. A very large excavation would have to be mounted if a proper knowledge of the contents of this cave is to be obtained.

3 Limekiln Hill Quarry, Mells (732486)

This large bone fissure was first reported in June 1971, and the management have been most co-operative. It is not as spectacular as the Westbury site, nor so rich in faunal finds.

The fissure is filled with a brown, sticky clay and some weathered limestones. At 10m from the top rock surface, is a bone-bearing band about 1m thick and 2–3m wide. The bones are very poorly preserved. Animals represented include *Bos sp.*, cervid sp., carnivore sp., and rodentia. There is a considerable quantity of charcoal, in the form of discrete pieces, indicating that man probably played a part in the accumulation of the deposit, which may have been washed in from a surface site. If so, then the topographical features must have been very different from those now prevailing.

Stratified material has been collected, and is stored in the geology department of the University of Bristol. So far, the deposit has not been dated, but it is likely to be quite early.

4 Hyaena Den, Wookey Hole (53234792)

This cave lies on the left bank of the River Axe, a few metres downstream from its resurgence at the foot of the cliff. Boyd Dawkins and his associates started digging out the cave in 1859 and continued for a number of years. He published two accounts. These give a fair amount of information, but much is lacking. A number of stone implements were found. They fall into two groups. A series, including bi-faces of undoubted Mousterian facies fig 94 p 392 and two others that equally obviously belong to the Early Upper Palaeolithic. The fauna found is an agreement with both groups of implements. The dominant carnivore was *Crocuta crocuta*, Ursidae were common, *Coelodonta antiquitatis* and *Dicerorhinus hemitoechus* occurred, though chiefly the former, as did other animals such as Cervidae and *Bos*. The presence of *D. hemitoechus* indicates that part of the deposit was at least as old as the later part of the Ipswichian temperate times (about 100000 BP). In 1966 UBSS started excavations to elucidate the stratification. This work was not entirely successful, as the former excavators had cleared out much more than had been thought. However, it was possible to set out a coherent account of the deposits, and to show that there had been at least two phases of occupation of the cave by man at different times. Pollen and granulometric analyses were done and these proved that the deposits did in fact cover a range from the end of the Ipswichian to the Holocene. (Tratman, Donovan and Campbell, 1971.)

5   *Uphill Bone Caves, Weston-super-Mare (316584)*

Both these caves have been quarried away. Roe has described (1968) a single Mousterian hand-axe (Middle Palaeolithic) from one of these caves and Davies (1926), has oppositely drawn attention to a small series of flint implements of early Upper Palaeolithic facies from one of the caves. It is not certain if the implements of both types came from the same cave or not. The fauna is much the same as that from the Hyaena Den, but *D. hemitoechus* is absent. Anthony Sutcliffe has also pointed out (personal communication) that the teeth of *F. leo spelaea* came from a small variety which would tend to put the date earlier (rather than later) than 50000 BP or the beginning of the Weichselian glaciation. The probability seems to be that there were two archaeological horizons of different age represented in these two caves.

6   *Picken's Hole, Crook Peak (39695500)*

An extensive exvacation has been mounted on the platform area outside the cave by the UBSS. The preliminary report (Tratman, 1964) sketched the sequence of deposits. The lowest bone-bearing layer was a red, clay-like cave earth, filling the hollows of an uneven rock surface. This surface was apparently an old roof-fall re-cemented with calcite. In the red cave earth was much bone, all in an extremely weathered condition. Two carnivores present were *Ursus arctos* and *Canis lupus*. Bovidae and Cervidae seem to have been their chief prey. Directly above, was an unconsolidated frost-shattered layer, with few bones of small animals. Above again, was a typical hyaena stratum with typical fauna of *Crocuta crocuta, Coelodonta antiquitatis, Mammuthus primigenius, F. leo spelaea, Bos sp., Rangifer tarandus, Alopex lagopus, Equus* but no *Ursus* or *Canis lupus.*

In this *Crocuta* layer were two human teeth and a number of nondescript pieces of poor quality flint, but unluckily, no definite implements of stone or bone. Difficulty has been encountered over radio-carbon dating, and the final report is not now likely to be ready till 1975. When these dates are available it should be possible to put this site into its proper place in the late Pleistocene sequence.

The next group of sites used by man, all belong to the Upper Palaeolithic, which is sub-divided into Early (or proto-Solutrean and Late (or Creswellian). In the Mendip caves there is no evidence of the Aurignacian culture, which, over considerable parts of Europe, preceded the Solutrean.

THE UPPER PALAEOLITHIC

7   *The Badger Hole, Wookey Hole (5344795)*
This is just above and slightly east of the Hyaena Den. The cave has a wide vestibule like the Hyaena Den, with a main passage running back to an inner chamber filled with a vast talus cone of material that has come through a roof-opening. Balch dug in the cave for twenty years (Ashworth, 1971). Unfortunately, the diaries of the excavation, as written by Balch, merely indicate extensive disturbance of the deposits and are virtually useless scientifically. However, an examination of the flint implements found by Balch, shows that they can all be referred to the early Upper Palaeolithic. The fauna includes *Crocuta crocuta, Coelondonta antiquitatis, Equus, Bos* and Cervidae. *Mammuthus primigenius* only occurred in the inner

chamber. More recently, McBurney (1961) and Campbell (personal communication, 1968) did some further excavation in areas left undug by Balch. Each found an Early Upper Palaeolithic implement, and one can agree with McBurney that the site showed only one occupation by man in the period.

To this period can be related, on the evidence of Balch's diaries, the two pieces of children's lower jaws. The diary entries were checked against the recollections of the finders of these pieces on the site. The jaws were contemporary with the hyaenas and other animals. They represent probably the earliest human bones recovered from any British cave.

8 Soldier's Hole, Cheddar (4687 5400)

This is a small shelter about 50m above the road on the south side. It was excavated under the direction of R. F. Parry (1931). This is a key site, for it is the only one in Mendip where the break in the sequence from Early to Later Upper Palaeolithic (LUP) can be demonstrated.

The 'lower working layers' of Parry, contained several EUP flint implements (and very fine ones they are too (fig 95). They should not be confused with the superficially similar Neolithic implements from the top layer (Gough's Cave Museum). The animal remains were scanty, and the following were represented: *Crocuta crocuta*, *F. leo spelaea*, *M. primigenius*, *U. arctos*, *R. tarandus* and *C. elaphus*, *Bos* and *Equus*. *C. antiquitatis* was not represented. The microtine fauna included various voles and lemmings.

Above these layers of compact cave earth were transition layers of more angular material, almost devoid of remains. Next upwards in the sequence was another red cave earth, lighter in colour and with less clay in it than the lowest cave earth. The transition was fairly abrupt. In this material were flint implements, belonging to the Creswellian. They included typical blunted back blades, somewhat reminiscent of penknife blades, and tending to be trapezoidal, though there were some of the specialised 'points' now known as 'Cheddar points' (fig 95). The fauna too had changed. *C. crocuta, F. leo spelaea and C. antiquitatis* had gone. There were now representatives of a tundra-steppe fauna and of a forest fauna. Included were *U. arctos, C. lupus, R. tarandus* as well as *C. elaphus, Equus, Vulpes vulpes* and *A. lagopus,* lemmings and voles and, of course, birds.

The deposits were sealed by a layer of stalagmite. On top of this were further thin deposits which contained Neolithic and later remains.

The layers at this site are all thin, due to its location which prevented rapid accumulation of deposits. Only fine material weathered from the cliff face above could enter, to which would be added larger material weathered off the shelter roof and walls, and the material that would accumulate through use of the cave by man. The time spread would be from probably Middle Weichselian through to the present time, or, in actual years, from about 40000 BP onwards.

There are three main caves in the Mendips that were used by man during the LUP. They are Sun Hole (also known as Sheep Hole), Gough's Cave, and Aveline's Hole. Between them they provide a record that covers the last phases of the Weichselian glaciation and the beginning of post-glacial times.

9 Sun Hole (Sheep Hole), Cheddar (46735408)

The cave lies about 50m above the road near the bottom of the Gorge on the north side. There had been (by treasure hunters) appreciable disturbance, of the superficial deposits down to the soft layer of stalagmite that covered the Pleistocene and Palaeolithic deposits. The latter were tested to a depth of 6m by the University of Bristol Speleological Society, and further work was done by J. B. Campbell. At the present time the cave is a pleasantly warm one even in the winter because the floor slopes up to the roof, and the back of the cave is closed. It was very different in the late Pleistocene. The basal portions of the deposit contain fine silts and gravels, which gradually change upwards to coarser, unweathered, angular rubbles which have come into the cave as a sort of slurry. Frost shattering of the walls of the cave near the entrance is greatly in evidence. At a depth of 1.5–2m in the Pleistocene deposits, flint implements of Creswellian type, human bones, and animal bones were found. Below, the deposits were sterile archaeologically, and above them the animal remains were very scanty. So this collection can be attributed to the intermittent occupation of the cave by man. The C^{14} date of this level has been obtained from a humerus of *U. arctos* (found by Campbell) as 10428 BC ± 150 (BM 524). The occupation was probably during the Alleröd interstadial of the Late Weichselian. A more detailed account was published by Tratman in 1955.

Above the stalagmite were layers containing Neolithic and later remains.

10   Gough's (New) Cave, Cheddar (46705391)
This is the present show cave. Gough's Old Cave is a short distance above and to the west of this cave.

Gough's Cave is the key site in the Mendips for the Late Upper Palaeolithic. It is only possible to give a brief summary of all that has been found and an interpretation of the finds. The cave has produced a series of objects that are unique for British caves. The only really satisfactory excavations of the archaeological deposits were those carried out by Parry (1929), and to these Donovan (1955) has added a close study of the sequence of the deposits.

From these studies, and my own, it can be deduced that the occupation of the cave began quite soon after it ceased to be a regular site of water resurgence. The deposits containing the archaeological remains were derived from weathering of the cliff face and from the immediate roof and walls at the entrance, together with accumulations directly due to the use of the cave by man. In addition, periodic flooding, which still takes place, added its quota of fine sand and silt. It is worth noting that even

(*right*) Wings of a Caddis Fly (Trichoptera) found in Cooks Wood Cave. The photograph is of the cast of the wings preserved in limestone as a fossil. The wing has a natural size of about 4mm. The larval form of modern species is frequently found in caves but the adult cannot survive underground for any length of time

(*left*) *Gammarus pulex* is a freshwater shrimp. It is best regarded as a trogloxene washed underground in flood. Specimens found underground are usually white but if returned to surface waters the normal colour soon returns. The natural length is about 11mm

(*right*) *Meta menardi* (Latreille) is sometimes known as the cave spider. It is normally found in the threshold zone of caves. The adult specimen illustrated has a body length of about 13mm and is shown beside an egg sac

Page 366

The infilled Pleistocene fissure at Westbury-sub-Mendip. The main bone bearing deposit extends from near the top for about 10m downwards. For scale note figures at bottom right

the major flood of July 1968 only transported material up to fine grade sand.

The flint industry is uniform and Creswellian in type, though it does have its own specialities known as Cheddar points, but this is not sufficient to dub it as a separate culture. Over 1,000 implements have been found and they form by far the finest collection for this period in the whole of Britain (fig 96).

The bone industry is quite extensive—much more so than at many other sites. The implements include a wide variety of points which have not yet been described adequately. Included in these is the tibia of a hare, that has down each of the long angles of the shaft, a series of deliberately made incisions arranged in groups. This is illustrated at top right of Plate on p 399, *u*. Continental examples are well known, but this is the only one at present adequately described for Britain. There are two so-called 'Batons de Commandment', which are shown in Plate on p 399, *u*. These are common at Continental sites but are the only two to be found in Britain. Both were made from reindeer antler. One was broken after much usage. The other shows comparatively little use. Their function was possibly for straightening arrows or even lance shafts or, more probably, for cleaning off tissue matter when preparing thongs for various purposes.

A piece of amber from the Baltic (Beck, 1965) has been found in the palaeolithic levels (see Plate p 399, *u*). It has been partly shaped by a pressure-flaking technique. Amber has never been found at such an early level in cave deposits in Britain before. The last, unique object, is a piece of animal rib (see Plate p 399, *l*) on which appears a very large series of man made incisions (Hawkes, Tratman and Powers, 1970). All these and many other items can be seen in the excellent local museum at the Cheddar caves.

The fauna belongs to a late glacial/post-glacial phase, and is very similar to that recorded for the Late Upper Palaeolithic in both Soldier's Hole and Sun Hole. The report on the human bones, other than Cheddar Man, includes a statement that they

M

were broken up in just the same way as the animal bones. A study of what is still available of these bones, confirms this judgement and so it is necessary to conclude that cannibalism was at least practised from time to time by this late Palaeolithic people.

'Cheddar Man' presents quite different problems. His bones were found quite accidentally, when a drainage trench was dug inside the cave. It is reasonably certain that the skeleton was originally complete in a crouched position, with the skull resting on the knees. Several finger bones were found inside the skull. So it seems that here is a deliberate burial put in more or less as bones, but when the ligaments were still, in part, holding the bones together. Now a burial implies a pit being dug to take the body, and it is also known that the skeleton was sealed by the general floor of stalagmite that seals the Pleistocene–Palaeolithic deposits over large areas of this cave. On the stratigraphical evidence, Cheddar Man belongs to the very end of the Palaeolithic occupation of the cave, and might even postdate this and be Mesolithic. So it is not surprising that the latest C^{14} date is given as 7130 BC $\pm$ 150 (BM 525).

No reliance whatsoever can be placed on the assumption that certain items, including one of the 'batons', were put in as grave goods with the burial. The circumstances of the discovery and removal of the bones most clearly deny the validity of any such assumption.

Cheddar Man was about twenty-two to twenty-five years old when he died. The state of wear of the teeth suggests the younger age. He was of slender build, and about 5ft 4in tall. He had a long skull but a broad face—a form of disharmony that bespeaks an element of Crômagnon Man in his make-up. Dressed in modern clothes he would be quite unremarkable in a mixed population, and any reconstructions to the contrary are without anatomical foundation. Finally, there are facets on the teeth of the lower jaw which show that he cleaned his teeth regularly and was very probably right-handed.

11 *Aveline's Hole, Burrington Combe (47615867)*

This is the cave that opens just off the road on the east side at the bottom of the Combe. It has had a long and rather complex history since its discovery, by accident, in 1797. It is taken last for the Palaeolithic because there is evidence that the occupation ended very late—around 6000 BC.

A constant feature in the accounts of the discovery is the quantity of human bones found partly 'embedded in black earth and partly covered with stalagmite' (see Davies, 1929). The cave suffered very considerable depredations by various persons including Dean Buckland, who is reputed to have removed fifty skulls and other material to Oxford. Only one has been traced. Boyd Dawkins made a major excavation, but fortunately sank his shaft in the inner chamber, leaving alone the outer chamber, which alone contained archaeological material.

The systematic excavation of the site was the work of the UBSS for more than a decade from 1919 onwards. It was thus all the more tragic that practically all the material, together with all the records, was destroyed in the war.

At the time of its discovery, the entrance to the cave was sealed by boulders and smaller rocks partly cemented with stalagmite. The UBSS, excavating in the outer chamber, found about one metre of cave earth containing remains resting on a lighter-coloured, laminated, non-plastic silt identical with that found in the inner chamber. Various degrees of disturbance were found. It was possible to separate the disturbed and undisturbed to a major extent.

It soon became apparent that the major mass of human bones, and the skulls found in an excavation made in 1914, were in the top of the deposit, and many were embedded in the stalagmite where this was present. Distinct from this major grouping, two burials were found in the lower part of the metre of cave earth near the bottom of the entrance slope as it then existed. These burials had been badly disturbed at the feet and by a treasure hunter's pit. At the head end, a large boulder had fallen out of the roof, crushing the skulls. Associated with the burials was a series of ornaments (fig 97) made from animal teeth and bone, and drilled for suspension, together with a number of sea-shells (*Neritoides obtusatus*) likewise drilled (see fig 97 p 395). There was a nest of seven ammonite body cases—fossils foreign to the area—and one other foreign fossil. Rather more gruesome was the find, near the shoulder of one burial, of the vertex of a child's skull, that had been cut off and placed, inverted, in the base of the same skull. Such discoveries are unique for Britain, but are paralleled from Continental sources. The significance of these finds is a matter for conjecture, but the vertex of a human skull could serve as a drinking vessel.

The flint industry was Creswellian, though rather more evolved than at Cheddar, and there were a number of micro-lithic forms. A harpoon made of stag antler, not reindeer, was of a very late type—equivalent to the French Magdalenian type 6B of Breuil (see fig 97 p 395). The immediate Continental connections are with Belgium and north-east France.

The human skeletal material from the topmost level and the stalagmite has proved most interesting. It includes long heads, broad heads, and hybrids of the two. One long-headed skull form, is almost identical with that of Cheddar Man. The differ-ences are probably due to sex, as the Aveline's skull was that of a woman. There was the same disharmony of facial features. This is the earliest occurrence of broad-headed people in Britain, and marks an influx of fresh folk from the Continent. Again the connections are with Belgium, and even further afield to Bavaria.

Only a very few jaw fragments were found. On the other hand, numerous single teeth were scattered through the deposit, mainly in the first thirty centimetres. The teeth were virtually free from caries of the modern fissure type, though there was some interstitial caries. There was ample evidence of poor gingival conditions and loss of teeth therefrom. A number of teeth showed gross caries-like lesions round their necks and spreading widely on to the roots. Much of this has turned out to be the outcome of post-mortem changes and not true caries. Probably the most interesting thing about the teeth is the evidence they present of the habitual use of tooth picks as cleaning agents. The lesions are unmistakable and indicate also that at least one individual was left-handed.

The main mass of human material seems to have been deposited within a short time. Some remains were probably put in as bones but one skeleton at least was put in articulated. Various explanations can be offered for this accumulation of human bones. Any such explanation must take into account the change in micro-climate within the cave. This change produced conditions favourable to the growth of massive flowstone deposits where there had been none formerly. A general climatic change may have been in part responsible for this. It is at least likely that the cave mouth was deliberately sealed by man after the last burials, and that the micro-climate within the cave was changed thereby. A natural collapse may also have closed the entrance. Such closure would stop air circulation.

The fauna calls for comment. From Aveline's Hole were recovered many remains of animals. They included shells (33 species), birds (39 species) and mammals (30 species). This gives an impressive total of 102 species, a total far larger than that from any other cave in Britain. The Mollusca, except one, can still be found locally. The thickness of the shells indicated a climate somewhat moister than today. One species of a mollusc, *Neritoides obtusatus*, the small periwinkle, had been fetched from the seashore to make a necklace. The avian species belong to those existing today, but not necessarily locally. The presence of such species as *Plectrophanes nivalis*, *Lagopus mutus*, *Lagopus sp.* (small form), and *Lagopus lagopus* impart a distinctly northern tinge to the climatic picture.

The mammal remains confirm this, for they include forms (now locally extinct) of northern distribution, such as *Ochotona spelaea* (*hpyerborea*?), *Dicrostonyx henseli* and *Lemmus lemmus*. The larger mammals include various forms of deer, *R. tarandus*,

C. elaphus and *Megaloceros giganteus*, but whether the species found at Aveline's Hole is identical with the Irish Giant Deer, or is a variant, is not fully established. The massive antlers of the Aveline's Hole specimens suggest that it may be a giant form of *C. elaphus. Equus, Bos sp.* and *Sus scrofa* are all represented.

The carnivora form quite an impressive array. They include *U. arctos, F. lynx, F. silvestris, V. vulpes, C. lupus, Canis sp.* and *M. putorius.* Aveline's Hole is thus one of the very few caves at which *F. lynx* has been found in Britain.

This is a fauna that is slightly later in facies than that of Gough's Cave, and there is an obvious admixture of steppe-tundra forms with forest forms. This places the time range from late Pleistocene on into the beginnings of post-Pleistocene times.

Two C^{14} dates are available from the British Museum Research Laboratory. One was obtained from a bone found in the deposits at an unknown depth (records destroyed in war), but not from the stalagmite. One from a skull found partly embedded in the stalagmite. These dates have not been published before. The bone gave 9114 BP±110 and the skull 8100 BP±50. Both dates are in agreement with other evidence. Between them they indicate a period of intermittent occupation of Aveline's Hole of a thousand years or more, and put the final date close to, if not actually into, the post-glacial cultural phase known as Mesolithic.

A few final comments on the Upper Palaeolithic must be made. Only cave sites have been dealt with, and a selection made of the more important ones. No consideration has been given to known open sites. No consideration has been given to sea level changes which have affected the whole of the skirts of Mendip. How many sites now lie buried under the many feet of alluvial deposits all round Mendip and for a long way out into the Bristol Channel, is unknown. There are probably many. Upper Palaeolithic man, like his predecessors, was a hunter/food gatherer. With a sea level at the beginning of the Weichselian glaciation far below that of the present day, there would have been good hunting country in the lowlands all around Mendip and out into the Bristol Channel as far as the edge of the buried channel. This is known to be 25m below OD at Avonmouth, and considerably deeper off the Mendips.

THE MESOLITHIC

The climatic change at the end of the Weichselian glaciation was fairly rapid. There was increasing warmth, precipitation and forest growth. The frequent occurrence of soft tufaceous stalagmitic deposits at the entrances and just inside a number of caves would seem to be related to this phase. They rest directly on Pleistocene material. It was during this time that the land bridge to Europe was finally ruptured.

New groups were obviously entering the country, and they brought with them new techniques, which included the use of minute flint implements meant to be held in bone or antler shafts. There was no abrupt transition. The evidence from open sites on the Mendips is that the newcomers joined up with the older inhabitants, and each learned from the other.

Caves ceased to be used as living sites. There are only two known to have been used, and both only very spasmodically or for only one short period. These are Rowberrow Cavern (45965802) (14) and Hay Wood rock shelter, Hutton (33995802) (20). At both sites, disturbance at later times had resulted in a mixture of deposits. It has already been shown that the last phase at Aveline's Hole and Cheddar Man could both be attributed to the opening stages of the Mesolithic without prejudice to the Late Upper Palaeolithic dating for the main occupation.

In Yorkshire, some Mesolithic sites have been C^{14} dated, in round figures, as early as 10000 BP (Flixton), and 9600 BP (Star Carr), and there is a general range of dates around 8000 BP. In the south there are comparable dates, eg Thatcham (Berks) 10400–8200 BP, Cherhill (Wilts) 7200 BP, Portland Bill (Dorset) 7100 BP and Westward Ho! (Devon) 6600 BP.

NEOLITHIC TIMES

The New Stone Age represents a whole series of changes brought into Britain by various sea routes. Such routes had already been in use for a long time in the preceding Mesolithic. The principle changes introduced by the newcomers were animal husbandry and agriculture, together with a range of new tools. Such evidence as there is does not point to an extinction of the earlier inhabitants but rather to an overlap and amalgamation.

The stone tools still include a wide variety of implements, chiefly of flint, made by flaking techniques. Tools of polished stone also appear. The axes form just one group of such polished tools, and a series of axe factories were developed in various parts of the country, and the axes were 'traded' afar. Though man was now living in larger and more permanently settled communities, movements of people were still going on. The earliest phases of the Neolithic in Britain are still poorly known. The first immigrants certainly arrived before 3500 BC and may be earlier than 4000 BC, but this remains to be proved. The later phases of the Neolithic are much better known, due to excavations at many sites.

In the Mendip caves, deposits at the entrance and just inside, continued to accumulate but at a slower rate than during the Pleistocene. Most of the material was in the form of partially weathered limestone pieces detached by vegetation processes and winter frosts from the cliff faces, roofs and walls at the cave mouths. Finer weathering products were produced in much smaller quantities. The result was a deposit of loose stones. So if man visited the site, or even made a more permanent residence there, the physical nature of the deposits would tend to allow objects to get out of their true stratigraphical position. Such loose deposits present major difficulties to satisfactory excavation.

The manner in which the material accumulates will inevitably involve the formation of a cone of dejection at the cave mouth. The material, if there are no rock walls to prevent it, will slide in all directions. The end result, if there is any platform at all outside the cave, will always be that the deposits on the platform will be considerably thicker outside the cave than inside, where they will tail off rapidly. The level of a given occupation inside and outside the cave will not be the same in relation to the surface for differing positions. This relative difference in level would be accentuated with the passage of time since the height of the cone outside the cave would increase more rapidly than the thickness of the material inside, and an almost step-like declivity would develop immediately under the cave arch.

Such evidence as there is from the caves implies that they were not used during the Neolithic except towards the end. At every site except one (Tom Tivey's Hole), the Neolithic horizon has produced native Neolithic pottery in association with the late Neolithic Beaker pottery, brought into Britain by a group of people mainly from the Rhine. The association could be a false one derived from an admixture of separate deposits in the very loose material comprising the determinable horizon. On the whole, from the evidence of sites other than caves it is more likely to be a true association than a false one. The approximate date would be in the range 2200–1800 BC. Some of it could be earlier by a century or so.

The cave sites to be considered lie in the Cheddar area, Ebbor Gorge, Burrington Combe and eastern Mendip.

8 Soldier's Hole

The soft tufaceous stalagmite sealing the Pleistocene–Palaeolithic deposits, had resting on it, and in some cases partly embedded in its topmost layer, a series of implements of Neolithic types, including a polished flint axe and a fine flint lance head, which was unpatinated. (Cheddar Museum.)

9 Sun Hole

The cone of dejection here stood about 30cm higher outside than just inside the cave arch. At a depth of 60cm outside the

M*

cave was a Neolithic horizon in very loose material. Because the Pleistocene deposits sloped steeply upwards inside the cave, the Neolithic horizon outcropped on the surface only 3m inside, (Henderson and Tratman, 1928). The Neolithic level rested on soft tufaceous stalagmite which sealed the Pleistocene ones.

Parts of Neolithic bowls, the bowl of a pottery spoon (a rare find), a few shards of 'Beaker' ware, and a series of flint implements were found. Some survived the war (UBSS Museum). Fragments from polished flint axe(s) were found, and also bone points, one of them being of the skewer form well known from many Neolithic sites.

12　*Chelm's Combe (46345447)*

The evidence from the rock shelter at Chelm's Combe, now quarried away, is not very satisfactory. The deposits here had two natural slopes, one inwards to the cliff overhang and one down the slope of the combe. The excavations were made in horizontal levels of arbitrary depth (Balch *et al*, 1927). Thus, in the published account, material which from its typology can be attributed to different periods, is recorded as coming from the same level.

However, it can be safely stated that there was quite a long period of occupation of the site in late Neolithic times. Two of the typical round-bottomed bowls have been reconstructed (Wells Museum). They can be matched against similar ones found at Windmill Hill in Wiltshire.

A little further down the slope a small rock-cut tomb was found in the cliff face. It was concealed under natural scree but all the same had been disturbed, for some of the bones were found outside the tomb. Five individuals were represented by the bones. No objects were found. The skull forms are closely comparable to those found in Neolithic long barrows. It is reasonably certain that this small tomb was cut, and used, by the Neolithic occupants of the shelter but there is no absolute proof.

In Ebbor Gorge, several small shelters with shallow deposits have been gutted at different times by various people. Some of the material found is on exhibition in the Wells Museum. All that can be said of this collection is that it contains some Neolithic items but that their stratigraphic relationship to other material, including human material, is quite uncertain.

13   Bridged Pot Shelter (Ebbor Gorge) (52604866)

It has this name from the rock bridge that was found to span the interior. This small site, only about 3m from front to back, was excavated by Balch. There was the usual cone of dejection outside and an abrupt drop down of about 60cm to the interior of the shelter, and then a slight slope down to the back.

At a depth of about 1m inside, Balch found a continuous floor of white tufa covering the whole of the interior, including the upper surface of the rock bridge. On this, and partly embedded in the tufa, were a polished flint axe and a splendid flint knife, densely patinated to white. The knife is not easily matched against other specimens from Mendip. There was no doubt of the association, and the axe is obviously of Neolithic date. The stratigraphic position confirms this and puts them fairly early in the Neolithic.

Below the tufa floor, Balch found only animal remains representing a very late glacial fauna with some admixture of post-glacial forms. At this stage, in order to be able to dig deeper at the back, the excavation was taken forward to cut through the talus cone on the platform. Immediately outside the cave arch on the north side, a hoard of eleven pieces of flint, either actual implements or roughouts for them, was found. These were hidden in a small recess, concealed perhaps by the boulders piled against the opening (the account is a little obscure on this point). Shortly after the discovery, the site was examined by several interested persons, including the author. The sealing layer of tufa could be traced outwards but ended short of the hoard site. But there was an obvious break upwards from the frost-shattered scree of the late glacial deposits, into the darker, humic post-glacial deposits. The change was quite distinct. The hoard-recess was at this level. On this evidence alone, the hoard cannot be earlier than the beginning of the post-glacial times.

The implements in the hoard show a somewhat different flaking technique to that of the knife associated with the polished axe. The hoard has been examined by a series of independent experts on flint implements. The unanimous opinion is that they are Neolithic. The difference in technique between the knife and the hoard would seem to point to a late date for the hoard, which could conceivably be of Bronze Age date. After all, the hoard was *concealed*, and at this site concealment would only be possible either by digging a pit or by piling up stones or a combination; so, if anything, the hoard was lying at a depth below its proper horizon. There is not one scrap of evidence from the stratigraphy, the fauna or the typology of the implements to suggest that they belong to the vastly older—by thousands of years—Solutrean or even the much older Mousterian, as hinted at by Balch.

14   Rowberrow Cavern (45965802)

Rowberrow Cavern yielded part of a round-bottomed Neolithic bowl in the spoil from a trench dug in Iron Age times. Below the trench were a few sherds of Beaker pottery. Together they indicate an occupation of short duration.

15   Bos Swallet (47095837)

From the mass of material in the hollow of this swallet, ox bones, many flint implements, and much beaker pottery (together with some cruder pottery) were found. The beaker pottery included two of the rare, handled forms. In the end it turned out that this whole deposit, including two pseudo-hearths, was nothing more than a miner's spoil-heap from a living site of the late Neolithic which they had destroyed. The living site was probably a little to the west of the swallet. It has not been found. (Taylor and ApSimon, 1964).

16   Cockles Wood, Nettlebridge (64644853)

The site is in eastern Mendip and consists of two small fissures in the Dolomitic Conglomerate. Both had been disturbed and both yielded some human bones and pottery. The lower cave had the better preserved deposits. It would seem to have served as both a living site and a burial site towards the end of the Neolithic. The usual combination of round-bottomed Neolithic pottery and beaker ware was found (Hickling and Seaby, 1952).

17   Tom Tivey's Hole, Leighton (70514447)

Outside this minute cave were found parts of the skeleton of a woman, together with a round-bottomed Neolithic bowl and a bone point. The pot can be matched in the series found at Windmill Hill. There was no grave, only a few placed stones and there had been some disturbance (Barrett, 1966).

THE BRONZE AGE

The title of this section is used to convey the idea of a major technological revolution and not of abrupt changes of people by invasion and conquest. The main change is the substitution of first copper, and then alloys of copper, eg tin to make bronze, for the manufacture of a large range of tools, weapons and ornaments. The use of stone, especially flint, continued to a very large extent, but such items of equipment as stone axes gradually disappeared as better metal tools became available. The distribution of living sites and burial sites indicates a great increase of population. In agriculture, wheat was largely supplanted by barley as the principal grain food. Animal husbandry continued and increased.

The sequence is very poorly represented indeed, in the Mendip caves. Rowberrow Cavern seems to have been used for a short while as a living site, and the thin hearth yielded two bronze awls (both destroyed in the war) and a few sherds of pottery. Sun Hole was apparently visited as there are a few potsherds from there, and likewise Chelm's Combe. 'The Slitter' at Cheddar

(Gough's Cave) yielded a single-looped, socketed bronze axe from the mass of scree sloping down from the Long Hole.

A small rift described as in Cook's Wood near Wookey (519486) (Mason, 1953) produced a couple of sherds of Bronze Age pottery, but it is thought that they fell in when a burial was made in the cave at a later date. Again in Hope Wood, Ebbor, came a plain, gold bracelet from a deposit just outside a tiny cave. It is of a late Bronze Age type (521485).

North of the Mendips, and north of Bristol at Combe Dingle, a minute horizontal slit of a cave in the side of the Trym valley held a small hoard of early types of bronze implements (55757726).

THE IRON AGE

This is again a convenient title to indicate another major technological change—the substitution of wrought iron for bronze for many utilitarian purposes. Bronze continued to be used, though mainly for ornamental purposes, and flint was still used though the manufacturing techniques seem to have suffered a severe decline. Fresh groups of people came into England during the Bronze Age and also in the Iron Age, and there is much evidence, particularly in the closing stages, of warfare between different groups of people. On the other hand there is much evidence of increased trading not only internally in Britain, but also to the Continent. There was obviously a very considerable increase in the population, and it may be surmised that this was one of the causes of warfare between groups of tribes.

The period can be divided into an earlier, or A phase and a later, or B phase, which carries the story up to the Roman conquest. At several cave sites it is not possible to separate the purely Iron Age levels from those of the Romano-British. The A phase is derived from the type site of Hallstatt in Austria, and the B from the type site of the lake village La Tène on Neuchatel in Switzerland.

For the A phase the Mendip caves have little to tell us. Sun

Hole and Chelm's Combe were certainly visited from time to time on the evidence of a few sherds of pottery of the period recovered from them. The occupation of the Great Cave of Wookey Hole (53184802) may have begun towards the end of the A phase around 250–300 BC.

18   Gough's (Old) Cave, Cheddar (46685388)

This is the only cave site shown to have been used as a living site in phase A. Though the deposits over most of the outer chamber of this cave had been badly disturbed, there was a limited area undisturbed. Under the topmost deposits were several distinct layers. Of these, the second or lower hearth proved to be of Iron Age A date (Tratman, 1960). This hearth rested directly on a floor of soft, white, tufaceous stalagmite. Some coarse and fine pottery was found, on which ApSimon (in Tratman, 1960) has reported. He compared it with pottery from other sites, notably with that from the ditch under the Roman Temple at Pagan's Hill near Chew Stoke. This pottery, he regards as some of the earliest, if not *the* earliest, Iron Age pottery in north Somerset, with a date in the fourth century BC (ApSimon, 1958).

The upper or first hearth was separated from the lower by 30cm of archaeologically sterile earth and stones. This must represent an appreciable gap in time between the two levels. In the upper hearth were a few sherds of Iron Age B pots (ie Glastonbury Lake Village ware) and a slight admixture of Roman pottery. On the whole, this hearth was native B and earlier than the Roman conquest; so the Roman pottery might properly be regarded as a later intrusion due to disturbance, particularly as the cave had been used as a dump for Roman pottery found elsewhere.

14   Rowberrow Cavern (45965802)

This particular cave had been used during the Iron Age for smelting iron on quite a large scale. This level lay well below the hearth dated by its pottery as Romano-British. So the lower hearth is appreciably older than this. A trench had been dug (Taylor, 1926) and lined with slabs of Old Red Sandstone. In this, iron ores had been smelted. Quantities of slag and charcoal were found, and one very large bloom. The heat generated during the process had been high enough to fuse some of the Old Red Sandstone slabs together. Very few objects were found, and all the material was destroyed in the war. The few scraps of pottery found were of the Glastonbury Lake Village type, and allow a date of around first century BC to be allocated to this iron-smelting phase. The site was abandoned well before the Roman conquest.

12   Chelm's Combe

A bowl furnace used for smelting iron was found here (Wells Museum). The account of its discovery is not clear, but the bowl probably dates from the Iron Age and is not Romano-British.

19   Read's Cavern, Burrington (46825844)

This is the last site with a purely Iron Age occupation. It was found in 1919 by the UBSS. The entrance descent in those days was rather dangerous because of the decidedly unstable nature of the material lodged down the descent route of about 15m. from the surface to the main chamber floor at the east end. From the point of view of the occupation, only the main chamber—some 50m long by 6m or so wide, and which runs west—was used. When found, it was a beautifully decorated cave; not the muddy horror it has become by deliberate destruction of all the speleothems.

On the first day of exploration, those in the party were astonished to find remains lying on the surface in different places showing that the cave had been occupied by man in the Iron Age. Ten years of patient excavation followed. The entrance used in Iron Age times was located and opened. It provided a safe and easy descent to the cave. It also emerged from the excavations that when the cave was used it was more of a deep shelter than a cave. Daylight would have penetrated to all parts of the main chamber. The cave was abandoned because there was a major collapse, which caught and killed some of the inhabitants. The whole of the overhanging cliff face came down, burying the prehistoric entrance with rock to a depth of 5m. Great pieces fell out of the roof. The micro-climate within the cave changed. It became wet as there were no longer air currents to keep it dry. Stalagmite-flows rapidly covered the floor, becoming as thick as 10cm over the hearth material. At a later date, minor shifts of the fallen material brought some of the bones of the victims down into the cave. Such shifts are still happening.

The finds included a wide variety of objects. In one area, a hole in the floor had been covered by hurdle work on top of which clay had been laid. The hurdle rotted, and the finds fell to a lower level to lie waiting to be picked up. This was near the eastern end of the north side and may have been the principal sleeping area, for even now it is a dry zone in an otherwise damp cave. Some of the iron work was very fine, particularly the beautifully designed horse hobbles (see Plate p 400, *l*). Much pottery, and some spindle whorls but no weaving combs were found. Two bronze brooches enable a date to be fixed between 200 and 100 BC; probably around 150 BC.

Much of the material was destroyed in the war but a fair amount was recovered from the ruins of the University and is now again on display in the UBSS Museum.

20   *Haywood Cave, Hutton (33995802)*
This small site was used for human burials in the pre-Roman Iron Age (see A. and R. Everton, 1972). Only one other such burial cave is known in the area and that is outside Mendip proper at Cheston Combe, Backwell (33995822). The site has been quarried away. Some material survived the war and is in UBSS Museum.

THE ROMAN CONQUEST

The Roman conquest produced many changes. Caves generally were abandoned as living sites, but not all. There was quite a long occupation at Gough's Cave where it may have started in the Iron Age. Unfortunately the chief area of occupation had been so badly disturbed, and so much of the top material had been carted away, that even Parry was unable to produce order out of chaos. The Great Cave of Wookey Hole (see below) continued to be used into the fourth century, for the latest coins found were those of Valentinian II AD 375.

The Long Hole or Roman Cave, a high-level cave above Gough's Old Cave, was once the site of occupation. It has since been gutted to rock bottom. It did yield a hoard of Roman coins (Boon, 1958) of late date. Numerous Romano-British remains have come from what is now a coach park, just up the road from Gough's Cave. The small cave opposite this coach park is known as Pride Evan's Hole, after the man who lived in it well into the twentieth century. He had cleared out all but the bottom of a tiny recess behind his fireplace. From this was recovered a small hoard of Roman coins, forty-seven in all. The remarkable thing about them is that the date for their minting is in the range AD 267–276.

Finds of Roman coins have been made in other caves, such as the small one at the south end of Callow rocks, Shipham (44785575). The faint indications are that when the Saxon raids began along the Somerset coast and many Roman villas were destroyed by fire, some resort was made to caves for shelter and protection. Since then very little use has been made of caves as living sites with the exception of Gough's Old Cave and Rowberrow Cave, and probably Wookey Hole, Great Cave.

21   *The Great Cave of Wookey Hole (53184802)*

This site has been left to the last because its archaeological contents fit best into the end of the sequence already described.

Further it is the site of Balch's major excavation and contribution to the archaeology of the Mendip caves.

There is no need to go into detail of the archaeology of this site. Two books by Balch, 1914 and 1947, are available and should be consulted.

The main occupation area was at the entrance. The Goatherd's Stable and the area around were dug, and a little work done in the First Chamber. Cave divers have since found remains in the Fourth Chamber which seemed to have been used as a cemetery during Roman times. It is now flooded because the dam across the river at the resurgence maintains the water level well above the natural level.

In the entrance parts, there was in excess of 1m of material below the Romano-British level, which was, on average, only 15cm thick. The whole of the lower layers contained Iron Age remains. They have been described in considerable detail. Amongst other things, Balch noted that bone pins were commonest near the fireplace. He thought that this was perhaps because the woman slept nearest to the fire, and the men further away. He also noted that there were some human bones in the hearth material and they seemed to have been treated in the same way as bones of animals. Occasional cannibalism must be suspected. That is not surprising in the light of accounts of the Celtic peoples given by classical writers. The total range of objects found is wide, and the collection in the Wells Museum well worth a visit. There is also a small amount of material in the museum attached to the cave car park.

The remains of the goatherd present problems. The artifacts illustrated seem to be of two ages. The key or latch-lifter is Iron Age and of a well known type. The bill-hook might be of any age from Iron Age onwards. It is an implement that in its essentials has remained unchanged down to the present day. The knife, with its triangular blade, could perhaps be Iron Age, but is much more likely to be medieval. The comb is a hair comb, not a weaving comb, and is not a type found at local Iron Age sites. It is more likely to be medieval. The single pot might be of any age from Iron Age to medieval. Finally there are the two femora. Anatomists have commented that they are not a pair. One is female and the other male. It must be concluded that the group represents a disturbed deposit of at least two persons, and that there had either been considerable disturbance of the site, or unskilled excavation. It may be inferred that there was at least one goatherd living in the cave in medieval times. This may have given rise to the famous legend of the witch.

In the First Chamber, pottery in the dripstone pools and in the mud of the river bank, confirms that the people did go as far into the cave as this fairly regularly; and for the special purposes of funerary rites in the Roman period, probably went as far as the Fourth Chamber.

One wonders what the river course would be like if there was no dam. It seems highly probable that it would be possible to go in at the river mouth and get as far as the Fourth Chamber, crossing and re-crossing the river. If so, this would fulfil the legend attached to Cheddar of being able to go a long way into caves 'crossing and re-crossing the river' etc. A transfer of location is not uncommon in legends, and certainly there is nothing near the resurgences at Cheddar that would fit the legend.

ROMAN

A number of cave sites have produced evidence of usage in Roman times. For example, Gough's Old Cave, Gough's (New) Cave [the present show cave], Rowberrow Cavern, Wookey Hole and several small sites in the Cheddar and Ebbor gorges. Indeed almost all caves in Mendip that were suitable for habitation were used, occasionally or for longer periods, as living sites. Just one cave calls for specific mention.

22   *White Woman's Cave, Leighton (70334433)*

This tiny cave is close to Tom Tivey's Hole. Its contents had been greatly disturbed. Careful, patient excavation directed by

J. H. Barrett over a period of years produced evidence that the cave had been used as a den by Roman counterfeiters. This is a unique discovery for Mendip (see Barrett and Boon, 1972).

POST-ROMAN TO RECENT

Caves have always attracted the adventurer, the treasure hunter, the picnicker and the homeless. This applies to Mendip. Suitable sites seem to have been visited from time to time. A few such as Gough's Old Cave and Pride Evan's Hole at Cheddar were adapted as permanent homes and were lived in till well into the twentieth century. The goatherd(s) of Wookey probably used the cave in medieval times; Rowberrow Cavern was certainly used then. Lamb Leer was found by miners who mined extensively there for lead ores. No doubt Mendip miners broke into other caves from their shafts and galleries. Sandford Hill is riddled with workings, some of which can be seen to have broken into natural cavities.

The human skeletons found in the first chamber of Ubley Hill Pot (51605693) may have been those of miners exploring for ores. They lay scattered beneath the shaft, which is entirely natural in its lower part and unclimbable without a rope. [This is not the shaft opened up by the Mendip Caving Group.] On the other hand the total absence of any traces of clothing or other equipment, makes it rather more likely that they were unclothed bodies flung down after some murderous quarrel long ago. There is plenty of evidence that the Mendip miners were a pretty rough crowd even by the standards of their own times.

NOTES ON MINOR SITES

Cheddar area

23   *Flint Jack's Cave (46325381)* : A rock shelter above the road below Gough's Cave. It yielded many late Upper Palaeolithic flints—hence its name—of which a few survive in the British Museum. There were human remains including skulls,

probably associated with the flint implements. (Oakley *et al*, 1958.)

24   *Long Hole (46685387)* : In addition to the Roman material, there is Pleistocene. All this seems to be entering the cave from a rift about 30m in on the left. It opens above the floor and is difficult of access. The bottom of a mass of angular limestone scree can be reached. This lies in a steeply ascending rift. Out of it fall bones of Pleistocene animals. Most belong to a fauna of probably Weichselian age, but *Dama dama* is represented so it may belong to the end of the Ipswichian. (Tratman, 1966, p 42)

25   *Sugarloaf Rock (46905415)* : This is a prominent rock, standing up from the road side about 100m up from Gough's Cave on the right. On the north side is a rift. There is some confusion about where the Pleistocene animal bones were found. Boyd Dawkins and Gough dug in the rift in the north face and cleared it out. The faunal remains are claimed by Balch to come from the fissure. Victor Painter claimed that they came from a still-visible rock shelter and its scree contents south of the rock at the back of the present car park. Painter did some of the digging himself. The animals included *Coelodonta antiquitatis, M. primigenius, F. leo spelaea, Crocuta crocuta* and *Ursus sp.*

26   *Bone Hole (Mr Long's Cave) (48045470)* : The accounts of this cave and its contents are most unsatisfactory. Many animal bones are said to have been found, but they could have been more recent than Pleistocene. A human skull was found, and perhaps some other human bones. At the back, a climb leads to the bottom of a steeply ascending passage, which is filled with an angular limestone scree partly cemented with soft stalagmite. This has been partially excavated and may have been the main source of the bones. The surface opening of the top of this passage has not been located, and there are no indications of its presence in the expected position.

27   *Totty Pot (48255357)* : On high ground, well away from the road at the top of Cheddar Gorge. A partial excavation has produced evidence of an occupation in Mesolithic and later

times. Human remains seem to be associated with Mesolithic level (unpubl).

28 *Quarry above road below Cliff Plantation (580542)*: Victor Painter asserted that when the scree material immediately adjacent to this small and now disused quarry was moved, bones of *M. primigenius* and *Coelodonta antiquitatis* were found. There seems no reason to doubt this statement.

29 *Rhino Rift, Longwood (48475557)*: In the preliminary excavation for an exploring cave here, a few teeth of *C. antiquitatis* and some bones of *Crocuta crocuta* were found. Some of the material survived the war in the UBSS Museum.

Wookey Hole

30 *Rhinoceros Hole (53234793)*: A tiny cave above and south of Hyaena Den. At present under excavation by UBSS. The platform area has material of two faunas, and has also yielded a few bone implements of crude workmanship. The two faunas belong to the Weichselian glaciation and the end of the preceding Eemian interglacial.

Burrington area

31 *Goatchurch Cavern (47585823)*: Entrance Gallery, The Traverse and the Dining Chamber have all provided scanty Pleistocene animal bones.

32 *Foxes Hole (Plumley's Den) (48235822)*: Boyd Dawkins dug here and found some Pleistocene animal bones in the outer chamber.

33 *Blagdon Bone Fissure*: Site lost. Teeth of *Coelodonta antiquitatis* and *Bos sp.* and some bones were found when it was discovered.

Western Mendip

34 *Sandford Hill (4259)*: One or more bone fissures or caves with bones found. Sites now lost. The extant material is in the

County Museum, Taunton. The fauna is late Pleistocene but not final Pleistocene.

35   *The Wolf Den, Wavering Down (39555634)* : A small cave named after the principal animal represented by the bones. A very late Pleistocene fauna was present.

36   *Loxton Cave (37425596)* : A cave with ramifying passages. There is at least one connection vertically up to the surface. There are bones in places and some may be as early as very late Pleistocene.

37   *Hutton Bone Cave (36115812)* : The entrance has recently been rediscovered and opened by members of the Axbridge Caving Club. Remnants of the bone deposits recorded by earlier explorers are present. They had all come down through roof openings. The recorded fauna is late Pleistocene and it is possible that some of the material is as early as the end of the Ipswichian. *R. tarandus* was the most common animal.

38   *Worlebury Hill* : There was a small cave here, now quarried away, which yielded some Pleistocene animal bones. (Weston Museum.)

39   *Brean Down (2959)* : There is a fissure in the south side about 95m west of the Sand Cliff Site. It contains similar material (ApSimon, Donovan and Taylor, 1961).

40   *Steep Holm* : Sea rift type caves are said to exist here and to be accessible at low tide. The appearance of the deposits suggests that they are identical with those of the Sand Cliff at Brean Down.

Eastern Mendip

41   *Dulcote Quarry (567443)* : A series of small rifts and caves have been exposed from time to time by quarrying, and have been destroyed. One or more of them contained late Pleistocene animal remains.

42   *Whatley Quarry (730482)* : A small cave that had served as a natural pitfall was exposed and quarried away. The animals represented were *M. primigenius*, *Equus sp.* and *Gulo gulo*. The

last is not often found in Mendip caves. This is a late Pleistocene fauna.

43 *Cockles Wood Cave (64644853)* : The late Neolithic material has been described. There are two caves here one above the other. It is not clear from the account what was found in each cave, but the main mass of animal bones came from the lower cave. It is probably this mass that contained the reindeer material which puts the beginning of the accumulation of bones considerably earlier than the late Neolithic represented by the pottery.

44 *Stoke St Michael or Stoke Lane Slocker (66874743)* : Beyond the first sump is a large chamber known as the Bone Chamber. This lies partly under a deep surface depression. There is much mud in the chamber and in the upper part of this mud were human remains. These have not yet been dated. But their appearance in the deposits and the nature of those deposits indicates that the bones are of no great antiquity. When I saw them *in situ*, shortly after their discovery, it seemed to me that some of the so-called charcoal was indeed produced by the burning of paper, and perhaps even newspaper.

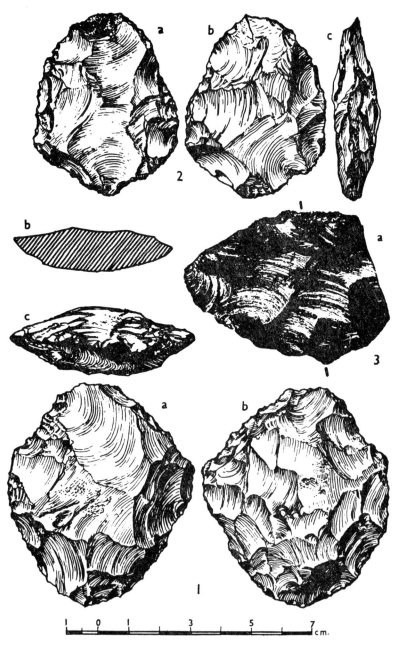

Fig 94 Hyaena Den (Wookey Hole). Bifacial flint tools from the
Mousterian levels. After Donovan, 1971.

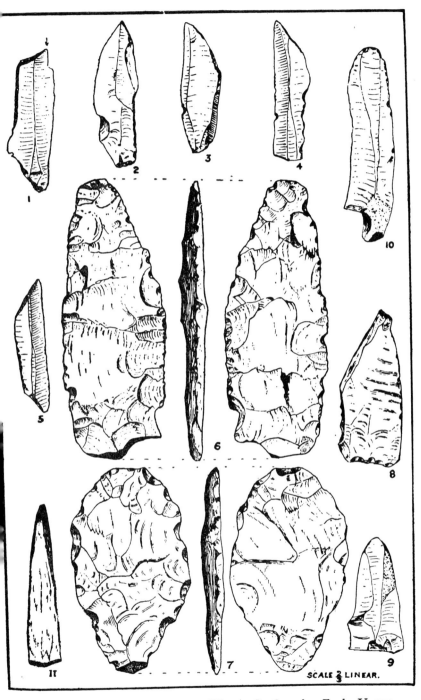

Fig 95 Soldier's Hole, Cheddar. Flint tools, 6 and 7 Early Upper
Palaeolithic, 1–5 Late Upper Palaeolithic. The contrast between
the two types is very evident. After Parry, 1931.

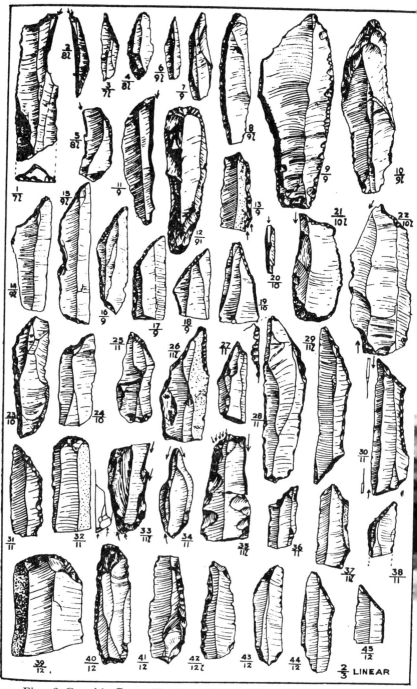

Fig 96 Gough's Cave, Cheddar. Series of Late Upper Palaeolithic flint tools. Blunt backed triangular forms (Cheddar points) and blunt backed trapezoidal forms are common, with scrapers and burins (engravers). After Davis, 1929.

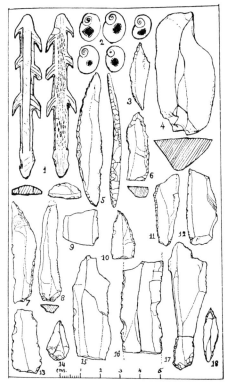

Fig 97 Aveline's Hole, Burrington. Harpoons of red deer antler,
part of a necklace of sea shells and flint tools, rather smaller than
the Cheddar examples. After Davis, 1921.

Latin	English equivalent
Hippopotamus amphibius	Hippopotamus
Mammuthus primigenius	Mammoth
Coelodonta antiquitatis	Woolly rhinoceros
Rhinoceros hemitoechus	Steppe rhinoceros
Dicerorhinus etruscus	Etruscan rhinoceros
Bos sp., *Bovidae*	Ox
Equus sp.	Horse
Cervus, Cervidae	Deer, deer family
Cervus elaphus	Red deer
Dama dama	Fallow deer
Megaloceros giganteus	Giant deer or Irish elk
Capreolus capreolus	Roe deer
Rangifer tarandus	Reindeer
Ursus, Ursidae	Bear, Bears
U. arctos	Brown bear
U. speleus	Cave bear
Crocuta crocuta (Erxleben)	Spotted or cave hyaena
Homotherium sp.	Sabre-toothed tiger
Felis leo spelaea	Cave lion
F. sylvestris	Wild cat
F. lynx	Lynx
Gulo gulo	Glutton or wolverine
Mustela putorius	Polecat

396

Canis sp.	Dog
Canis lupus	Wolf
Vulpes vulpes	Red fox
Alopex lagopus	Arctic fox
Sus scrofa	Pig
Lemmus lemmus	Lemming (Norwegian)
Dicrostonyx henseli	Banded or Hensel's lemming
Ochotona spelaea	Cave pika (a small tailless hare)
Neritoides obtusatus	Small periwinkle
Plectrophanes nivalis	Snow bunting
Lagopus mutus	Ptarmigan
Lagopus lagopus	Red grouse
Lagopus sp.	Ptarmigan (small variety)

County Museum, Taunton Castle, Taunton	Mainly animal remains from the Sandford and Beard Collections. Mostly in store.
Borough Museum, The Boulevard, Weston-super-Mare	A small collection of flint implements from the Uphill caves, and some alleged to be from Banwell and Flint Jack's caves. Animal bones from various Pleistocene sites.
Gough's Cave Museum, Cheddar	A splendid collection of material from the Cheddar caves, especially Soldier's Hole and Gough's (New) Cave. Cheddar Man. Reserve collections.
Axbridge Museum	A limited amount of material including *Coelodonta antiquitatis* from the Triple H Cave (53214802).
Wells Museum, Wells	Mostly in the Balch Room. Material from Milton Hill, Hyaena and Badger Hole at Wookey Hole. The majority of finds from the Great Cave of Wookey Hole. Finds from Ebbor shelters and Chelm's Combe.
Wookey Hole Caves Museum	Limited amount of material from the Great Cave and Hyaena Den and from sites in Ebbor Gorge.

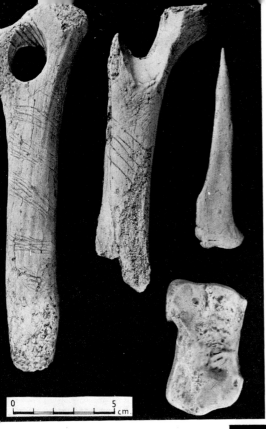

Page 399

(left) Baton de Commandment, hare tibia tally mark and a piece of partly shaped Baltic amber from Gough's Cave (below) Piece of animal rib 'decorated' with a large series of incisions, from Gough's Cave. Each is approximately 12cm long

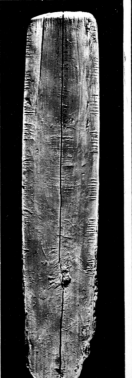
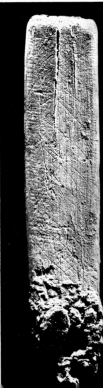

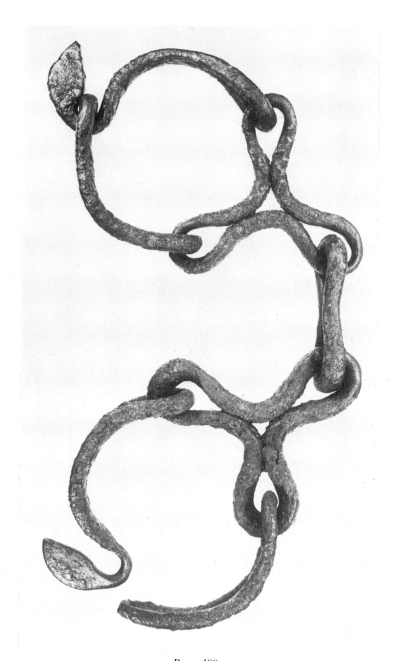

Page 400

Iron horse hobbles from Read's Cavern, Burrington. Actual length from extremity to extremity is 32.5cm

City Museum, Queen's Road, Bristol

Most of the cave material was destroyed in 1940. Still has material from Uphill caves and Walton (Clevedon) cave. Combe Dingle Bronze Age hoard.

University of Bristol, Dept of Geology

Bones and teeth from Durdham Downs Fissure. Walton (Clevedon) and Uphill caves. Except for Walton the amount of material is small. Quarry, Westbury-sub-Mendip bone fissure—all material recovered 1969–71. All material, Lime Kiln Hill quarry Mells, 1971.

University of Bristol Speleological Society

(Much material destroyed in 1940.) Aveline's Hole, Sun Hole, Gough's Old Cave, Picken's Hole, Wookey Hole, Hyaena Den and Rhinoceros Hole, Read's Cavern, Rowberrow Cavern, Brean Down (Sand cliff and cave site). Banwell (a few bones), Bos Swallet.

Also material from Alveston Bone Fissure (Glos). King Arthur's Cave and Merlin's Cave (Wye Valley). For Merlins Cave only Pleistocene rodents survived 1940.

N

Throughout this chapter, references have been kept to a minimum. If all the references had been put in they would run to several hundred entries. Essential entries have been made and full details given in the bibliography on pp 401–419. Books that can be consulted are :

Wookey Hole, Its Caves and Cave Dwellers	Balch, H. E. 1914
Mendip—The Great Cave of Wookey Hole	Balch, H. E. 3rd ed 1947
Mendip—Cheddar. Its Gorge and Caves	Balch, H. E. 2nd ed 1947
Mendip—Its Swallet Caves and Rock-shelters	Balch, H. E. 2nd ed 1947
The Complete Caves of Mendip	Barrington, N. and Stanton, W. 2nd ed 1972

The *Proceedings of the University of Bristol Speleological Society* contain most of the original worthwhile papers on cave archaeology published since 1920. An author index to all papers appeared in 1969, Vol 12(1), the Jubilee issue. Occasional worthwhile papers have appeared in the *Proceedings of the Somersetshire Archaeological and Natural History Society*. Most of these are individually cited in the bibliography. The *Journal of the Mendip Nature Research Committee of the Wells Natural History and Archaeological Society* provides occasional pieces of information. So, too, do the News Letters and *Journal of the Axbridge Caving Group and Archaeological Society*.

Two papers by Donovan (1954, 1964) present a valuable bibliography for the Palaeolithic–Pleistocene periods. In these papers are given all the known sources of information.

Another valuable reference source is the Mendip Cave Registry. A loose-leaf compilation, which is available for study in the Central Reference Library, College Green, Bristol.

The Notes on Minor Sites covers the majority, but not all, of the sites not mentioned in the general text.

Bibliography

APSIMON, A. M. & DONOVAN, D. T. (1956). 'Marine Pleistocene deposits in the Vale of Gordano, Somerset', *Proc Univ Bristol Spel Soc*, 7 (3), 130–6.

APSIMON, A. M. (1958). 'The Iron Age "A" Ditch and Pottery at Pagan's Hill, Chew Stoke', *Proc Univ Bristol Spel Soc*, 8 (2), 97–105.

APSIMON, A. M. (1960). 'Notes on the Pottery from Gough's Cave', *Proc Univ Bristol Spel Soc*, 9 (1), 19.

APSIMON, A. M., DONOVAN, D. T. & TAYLOR, M. (1961). 'The stratigraphy and archaeology of the Late-Glacial and Post-Glacial deposits at Brean Down, Somerset', *Proc Univ Bristol Spel Soc*, 9 (2), 67–136.

ASHWORTH, H. W. W. (1971). 'Fourteen Years at the Badger Hole', (From diaries of Balch, H. E.), *Wells Nat Hist and Archaeol Soc*.

ATKINSON, T. C. (1966). 'Now at last it can be told—extensions in the fossil series of Swildon's Hole', *J. Wessex Cave Club*, 9 (10), 59–64.

ATKINSON, T. C. (1967). 'The geomorphology of Longwood Swallet, Charterhouse-on-Mendip, *Proc Univ Bristol Spel Soc*, 11 (2), 161–85.

ATKINSON, T. C. (1968). 'The earliest stages of underground drainage in limestones—a speculative discussion', *Proc British Spel Ass*, 6, 53–70.

ATKINSON, T. C. (1970). 'Water tracing on Mendip', *J Wessex Cave Club*, 11 (130), p 98.

ATKINSON, T. C. (1971). 'Hydrology and erosion in a limestone terrain', *Unpublished PhD thesis, Univ of Bristol*.

BALCH, H. E. *The Netherworld of Mendip* (1907).

BALCH, H. E. *et al* (1927). 'Excavations at Chelm's Combe, Cheddar', *Proc Somerset Archaeol Nat Hist*, 72 (2), 97–100.

BALCH, H. E. *Mendip : the Great Cave of Wookey Hole* (1929).

BALCH, H. E. *Mendip, its swallet caves and rock shelters* (1937).

BALCHIN, W. G. V. (1952). 'The erosion surfaces of Exmoor', *Geog J*, 118, 453–76.

BALFOUR-BROWNE, F. (1950). 'British water beetles', *Ray Soc Pub*, V 2, nos 127 and 143.

BAMBER, A. E. (1924). 'The Avonian of the west Mendips from Cheddar valley to the sea', *Proc Bristol Nat Soc*, 6 (4), 75–91.

BARRETT, J. H. (1966). 'Tom Tivey's Hole Shelter, near Leighton, Somerset', *Proc Univ Bristol Spel Soc*, 11 (1), 9–24.

BARRETT, J. H. & BOON, G. C. (1972). 'A Roman counterfeiter's hide, White Woman's Hole', *Proc Univ Bristol Spel Soc*, 13 (1), 61–9.

BARRINGTON, N. & STANTON, W. I. *The complete caves of Mendip* (1972). Cheddar. 2nd edition.

BECK, KURT W. (1965). 'The Origin of the amber found at Gough's Cave, Cheddar, Somerset', *Proc Univ Bristol Spel Soc*, 10 (3), 272–6.

BLUCK, B. J. (1965). 'The sedimentary history of some Triassic conglomerates in the Vale of Glamorgan, South Wales', *Sedimentology*, 4, 225–45.

BÖGLI, A. (1964). 'Mischungskorrosion—ein Beitrag zur Verkerstungsproblem', *Erdkunde*, 18 (2), 83–92.

BÖHMERS, A. (1956). 'A preliminary report on the Younger Palaeolithic of Northwestern Europe', *Palaeohistoria*, 5, 7–26.

BOON, G. C. (1958). 'Roman coins from Gough's Old Cave and The Slitter, Cheddar', *Numis Chrnc*, 17, 231–7.

BRETZ, J. H. (1942). 'Vadose and phreatic features of limestone caverns', *J Geol*, 50, 675–811.

BRISTOL EXPLORATION CLUB (1968). *Caving Report*, no 13, St Cuthbert's Swallet, Parts A–O.

N*

406　　　　　Bibliography

BRUNSDEN, D. (1963). 'The denudation chronology of the River Dart', *Trans Inst Brit Geogr*, 32, 49–63.

CALLAWAY, C. (1902). 'The zig-zag course of Cheddar Gorge', *Geol Mag*, ix, 67–9.

CAMPBELL, J. B., ELKINGTON, D., FOWLER, P. J. & GRINSELL, L. V. (1970). 'The Mendip Hills in Prehistoric and Roman Times', *Bristol Archaeol Res Gp*, 36 p.

CLAYDEN, B. W. & FINDLAY, D. C. (1960). 'Mendip derived gravels and their relationship to combes', *Abstracts Proc 3rd Conf Geol and Geomorph SW England, Royal Geol Soc of Cornwall*, p 24.

COLEMAN, A. M. & BALCHIN, W. G. V. (1959). 'The origin and development of surface depressions in the Mendip Hills', *Proc Geol Assoc London*, 70, 291–309.

CORBEL, J. (1957). 'Les karsts du nord-ouest de l'Europe', *Inst des Etudes Rhodaniennes*, Lyon, mem 12.

CUMMINGS, R. H. (1958). 'The faunal analysis and stratigraphical application of Upper Palaeozoic smaller foraminifera', *Micro palaeotology*, 4 (1), 1–24.

CVIJIĆ, J. (1918). 'L'Hydrographie souterraine et l'évolution morphologique du karst', *Revue Géogr alp*, 6, 375–426.

DAVIES, J. A. (1921). 'Aveline's Hole, Burrington Combe', *Proc Univ Bristol Spel Soc*, 1, 61–78.

DAVIES, J. A. (1926). 'Notes on Upper Palaeolithic implements from some Mendip caves', *Proc Univ Bristol Spel Soc*, 2 (3), 261–73.

DAVIES, W. E. (1960). 'Origin of caves in folded limestone', *Nat Spel Soc Bull*, 22 (1), 5–18.

DAVIS, S. N. (1966). 'Initiation of ground-water flow in jointed limestone', *Nat Spel Soc Bull*, 28 (3), 111–18.

DAVIS, W. M. (1899). 'The geological cycle', *Geog J*, 14, 481–504.

DAVIS, W. M. (1930). 'Origin of limestone caverns', *Bull Geol Soc Amer*, 41, 475–628.

DAWKINS, W. B. (1862). 'On a Hyaena-den at Wookey Hole, near Wells', *Q J Geol Soc Lond*, 18, 115–25.

DE MARTONNE, E. *Traité de géographie physique* (1926), Vol 2, Paris.

DINES, H. G., EDWARDS, W., HOLLINGWORTH, S. E., BUCHAN, S. & WELCH, F. B. A. (1940). 'The mapping of head deposits', *Geol Mag*, 77, 198–226.

DONOVAN, D. T. (1954). A bibliography of the Palaeolithic and Pleistocene sites of the Mendip, Bath and Bristol area', *Proc Univ Bristol Spel Soc*, 7 (1), 23–34.

DONOVAN, D. T. (1955). 'The Pleistocene deposits of Gough's Cave, Cheddar, including an account of recent excavations', *Proc Univ Bristol Spel Soc*, 7 (2), 76–104.

DONOVAN, D. T. (1958). 'Easter field meeting: the Lower and Middle Triassic rocks of the Bristol District', *Proc Geol Assoc London*, 69, 130–40.

DONOVAN, D. T. (1964). 'A bibliography of the Palaeolithic and Pleistocene sites of the Mendip, Bath and Bristol area. First supplement', *Proc Univ Bristol Spel Soc*, 10 (2), 89–97.

DONOVAN, D. T. (1968). 'The ammonites and other fossils from Aveline's Hole (Burrington Combe, Somerset)', *Proc Univ Bristol Spel Soc*, 11 (3), 237–42.

DONOVAN, D. T. (1969a). 'Geomorphology and hydrology of the central Mendips', *Proc Univ Bristol Spel Soc*, 12 (1), 63–74.

DONOVAN, D. T. (1969b). 'Letter to the editor', *Proc Geol Assoc London*, 80, p 379.

DOUGLAS, I. (1964). 'Intensity and periodicity in denudation processes with special reference to the removal of material in solution by rivers', *Z Geomorph*, 8, 453–73.

DREW, D. P. (1964). 'The Origin and Development of the Cave Systems of the Stoke Lane area, East Mendip, in relation to the evolution of surface topography', *Unpublished B. A. Dissertation, Department of Geography, Univ of Nottingham*.

DREW, D. P. (1966). 'The water-table concept in limestones', *Proc Brit Spel Assoc*, 4, 57–67.

DREW, D. P. (1967). 'Aspects of the limestone hydrology of the Mendip Hills', *Unpublished PhD thesis, Univ of Bristol*.

DREW, D. P. (1968). 'A study of the limestone hydrology of the St Dunstan's Well and Ashwick drainage basins, eastern Mendip, Somerset', *Proc Univ Bristol Spel Soc*, 11 (3), 257–76.

DREW, D. P. (1970a). 'Limestone solution in the east Mendip area, Somerset', *Trans Cave Res Gp GB*, 12 (4), 259–70.

DREW, D. P. (1970b). 'The significance of percolation water in limestone catchments', *Groundwater*, 8 (5), 5–11.

DREW, D. P., NEWSON, M. D. & SMITH, D. I. (1970). 'Water-tracing of the Severn Tunnel Great Spring', *Proc Univ Bristol Spel Soc*, 12 (2), 203–12.

DREW, D. P. & SMITH, D. I. (1972). 'An account of an oolitic limestone cave : Cloford Quarry Cave, eastern Mendip', *Proc Univ Bristol Spel Soc*, 13 (1), 89–104.

DRISCOLL, E. M. (1958). 'The denudation chronology of the Vale of Glamorgan', *Trans Inst Brit Geogr*, 26, 45–57.

EK, C., GILEWSKA, S., KASKOWSKI, L., KOBYLECKI, A., OLECKSYNOWNA, K. & OLECKSYNOWNA, B. (1969). 'Some analyses of CO_2 content of air in five Polish caves', *Z Geomorph*, 13 (3), 267–86.

EVERTON, A. & EVERTON, R. (1972). 'Hay Wood Cave Burials, Mendip Hills, Somerset', *Proc Univ Bristol Spel Soc*, 13 (1), 5–29.

FAGG, C. C. (1923). 'The recession of the Chalk escarpment', *Proc Trans Croydon Nat Hist Scient Soc*, 9, 93–112.

FAIRBRIDGE, R. W. (1961). 'Eustatic changes in sea level', *Physics and Chemistry of the Earth*, 5, 99–185.

FINDLAY, D. C. (1965). 'The soils of the Mendip district of Somerset', *Mem Soil Surv Gt Br*.

FORD, D. C. (1960). 'Report on a C.R.G. Grade 5 survey of Swildon's IV and Blue Pencil Passage', *J Wessex Cave Club*, 6 (76), 31–40.

FORD, D. C. (1962). 'On the unknown course of Swildon's Hole', *J Wessex Cave Club*, 7 (87), 125–7.

FORD, D. C. (1963). 'Aspects of the geomorphology of the Mendip Hills', *Unpublished PhD thesis, Univ of Oxford*.

FORD, D. C. (1964a). 'On the geomorphic history of GB Cave, Charterhouse-on-Mendip, Somerset', *Proc Univ Bristol Spel Soc*, 10 (2), 149–88.

FORD, D. C. (1964b). 'The sequence of development in St Cuthbert's Swallet I', *Belfry Bull*, 200, 9–16.

FORD, D. C. (1964c). 'The sequence of development in St Cuthbert's Swallet II', *Belfry Bull*, 201, 2–6.

FORD, D. C. (1965a). 'The origin of limestone caves—a model from the Central Mendip Hills, England', *Nat Spel Soc Bull*, 27 (4), 109–32.

FORD, D. C. (1965*b*). 'The sequence of Development in Swildon's Hole', *J Wessex Cave Club*, 8 (99), 198–205.

FORD, D. C. (1965*c*). 'Stream potholes as indicators of erosion phases in limestone caves', *Nat Spel Soc Bull*, 27 (1), 27–32.

FORD, D. C. (1966). 'Calcium carbonate solution in some central Mendip caves, Somerset', *Proc Univ Bristol Spel Soc*, 11 (1), 46–53.

FORD, D. C. (1968). 'Features of cavern development in Central Mendip', *Trans Cave Res Gp, GB*, 10 (1), 11–25.

FORD, D. C. (1971). 'Geologic structure and a new explanation of limestone cavern genesis', *Trans Cave Res Gp, GB*, 13 (2), 81–94.

FORD, D. C. & STANTON, W. I. (1968). 'The geomorphology of the south-central Mendip Hills', *Proc Geol Assoc London*, 401–27.

GARDNER, J. H. (1935). 'Origin and development of limestone caverns', *Bull Geol Soc Amer*, 46, 1255–74.

GARROD, D. A. E. *The Upper Palaeolithic Age in Britain* (1926). Oxford.

GEORGE, T. N. (1958). 'Lower Carboniferous palaeogeography of the British Isles', *Proc Yorks Geol Soc*, 31 (3), 227–318.

GILBERT, E, (1960). 'Some aspects of surface and underground drainage in the Mendip region', *Unpublished BSc Dissertation, Department of Geography, Univ of Bristol*.

GLENNIE, E. A. (1954). 'Artesian flow and cave formation', *Trans Cave Res Gp, G B*, 3 (1), 55–71.

GLENNIE, E. A. (1967). 'The distribution of hypogean Amphipods in Britain', *Trans Cave Res Gp, GB*, 9 (3), 132–6.

GLENNIE, E. A. & HAZELTON, M. (1962). 'Cave fauna and flora', Chpt 9 in *British Caving*, C. H. D. Cullingford (Ed), Routledge, London. 2nd edn, 592 p.

GODWIN, H. (1955). 'Botanical and geological history of the Somerset Levels', *Advmt Soc Lond*, 12, 310–22.

GODWIN, H. (1960). 'Prehistoric wooden trackways of the Somerset Levels; their construction, age and relation to climatic change', *Proc Prehist Soc*, 26, 1–36.

GOUGH, J. W. (1967). *The Mines of Mendip*, 2nd edition.

GREEN, G. W. (1958). 'The central Mendip lead-zinc orefield', *Bull Geol Surv, GB*, 14, 70–90.

GREEN, G. W. & WELCH, F. B. A. (1965). 'Geology of the country around Wells and Cheddar', *Mem Geol Surv, UK*

GREGORY, K. J. & WALLING, D. E. (1971). 'Field measurements in the drainage basin', *Geography*, 56 (1), 277–92.

GRUND, A. (1903). 'Die Karsthydrographie', *Geogr Abh*, 7 (3).

HALSTEAD, L. B. & NICOLL, P. G. (1971). 'Fossilized caves of Mendip', *Studies in Speleology*, 2 (3–4), 93–102.

HAM, W. E. (1962). 'Classification of carbonate rocks—a symposium', *Mem Am Assoc Petrol Geol*, 1.

HANWELL, J. D. (1970). 'Digger meets diver', *J Wessex Cave Club*, 11 (128), 34–9.

HANWELL, J. D. & NEWSON, M. D. (1970). 'The great storms and floods of July 1968 on Mendip', *Occ Pub Wessex Cave Club*, ser 1, (2).

HARMER, F. W. (1907). 'On the origin of certain canon-like valleys associated with lake-like areas of depression', *Q J Geol Soc Lond*, 63, 470–514.

HAWKES, C. J., TRATMAN, E. K. & POWERS, ROSEMARY (1970). 'Decorated piece of rib bone from the Palaeolithic levels at Gough's Cave, Cheddar, Somerset', *Proc Univ Bristol Spel Soc*, 12 (2), 137–42.

HAWKINS, A. B. (1970). 'Late Quaternary geology of the Severn Estuary', *Unpublished PhD thesis Univ of Bristol*.

HAWKINS, A. B. & KELLAWAY, G. A. (1971). 'Field meeting at Bristol and Bath with special reference to new evidence of glaciation', *Proc Geol Assoc London*, 82 (2), 267–92.

HAZELTON, M. (1955–63). Biological supplement, publd by *Cave Res Gp, GB*

Pt 1 1955   Records for 1938–9
Pt 2 1956   "   "   1940–6
Pt 3 1958   "   "   1947
Pt 4 1959   "   "   1948–9
Pt 5 1960   "   "   1950–3
Title Biological Records :
Pt 6 1960   Records for 1954–6

Pt 7 1961   Records for 1957–9
Pt 8 1963   "   "   1960–2
HAZELTON, M. (1965–71). 'British Hypogean Fauna and Biological Records'.

1965 *Trans Cave Res Gp GB*, 7 (3) for 1963
1967   "   "   "   "   "   9 (3) for 1964–5
1968   "   "   "   "   " 10 (3) for 1967
1970   "   "   "   "   " 12 (1) for 1968
1971   "   "   "   "   " 13 (3) for 1969

HEAL, G. J. (1970). 'A new Pleistocene mammal site, Mendip Hills, Somerset', *Proc Univ Bristol Spel Soc*, 12 (2), 135–6.

HENDERSON, G. T. D. & TRATMAN, E. K. (1928). 'First report on the excavations at Sun Hole, Cheddar (levels above the Pleistocene)', *Proc Univ Bristol Spel Soc*, 3 (2), 84–97.

HEPWORTH, J. V. & STRIDE, A. H. (1950). 'A sequence from the Old Red Sandstone to Lower Carboniferous, near Burrington, Somerset', *Proc Bristol Nat Soc*, 28, 135–8.

HICKLING, M. J. L. & SEABY, W. A. (1952). 'Finds from Cockles Wood Cave, Nettlebridge, Somerset', *Proc Somerset Archaeol Nat Hist*, 96, 193–202.

HOWARD, A. (1964). 'Processes of limestone cave development', *Intern J Spel*, 1, 47–60.

HUBBERT, M. K. (1940). 'The theory of groundwater motion', *J Geol*, 48, 785–944.

HUNT, J. (1966). 'Banwell Bone Cave', *J Axbridge Caving Gp and Archaeol Soc*, 31–43.

JEANNEL, R. *Faune cavernicole de la France* (1926). Paris.

JOHNSON, P. *The history of Mendip caving* (1967). Newton Abbot.

JONES, O. T. (1931). 'Some episodes in the geological history of the Bristol Channel region', *Rep Br Assoc*, 57–82.

KATZER, F. (1909). 'Karst and Karsthydrographie', *Zur Kunde der Balkanhalbinsel*, 8, Sarajevo.

KELLAWAY, G. A. & WELCH, F. B. A. (1948). 'Bristol and Gloucester district', *Mem Geol Surv*.

KELLAWAY, G. A. & WELCH, F. B. A. (1955a). 'The Upper Old Red Sandstone and Lower Carboniferous rocks of Bristol and the Mendips compared to those of Chepstow and the Forest of Dean', *Bull Geol Surv GB*, 9, 1–21.

KELLAWAY, G. A. & WELCH, F. B. A. (1955*b*). 'Upper Old Red Sandstone and Carboniferous rock', 9–23 in *Bristol and its adjoining counties*, Eds. C. M. MacInnes and W. F. Whittard, Bristol.

KENDALL, O. D. (1955). 'Physiography' in *Bristol and its adjoining counties*, 35–47, Eds C. M. MacInnes and W. F. Whittard. Bristol.

KÜHNE, W. G. (1946). 'The geology of the fissure-filling 'Holwell 2'; the age-determination of the mammalian teeth therein; and a report of the technique employed when collecting the teeth of Eozostrodon and Microleptidae, *Proc Zool Soc Lond*, 116 (2 & 3), 729–33.

KURTÉN, BJÖORN. *Pleistocene mammals of Europe* (1968).

LERUTH, R. *La biologie du domaine souterrain et la fauna cavernicole de la Belgique* (1939). Brussels.

LLOYD, O. C. (1971). 'Wookey 22', *Cave Diving Gp Newsletter*, New series no 20, 18–20.

LUCY, W. C. (1874). 'Glaciation in west Somerset', *Geol Mag*, 1, (New Series), 255–6.

McBURNEY, C. M. (1959). 'Report on the first season's field work on British Upper Palaeolithic Cave deposits', *Proc Prehist Soc*, 25, 260–9.

McBURNEY, C. M. (1961). 'Two soundings in the Badger Hole near Wookey Hole in 1958 and their bearing on the Palaeolithic finds of the late H. E. Balch', *71st and 72nd Ann Rprts Wells Nat Hist Archaeol Soc*, 19–27.

MALOTT, C. A. (1938). 'Invasion theory of cavern development', *Bull Geol Soc Amer*, (abs for 1937), p 323.

MANDEL, S. (1965). 'A conceptual model of karstic erosion by groundwater', in *Hydrology of Fractured Rocks*. Dubrovnik. 662–4.

MARTEL, E. *Nouveau traité des eaux souterraines* (1921). Paris.

MASON, D. (1953). 'Note on human skeleton found at Cook's Hill Wood, near Wookey Hole', *Proc Somerset Archaeol Nat Hist*, 97, 186–7.

MASON, E. J. & MASON, D. (1952). 'Report on human remains and material recovered from the River Axe, Wookey Hole, 1947–1949', *Proc Somerset Archaeol Nat Hist*, 96, 238–43.

MAURIN, V. & ZÖTL, J. (1959). 'Die Untersuchung der Zusammenhänge unterirdischer Wasser mit besonderer Berücksichtigung der Karstverhältnisse', *Steirische Beitrage zur Hydrogeologie*, Neue Folge (1–2).

MILLIMAN, J. D. & EMERY, K. O. (1968). 'Sea levels during the past 35,000 years', *Science*, 162, 1121–3.

MITCHELL, G. F. (1960). 'The Pleistocene history of the Irish Sea', *Advmt Sci Lond*, 17, 313–25.

MITCHELL, G. F. & ORME, A. R. (1967). 'The Pleistocene deposits of the Isles of Scilly', *Q J Geol Soc Lond*, 123, 59–92.

MOORE, C. (1867). 'On abnormal conditions of secondary deposits when connected with the Somersetshire and South Wales coal-basin; and on the age of the Sutton and Southerndown Series', *Q J Geol Soc Lond*, 23, 449–568.

MORGAN, C. LLOYD (1888). 'The Mendips : a geological reverie', *Proc Bristol Nat Soc*, 5, 236–60.

NEWSON, M. D. (1969). 'Erosion in the limestone stream system— some recent results and observations', *Proc Brit Spel Assoc*, 7, 17–25.

NEWSON, M. D. (1970). 'Studies of chemical and mechanical erosion by streams in limestone areas', *Unpublished PhD thesis, Univ of Bristol*.

NEWSON, M. D. (1971a). 'The role of abrasion in cavern development', *Trans Cave Res Gp GB*, 13 (2), 101–7.

NEWSON, M. D. (1971b). 'A model of subterranean limestone erosion in the British Isles', *Trans Inst Brit Geog*, 54, 55–70.

NORTH, C. (1968). 'Contour Cavern', *Axbridge Caving Gp and Archaeol Soc Newsletter*, April, p 31.

OAKLEY, K. P. *et al* (1958). 'Antiquity of the skulls reputed to be from Flint Jack's Cave, Cheddar, Somerset', *Proc Univ Bristol Spel Soc*, 8 (2), 76–88.

PARRY, R. F. (1929). 'Excavations at The Caves, Cheddar', *Proc Somerset Archaeol Nat Hist*, 74, 102–21.

PARRY, R. F. (1931). 'Excavations at Cheddar', *Proc Somerset Archaeol Nat Hist*, 76, 46–62.

PICKNETT, R. G. (1964). 'A study of calcite solutions at 10°C', *Trans Cave Res Gp GB*, 7 (1), 39–62.

PITTY, A. F. (1966). 'An approach to the study of karst water', *Univ Hull Occ Paper in Geog*, 5, 70 p.

PONSFORD, D. R. A. (1970). Letter to the editor, *Proc Geol Assoc*, 80, 167–8.

PYKE, R. (1962). 'South-East Inlets—Swildon's Hole', *J Wessex Cave Club*, 7 (85), 68–71.

RAUCH, H. & WHITE, W. B. (1970). 'Lithologic controls on the development of solution porosity in carbonate aquifers', *Water Resources Res*, 6 (4), 1175–92.

REYNOLDS, S. H. (1907). 'A Silurian inlier in the eastern Mendips', *Q J Geol Soc Lond*, 63, 217–40.

REYNOLDS, S. H. (1912a). 'Further work on the Silurian rocks of the eastern Mendips, *Proc Bristol Nat Soc*, 3 (4), 76–82.

REYNOLDS, S. H. *A geological excursion handbook for the Bristol district* (1912b). Bristol.

REYNOLDS, S. M. (1927). 'The Mendips', *Geography*, 14, 187–92.

REYNOLDS, S. M. (1929a). 'The geology of the Bristol district', *Proc Geol Assoc London*, 40, 77–103.

REYNOLDS, S. M. (1929b). 'Limestone scenery', *Proc Bristol Nat Soc*, 7 (2), 114–19.

REYNOLDS, S. M. & VAUGHAN, A. (1911). 'Faunal and lithological sequence in the Carboniferous Limestone Series (Avonian) of Burrington Combe (Somerset)', *Q J Geol Soc Lond*, 67, 342–92.

REYNOLDS, T. E. (1970). 'Wookey 20 and beyond', *J Wessex Cave Club*, 11 (128), 28–33.

RHOADES, R. & SINACORI, M. N. (1941). 'Patterns of groundwater flow and solution', *J Geol*, 49, 785–94.

ROBERTSON, T., SIMPSON, J. B. & ANDERSON, J. G. C. (1949). 'The limestones of Scotland', *Mem Geol Surv Spec Rep Miner Resour GB*, 30.

ROBINSON, P. L. (1957). 'The Mesozoic fissures of the Bristol Channel area and their vertebrate faunas', *J Linn Soc (Zool)*, 43, 260–82.

ROE, D. A. *A gazetteer of British Lower and Middle Palaeolithic Sites*. Council for British Archaeology, (1968), Research Rprt 8.

ROQUES, H. (1969). 'A review of present day problems in the physical chemistry of carbonates in solution', *Trans Cave Res Gp GB*, 11 (3), 139–64.

SAVAGE, R. J. G. (1962). 'Rhaetic exposures at Emborough', *Proc Bristol Nat Soc*, 30, 275–8.

SAVAGE, R. J. G. (1969). 'Pleistocene Mammal Faunas', *Proc Univ Bristol Spel Soc*, 12 (1), 57–62.

SCHWARZENBACH, M. & FLASCHKA, H. *Complexiometric Titrations* (1969).

SIBLY, T. F. (1905). 'The Carboniferous Limestone of Burrington Combe', *Proc Bristol Nat Soc*, 4 (1), 14–41.

SIBLY, T. F. (1906). 'On the Carboniferous Limestone of the Mendip area (Somerset) with especial reference to the palaeontological sequence', *Q J Geol Soc Lond*, 62, 324–80.

SISSONS, J. B. *The evolution of Scotland's scenery* (1967).

SMITH, D. I. (1968). 'A study of the calcium and magnesium content of waters in limestone areas', *Proc 4th Int Cong Spel Ljublana*, 3, 213–18.

SMITH, D. I. (1971). 'The concepts of water flow and water-tables in limestones', *Trans Cave Res Gp GB*, 13 (2), 95–9.

SMITH, D. I. & MEAD, D. G. (1962). 'The solution of limestone with special reference to Mendip', *Proc Univ Bristol Spel Soc*, 9 (3), 188–211.

SMITH, D. I. & NICHOLSON, F. H. (1964). 'A study of limestone solution in northwest Co. Clare, Eire', *Proc Univ Bristol Spel Soc*, 10 (2), 119–38.

SMITH, D. I. & NEWSON, M. D. (1974). 'The dynamics of solutional and mechanical erosion in limestone catchments on the Mendip Hills, Somerset', *Inst Brit Geog*, spec Publ, n. 6, 155–67.

SMITH, R. A. (1963). 'The geomorphology of south Gloucestershire', *Unpublished PhD thesis, Univ of Bristol*.

STANTON, W. I. (1965a). 'A scalloped passage of Triassic age near Cheddar', *J Wessex Cave Club*, 8 (102), 277–83.

STANTON, W. I. (1965b). 'The digging at the end of Gough's Cave and its bearing on the chances at Cheddar', *J Wessex Cave Club*, 8 (102), 277–83.

STANTON, W. I. (1969a). 'Pioneer under the Mendips. Herbert Ernest Balch of Wells', *Wessex Cave Club Occ Pub*, 1 (1), 123p.

STANTON, W. I. (1969b). 'Hosepipe hysteria', *J Wessex Cave Club*, 10 (126), 438–42.

STANTON, W. I. (1970). 'Lionel's Hole : Survey notes and other trifles', *J Wessex Cave Club*, 11 (132), 160–3.

STENNER, R. D. (1966). 'The variation of temperature and hardness in St Cuthbert's Swallet, a progress report', *Belfry Bull*, 21 (1), 117–22.

STENNER, R. D. (1969). 'The measurement of aggressiveness of water towards calcium carbonate', *Trans Cave Res Gp GB*, 11 (3), 175–200.

STENNER, R. D. (1970). 'Preliminary results of an application of the procedure for the measurement of aggressiveness of water to calcium carbonate', *Trans Cave Res Gp GB*, 12 (4), 283–9.

STENNER, R. D. (1971). 'The measurement of aggressiveness of water to calcium carbonate, parts II and III', *Trans Cave Res Gp GB*, 13 (4), 283–96.

STEVENS, A. J. (1959). 'Surfaces, soils and land use in north-east Hampshire', *Trans Inst Br Geogr*, 26, 51–66.

STRIDE, A. H. & STRIDE, R. D. (1949). 'The formation of the Mendip Caves', *Br Caver*, 19, 6–25.

SUTCLIFFE, A. J. (1955). 'A preliminary report on the Reindeer remains from Banwell Bone Cave—antler bases', *J Axbridge Cave Gp and Archaeol Soc*, 2 (4), 36–40.

SWEETING, M. M. (1950). 'Erosion cycles and limestone caverns in the Ingleborough district', *Geog J* 115, 63–78.

SWEETING, M. M. (1958). 'The karstlands of Jamaica', *Geog J*, 124, 184–99.

SWINNERTON, A. C. (1932). 'Origin of limestone caves', *Bull Geol Soc Amer*, 43, 663–93.

TAYLOR, H. (1926). 'Fifth Report on Rowberrow Cavern', *Proc Univ Bristol Spel Soc*. 2 (3), 190–210.

TAYLOR, H. & APSIMON, A. M. (1964). 'Bos Swallet, Mendip, Somerset', *Proc Univ Bristol Spel Soc*, 10 (2), 98–111.

THOMAS, T. M. (1963). 'Solution subsidence in south-east Carmarthenshire and south-west Breconshire', *Trans Inst Br Geogr*, 33, 45–60.

THRAILKILL, J. (1968). 'Chemical and hydrologic factors in the excavation of limestone caves', *Bull Geol Soc Amer*, 79, 19–46.

TRATMAN, E. K. *et al* (1938). 'Excavation of Backwell Cave, Somerset', *Proc Univ Bristol Spel Soc*, 5 (1), 57–74.

TRATMAN, E. K. (1955). 'Second report on the excavations at Sun Hole, Cheddar (the Pleistocene levels)', *Proc Univ Bristol Spel Soc*, 7 (2), 61–75.

TRATMAN, E. K. (1960). 'Gough's Old Cave, Cheddar', *Proc Univ Bristol Spel Soc*, 9 (1), 7–21.

TRATMAN, E. K. (1963a). 'The hydrology of the Burrington area, Somerset', *Proc Univ Bristol Spel Soc*, 10 (1), 22–57.

TRATMAN, E. K. (1963b). 'Reports on the investigation of Pen Park Hole, Bristol', *Cave Res Gp Occ Pub*, no 12.

TRATMAN, E. K. (1964). 'Picken's Hole, Crook Peak, Somerset. A Pleistocene Site', *Proc Univ Bristol Spel Soc*, 10 (2), 42–5.

TRATMAN, E. K. (1966). 'Trial excavations at and the Pleistocene fauna from the Long Hole, Cheddar', *Proc Univ Bristol Spel Soc*, 11 (1), 42–3.

TRATMAN, E. K., DONOVAN, D. T., & CAMPBELL, J. B. (1971). 'The Hyaena Den (Wookey Hole), Mendip Hills, Somerset', *Proc Univ Bristol Spel Soc*, 12 (3), 245–79.

TROMBE, F. *Traité de spéléolgie* (1952). Paris.

TRUEMAN, A. E. (1939). 'Erosion levels in the Bristol district, and their relation to the development of scenery', *Proc Bristol Nat Soc*, 8 (4), 402–28.

TUCKER, J. H. (1964). 'The hibernation of the Herald and Tissue Moths (*Scoliopterix libratrix* L., and *Triphosa dubitata* L.) in caves of the Mendip region', *Newsletter Cave Res Gp*, no. 90/91, 2–7.

TUCKER, J. H. (1966). 'Banwell Bone Cave survey—Stage I 1966', *J Axbridge Caving Gp and Archaeol Soc*, 26–30.

TURK, F. A. (1967). 'The non-Aranean Arachnid Orders and the Myriapods of British caves and mines', *Trans Cave Res Gp GB*, 9 (3), 142–61.

VAN DE KAMP, P. C. (1969). 'The Silurian volcanic rocks of the Mendip Hills, Somerset; and the Tortworth area, Gloucestershire, England, *Geol Mag*, 106, 542–53.

VANDEL, A. *Biospeleology* (1965).

VAUGHAN, A. (1905). 'The palaeontological sequence in the Carboniferous Limestone of the Bristol area', *Q J Geol Soc Lond*, 61, 181–305.

VAUGHAN, A. (1906). 'The Carboniferous Limestone Series (Avonian) of the Avon Gorge', *Proc Bristol Nat Soc*, 4 (1), 74–168.

VAUGHAN, A. & REYNOLDS, S. H. (1935). 'The Carboniferous Limestone Series (Avonian) of the Avon Gorge', *Proc Bristol Nat Soc*, 8 (1), 29–90.

WARBURTON, D. (1967). 'Sketch plan of New Cave, Boveways Field, Eastwater', *J Wessex Cave Club*, 9 (113), p 273.

WARWICK, G. T. (1952). 'Fossil Cave System', *Cave Res Gp GB Newsletter*, 41, 10–11.

WARWICK, G. T. (1955). 'Views on the origin and development of Chelm's Combe Cave, Cheddar', *J Axbridge Caving Gp and Archaeol Soc*, 2 (3), 6–13.

WARWICK, G. T. (1962). 'The origin of limestone caverns', chpt 3 in *British Caving*. C. H. D. Cullingford (Ed) 2nd edn, 592p.

WARWICK, G. T. (1971). 'Caves and the Ice Age', *Trans Cave Res Gp GB*, 13 (2), 123–30.

WELCH, F. B. A. (1929). 'The geological structure of the central Mendips', *Q J Geol Soc Lond*, 85, 45–76.

WELCH, F. B. A. (1932a). 'The geological succession of the Blackdown pericline', *Proc Bristol Nat Soc*, 7 (4), 388–96.

WELCH, F. B. A. (1932b). 'The hydrology of the Stoke Lane area (Somerset)', *Proc Cotteswold Naturalist Field Club*, 24 (1), 87–96.

WELCH, F. B. A. (1933). 'The geological structure of the eastern Mendips', *Q J Geol Soc Lond*, 89, 14–52.

WELLS, O. (1955). 'Eastwater Cavern', *J Wessex Cave Club*, 49, 10–19.

WEST, R. G. *Pleistocene geology and biology* (1968).

WEYL, P. K. (1958). 'The solution kinetics of calcite', *J Geol*, 66, 163–76.

WEYL, P. K. (1961). 'The carbonate saturometer', *J Geol*, 69, 32–44.

WEYMAN, D. (1970). 'Some simple empirical models of slope hydrology', *Area*, 3, p 58.

WHITAKER, R. J. (1969). 'The discovery and exploration of Shatter Cave (Fairy Cave No 15), Fairy Cave Quarry', *J Wessex Cave Club*, 10 (124), 344–48.

WHITE, W. B. (1969). 'Conceptual models for carbonate aquifers', *Groundwater*, 7, 15–21.

WHITE, W. B. & LONGYEAR, J. (1962). 'Some limitations on speleogenetic speculation imposed by the hydraulics of groundwater flow in limestones', *Nittany Grotto Newsletter*, 10 (9), 155–67.

WHITTARD, W. F. (1949). 'Boreholes on Mendip', *Proc Bristol Nat Soc*, 29, 479–82.

WINWOOD, H. H. & WOODWARD, H. B. (1891). 'Excursion to the Mendip Hills', *Proc Geol Ass London*, 11, clxxi–ccxvi.

WOODWARD, H. (1961). 'A stream piracy theory of cave formation', *Nat Spel Soc Bull*, 23, 39–58.

WOODWARD, H. B. (1876). 'Geology of the east Somerset and Bristol coal-fields', *Mem Geol Surv*.

WOODWARD, H. B. (1891). 'Brief notes on the geology of the Mendip Hills', *Proc Geol Ass London*, 11, 481–94.

WOOLDRIDGE, S. W. (1960). 'The Radstock Plateau—a note on the physiography of the Bristol district', *Proc Bristol Nat Soc*, 30, 151–62.

WOOLDRIDGE, S. W. & LINTON, D. L. *Structure, surface and drainage in south-east England* (1955).

YATES, R. A. (1950). 'Erosion levels in the River Avon drainage basin', *Unpublished MSc thesis, Univ of Bristol*.

Location Index

A fully comprehensive index is not included because of the systematic chapter treatment of the various subjects. The names of passages within individual caves named in the biological records of Chapter 7 are not therefore included.